'Anna Westin provides us with a cogent and
traumatic subjectivity. Her interdisciplinary stud
of trauma illuminates the roots of suffering and
belonging'.

– **Prof. Richard Kearne** ssor in
Philosophy, Boston Co ge, Philosophy Department

'Anna Westin's wide-ranging and yet always focused conversations on trauma are deeply rewarding. She shows us—with careful scholarship and ethical urgency—that we cannot hope to make sense of and heal trauma without taking seriously the many dimensions of our lived, bodily coexistence with other people'.

– **René Rosfort,** Associate Professor of Ethics and Philosophy of Religion, University of Copenhagen

'Etymologically linked to the act of piercing, trauma carries with itself the Sanskrit sense of moving to the other side – now associated with the meaning of being "trespassed", violated, invaded, lacerated: a body-mind-soul perforation. Anna Westin's conversations are a deep journey through and out of the mystery of the black hole of the experience of trauma. Determinately stitched together by existential phenomenology – Lévinas' reading chiefly, but also Merleau-Ponty and Ricœur's thought – this narrative travel unravels, land after land, the complex geography of trauma. The mapping is multidimensional, in time, space, and perspective, yet woven along three foundation axes: the embodied self, the other, and place. With a self-reflexive and hermeneutical sail, Westin accompanies readers through an oceanic corpus stretching from Greco-Roman mythology, where suffering could transform us in stone, to dystopian Anthropocenic views around the eco-traumatic effects on humans of ecological disintegration. In high seas, readers navigate early analytic accounts of trauma, Freudian and post-Freudian psychoanalytic debates, van der Kolk and Levine somatic readings, the arrival of PTSD taxonomy and its critiques, phenomenological views around the relational, linguistic, corporeal and situated founding of the (traumatised) subject, up to explorations of collective, historico-political trauma – in the Isreali-Palestinian conflict, the Canadian First Nations issue and slavery and colonisation at large, the discourse of universal human rights of children in the context of human trafficking. Routes of healing are finally depicted, where mainstream conceptions of healing are questioned and paradigms of verbal catharsis are sailed through, to land into relational and body-based practices which focus on the body, the spirit, society and our homes/places/lands.

Sensitively mastering an impressive plethora of coordinates, Westin does not lose her direction – not even when we finally reach back home, another home, and she is herself sensorially confronted with vivid social suffering. As the traumatic metamorphosis forcing re-orienting subjectivity and ethics, Westin transforms first reactions of romanticisation and rejection into deeper awareness, hope, and further impetus to act for a more just world where interpersonal, social, and political healing becomes reality.

Westin's book is a fresh philosophical tool re-positioning trauma studies back to the uniqueness of the lived experience, and a loud call to our ethical and political engagement with it'.

– **Dr. Runa Lazzarino,** Bakhita Centre for Research on Slavery, Exploitation and Abuse, St Mary's University, Twickenham, London

EMBODIED TRAUMA AND HEALING

What if philosophy could solve the psychological puzzle of trauma? *Embodied Trauma and Healing* argues just that, suggesting that one might be needed in order to understand the other. The book demonstrates how the body-mind problem that haunted Descartes was addressed by phenomenologists, whilst also proposing that the human experience is lived subjectively as embodied consciousness.

Throughout this book, the author suggests that the phenomenological tools that are used to explore the body can also be an effective way to discuss the physical and mental aspects of embodied trauma. Drawing on the work of Paul Ricœur, Maurice Merleau-Ponty and Emmanuel Lévinas, the book outlines a phenomenological approach to the embodied and relational subject. It offers a reading of embodied trauma that can connect it to wider conversations in psychological underpinnings of trauma through Peter Levine's somatic research and Bessel van der Kolk's embodied remembering. Connecting to the analytic tradition, the book suggests that phenomenology can unify both language- and body-based therapeutic practices. It also presents a compelling discussion that ties the embodied experience of relation in trauma to the wider causal factors of social suffering and relational rupture, intergenerational trauma and the trauma of land, as informed by phenomenology.

Embodied Trauma and Healing is essential reading for researchers within the fields of philosophy, psychology and medical humanities for it actively engages with contemporary configurations of trauma theory and recent research developments in healing and mental disorder diagnosis.

Anna Westin is an Honorary Visiting Fellow at St. Mary's University, Bakhita Centre for Research on Slavery, Exploitation and Abuse, Lecturer at St. Mellitus College, and an Honorary Visiting Lecturer at The University of Kent. She is also Director of The JAM Network UK, a survivor-focused anti-trafficking community.

CRITICAL APPROACHES TO HEALTH

Series Editors
Kerry Chamberlain & Antonia Lyons

The Routledge *Critical Approaches to Health* series, in association with the International Society of Critical Health Psychology (ISCHP) aims to present critical, inter-disciplinary books around psychological, social and cultural issues related to health. Each volume in the series provides a critical approach to a particular issue or important topic, and is of interest and relevance to students and practitioners across the social sciences.

Titles in the series:

Constructing Pain
Historical, psychological and critical perspectives
Robert Kugelmann

Embodied Trauma and Healing
Critical Conversations on the Concept of Health
Anna Westin

EMBODIED TRAUMA AND HEALING

Critical Conversations on the Concept of Health

Anna Westin

LONDON AND NEW YORK

First published 2022
by Routledge
2 Park Square, Milton Park, Abingdon, Oxon OX14 4RN

and by Routledge
605 Third Avenue, New York, NY 10158

Routledge is an imprint of the Taylor & Francis Group, an informa business

British Library Cataloguing-in-Publication Data
A catalogue record for this book is available from the British Library

Library of Congress Cataloging-in-Publication Data
Names: Westin, Anna, 1988– author.
Title: Embodied trauma and healing : critical conversations on the concept of health / Anna Westin.
Description: Abingdon, Oxon ; New York, NY : Routledge, 2022. |
Series: Critical approaches to health |
Includes bibliographical references. |
Summary: Identifiers: LCCN 2021043950 (print) | LCCN 2021043951 (ebook) |
ISBN 9780367406127 (hardback) | ISBN 9780367406134 (paperback) |
ISBN 9780367800017 (ebook)
Subjects: LCSH: Psychic trauma. | Healing. | Philosophy–Therapeutic use.
Classification: LCC BF175.5.P75 W378 2022 (print) |
LCC BF175.5.P75 (ebook) | DDC 155.9/3–dc23
LC record available at https://lccn.loc.gov/2021043950
LC ebook record available at https://lccn.loc.gov/2021043951

ISBN: 978-0-367-40612-7 (hbk)
ISBN: 978-0-367-40613-4 (pbk)
ISBN: 978-0-367-80001-7 (ebk)

DOI: 10.4324/9780367800017

Typeset in Bembo
by Newgen Publishing UK

For Miriam and the little ones.

Thank You

I am deeply indebted to the many individuals whose insights, time, shared stories and critical perspectives gave substance and shape to this work.

I am thankful for the academic support from Carole Murphy and Todd Mei in initial conversations of the project. Gratitude is extended to the publishing team at Routledge for bringing the publication to completion and Lacey Decker for editing guidance. To my friends, colleagues and survivors who are engaged in anti-trafficking work, and in particular, Cheryl and Manny Deb P., my somatic mentors, Bettina Bergo, and the Ateliers Ricoeur community, Deana and Holly at Pi Studios, I am grateful for you. Thanks is also extended to conversations with my friend Amira,[1] and to the organisational and community leaders of Musalaha, Sadeh and Canticle Farm that I had the privilege of conversing with.

Much of this conversation was matured through the support of my family, Carolyn and John Paul, who engage with trauma work on a daily basis, and my two sisters, Miriam and Lucia. Col's critical and creative combing through of multiple early drafts has greatly helped me find how to best express this content 'for myself'. To this collective voice, I am deeply grateful.

Note

1 I have changed her original name for anonymity.

CONTENTS

Series Editor Preface *xi*
Preface *xiii*

PART I
Critical Discourses on Embodied Trauma **1**

1 Trauma and the Subject 3

2 Trauma, Ego and the Body 11

3 Labelling Traumatic Ambiguity 28

PART II
Phenomenology and the Traumatised Subject **49**

4 The Phenomenology of Lévinas 51

5 Ricœur on Narrative Experiences 64

6 Merleau-Ponty on Embodiment 77

PART III
Living Trauma in Relationship **89**

7 Silence and Communicability: Speaking Truths 91

8 Homelessness and At-Homeness: The Body as a Site of Integration 100

9 The Intersubjectivity of Trauma: Politics, Rights and Decolonisation 110

PART IV
Living Trauma as Health **129**

10 Individual Healing: The Subject and Her Relationships 131

11 Relational Healing: The Refiguration of a Place 164

12 Conclusion 173

Bibliography *180*
Index *196*

SERIES EDITOR PREFACE

Critical Approaches to Health

Antonia Lyons and Kerry Chamberlain

Health is a major issue for people all around the world and is fundamental to individual well-being, personal achievements and satisfaction, as well as to families, communities and societies. It is also embedded in social notions of participation and citizenship. Much has been written about health, from a variety of perspectives and disciplines, but a lot of this writing takes a biomedical and causally positivist approach to health matters, neglecting the historical, social and cultural contexts and environments within which health is experienced, understood and practiced. It is timely for a new series of books that offer critical, social science perspectives on important health topics.

The *Critical Approaches to Health* series aims to provide new critical writing on health by presenting critical, interdisciplinary and theoretical writing about health, where matters of health are framed quite broadly. The series seeks to include books that range across important health matters, including general health-related issues (such as gender and media), major social issues for health (such as medicalisation, obesity and palliative care), particular health concerns (such as pain, doctor-patient interaction, health services and health technologies), particular health problems (such as diabetes, autoimmune disease and medically unexplained illness), or health for specific groups of people (such as the health of migrants, the homeless and the aged) or combinations of these.

The series seeks above all to promote critical thought about health matters. By critical, we mean going beyond the critique of the topic and work in the field, to more general considerations of power and benefit, and in particular, to addressing concerns about whose understandings and interests are upheld and whose are marginalised by the approaches, findings and practices in these various domains of health. Such critical agendas involve reflections on what constitutes knowledge, how it is created and how it is used. Accordingly, critical approaches consider epistemological and theoretical positioning, as well as issues of methodology and practice, and seek to examine how health is enmeshed within broader social relations and structures. Books within this series take up this challenge and seek to provide new insights and understandings by applying a critical agenda to their topics.

In this book, *Embodied Trauma and Healing: Critical Conversations on the Concept of Health*, Anna Westin reflects on traumas that are caused and experienced in complex contexts of suffering and considers the ongoing lived and embodied experience of trauma. Westin draws on her work in addiction and trauma, her experience as a Pilates instructor, alongside her academic scholarly work in philosophy, to provide a unique, wide-ranging and engaging view of trauma. She employs phenomenology and psychoanalysis to provide insights and understandings into the ambiguity of trauma, how it is an embodied experience, and how it can be reperceived in terms of connections: to the story of oneself, as well as connection to place and others. It focuses on the capacity for transformation.

Westin frames the book as a conversation between scholars from different disciplines, including somatic theorists, phenomenologists, psychoanalysts and others concerned with the unconscious, all of whom have particular views, interpretations and lenses on trauma. The book is organised in three parts. In Part I, Westin explores critical discourses on trauma and how trauma has been understood and defined historically. In Part II, she considers phenomenology and the traumatised subject, bringing the work of Lévinas, Merleau-Ponty and Ricœur to bear. In Part III, she focuses on the lived experience of trauma in relationship. In providing such a broad, sweeping account of embodied trauma, Westin successfully keeps the work grounded through specific examples from her own work and experiences. She invites us to explore the topic as the work of reconnection and transformation.

In the final parts of the book, Westin applies the theoretical insights on trauma she has explored – specifically around how trauma is *lived* – and reflects on what this means for both individual and community healing processes. Trauma is multidimensional, as well as deeply personal and individual, yet it also inherently relational – it allows for witnessing and hearing of a person's trauma. In this way, it has capacity to connect people through a shared experience. It requires consideration of the material body, social relationships and the collective experience of being human.

As Westin convincingly argues, discussions about trauma are conversations about health and its complexity, including considerations of subjectivity, the relationship of consciousness to the world, self-narratives, bodies, perceptions and responses. She argues that at its most fundamental, health is about understanding human subjectivity and its relationship with the world in which we live. This is a thought-provoking and original addition to the *Critical Approaches to Health* series, providing important new perspectives on suffering, trauma, transformation and healing.

PREFACE

This reflection on trauma, its rupture and its mending, has been the result of a journey over a number of years. In the last couple of years, as a partial result of finishing studies on addiction and working with survivors of trafficking in England, I realised that I needed to learn more about the traumas that are caused in complex contexts of suffering. But as a philosopher and a Pilates instructor, I felt I was wrongly equipped for what I needed to do. So I decided to go on a journey with these seemingly ill-fitting tools and converse with people around the world who had worked with traumatised people, or, in some instances, were traumatised themselves. What I found was the need for reflection on the experience as a whole, which as I philosopher I could do, and a required understanding of how the body works, which my studies in anatomy somewhat allowed me. The rest was a process of listening.

As I travelled to various places in North America, the United Kingdom and Israel and Palestine, meeting with communities, activists, grassroots healers, academics, ex-inmates and urban farmers, I was inspired to hear how they live particular forms of healing that their own experiences require. I noticed the fundamental ambiguity of the variety of traumas represented in each place. In the British seaside town where I lived which included the poorest region of England, trauma was reflected in family abuse, in stories of sex traffic survivors and in economic depression. In Israel and Palestine, I witnessed the stories of survivors of the Holocaust and the outbursts of attacks in Israel existing alongside the traumas of the Palestinians experienced through the Intifadas. In America, trauma was told through stories of racial inequality, through the lives of Hispanic communities outside of San Francisco, and narratives of black men doing 'life' for crimes they did not commit. I saw it when speaking to academics about the opioid crisis in midwest America and the analysts in New York studying the intergenerational trauma of refugees.

But it was in Vancouver, on the West Coast of Canada that I came face to face with my own country's living and lived trauma. I had taken a flight in from the East Coast and was making my way with a heaving backpack to the other side of the city. The map told me to take a right once I left the coffee shop. I turn onto East Hastings, lugging the black canvas bag on my back, and the smaller bag of books beside – a notebook, the laptop, the various volumes of Sontag and philosophy. I reached the edge of another tall building. A figure huddled in her sleeping bag, tucked behind three umbrellas. The wide plastic sheet wheels covered her torso, like a makeshift home. Beside her, four tea candles flickered softly. I felt a stirring kind of romantic compassion as I looked, as if a distanced voyeur. There was a sense of the poetic in the figure, cradled in the corner of this building. I recognised this later in my research – the temptation to romanticise traumatic pain.

But any dissociative poetry I found in Gastown vanished abruptly as I started walking the street. It was long and wide, stretching steel and glass and grey, parallel to the waterfront. Figures huddled close and thick; thin bone frames, grey faces. One man was shaking convulsively. His jeans hung loose low on his bony hips, his eyes were open white and wild and black hair was matted beneath a grey hood. Everything was grey. I felt overwhelmed; felt a sudden exposure like I was a witness, and I did not want to see.

The sky spit cold and dark in mid-afternoon. It was the end of December. The people lining the streets had been bussed from the Prairies for the services. This strip of East Hastings was filled with service providers, cheap coffee shops and neon plastic crosses and shelters. Shame crept thick through the openings of my eyes. I could not unsee the thick crowds of hungry, displaced humans here, the anger and sharp sputtered laughs and trembling hands passing things back and forth. A man beside me wore his sunglasses low, though the sky was dark. There was a continuous twitching. Mouths wide, closed, moving, taut. Emmanuel Lévinas tells us shame turns us to face the other; that is the experience of revelation.

But I turned left because I felt I could not do any more of it. I turned down a thin side street. It spilt out onto a cinderblock church and a blue house with a 'Sisters of Mercy' sign in black marker and three figures huddled outside. One of the men stood, all bulk and tall, dripping in his wet leather coat, a thick metal chain around a tattooed neck. The rest were there too, in jeans and grey and shivering. I hated it. I hated this reckoning and these streets. I hated what I was seeing. I thought about waving down a taxi and felt annoyed with myself for being so sensitive. I realised then that all this phenomenological research was being lived in front of me. I realised in that moment what I had been writing about all along, that somehow, in this distance of an experience that I could not understand, that these people in front of me were the others I had written so extensively about. I hated Vancouver because it was making me see and showing me just how disruptive entering into another's experience can be.

At the edge of the Pacific, my country has cast its children off. The Country, strong and free, was all here in front of me, trembling and angry and cold. All the thousand failings were borne in bodies that were wet and homeless and waiting around. I left the east coast, buoyant and atoned. I came here, hours, later, confronted with shame. I looked ahead, past the church. The ball field was covered in tents. It was too cold for them on the Prairies in winter, someone told me later. So they came here. Some days the winter winds gust to -40. I could not imagine sitting on the edge of a prairie town when the dry air blows through. You breathe and the moist air freezes your lips to ice.

The services are good in this part of Vancouver. But there were so many people requiring them. Like I saw in many of the other communities, the process of healing takes time and faces overwhelming need. This walk was uncomfortable to me. It brought the theoretical discourse into the body, into the history of me, implicated in this moment of time, with the faces in front of me. I remembered Stauffer, who had written that the work of testimony needed to go deeper than just hearing a person's story. It needed to invoke an 'openness where what is said might be heard even if it threatens to break the order of the known world for those who listen' (2015, p. 112). I realised in some small way that my ordered phenomenological experience of life in Canada was breaking. But I still did not know what the response would be.

This book is a puzzling through of this. If living trauma is subjective, then it requires careful reorientation and transformation that can only come about through listening, and being willing to be broken. But it also requires us to know that there is a capacity for transformation. 'We are a part of the brokenness, but we are also a part of the blessing', a woman had told me, as she worked the urban farm outside of San Francisco that was home to ex-inmates, environmentalists and others seeking refuge. Kearney writes that, for Ricœur, the presence of the other to the suffering person is '…the connotations of promise, becoming and futurity…an eschatology of the possible' (pp. 178, 180). The blessing, bearing witness to the brokenness – the rupture, loss and displacement are each experiences that we are implicated in. They are also experiences that we often feel unable to fully bear.

This is where the work starts – often quite simple and small. As I witnessed in my travels, the road to health and healing is often built in the unseen and unspoken spaces. Countless hours were spent by clinicians, volunteers, grassroots activists, mothers and carers, on unseen work, on trying to find funding for buildings to house people or hoping to build a connection with an individual who is then relocated elsewhere. This really is the long and humble work of reconnection and transformation that is so essential. Lévinas reminds us that the ethical relationship always starts with the individual face that we are called to respond to. Wherever I went, levels of education fluctuated, as did social status, nationality and, to some degree, political opinions. But each healer evidenced similarities: a concern for the other, a connection between the body and its place in the world and an understanding of narrative. In this book, I explore how living trauma is a bodied experience; accounts of it require understanding how the body 'keeps' the memory in the brain and muscle and cells, as the somatic theorists tell us. But it also requires exploring the unconscious; what is not said, or cannot be said, the silence between speech and the fragment of narrative. For this, we need the tools of psychoanalysis.

However, even more than this merely being a connective conversation between psychological disciplines, between body specialists and readers of the unconscious, Lévinas, Merleau-Ponty and Ricœur point us to further experiences of interconnection. They give us texts that show how trauma might be lived socially and politically. They also show how our experience of place, and the place that we occupy in the world, is affected by our experience of trauma. They explain how our relational self can be affected by others; I will suggest that this is not only a current experience, but it can encompass intergenerational relationships that we embody in ourselves in a variety of ways.

Phenomenology can help us to understand and clarify the ambiguity of trauma by helping us to reperceive how our bodied experiences of the world around us connect us to the story of ourselves that inherently involves our connection to place, story and others. This book also connects the trauma conversation to the wider phenomenology of healing. As we explore how trauma is lived in the body, through our relationships and recreated in the rupture of social-, institutional- and land-based relationships, we are given the opportunity to reperceive and reorient the living. This is not a moral imperative; nor is it a clearly defined diagnostic application. Rather, it is an invitation to exploring the work of reconnection and transformation. This work involves lamenting and listening, silence and effort, for the self as traumatised and for the community that bears witness to her.

PART I

Critical Discourses on Embodied Trauma

1

TRAUMA AND THE SUBJECT

In the middle of the last century, Simone Weil wrote her philosophical reflections on the experience of upheaval in the world around her. She penned that '[t]o be rooted is perhaps the most important and least recognised need of the human soul. It is [also] one of the hardest to define' (1952, p. 43). From my observations and conversations that have formed this book, I have seen how trauma and uprootedness go hand in hand. The need for roots that Weil laments as the basic human requirement of her time has resulted in the traumatised history that we live out today. But Weil also notes how hard it is to define what it means to be rooted and uprooted. This book argues that the difficulty in defining traumatic experience points to the wider damage of a human experience of rupture, displacement, loss and silence.

At its core, discussions about trauma are conversations about health. Trauma is explored, not in order to glorify the shocking details of an event, but rather these dominating experiences of memory can be understood and integrated into the wider experience of a person's life. In this book, we look at contributions to health discourse from various disciplines, through the lens of phenomenology. By this, we mean, what health means as an experience of consciousness, oriented towards particular phenomena. In this case, the relationship of consciousness to the world around us means examining health through subjectivity; that is, through our perceptions and responses, our self-narratives and relationships to the world around us. In studying the different definitions of trauma and the experiences of traumatised people, we are confronted with the complexity of health. Trauma maintains that ambiguous experience because of its interconnection to so many different phenomena. To really understand what is going on, to enter into Weil's claim that 'uprootedness is by far the most dangerous malady to which human societies are exposed', we need to get under the assumptions and theories that we have already claimed about our relationship to the world. Trauma requires an almost

DOI: 10.4324/9780367800017-2

'naïve' return to basics: understanding human subjectivity and our relationships with the world around us.

Since the beginning of human history, there have been countless documentations of trauma. But it is not until more recently that it was critically explored, as a situation that deviated from the experience of full health. When developing his initial theory, Sigmund Freud defined trauma as an excitation so powerful that it 'breaks through the protective shield' of consciousness, meaning that a person's mental experience is flooded and bound 'with large amounts of stimulus' (ct. in Bulut 2019, p. 1). He later wrote that trauma is an 'experience of helplessness' (Perelberg 2015, p. 1453). Judith Herman, on the other hand, defines trauma by pointing to the terror of the event that causes it. For her, trauma is a paradox: an alternating experience 'between feeling numb and reliving the event' (1992, p. 1). The diversity of definitions continues. The different accounts reveal a complex relationship between rupture, suffering and memory, somewhat ambiguously interconnected and understood.

In this book, I want to explore how we have historically tried to understand trauma. What we see quite quickly is that there are many kinds of traumas. There are childhood traumas, where wounding takes place early on to rupture a child's perception of relationship to a trustworthy world. Episodic traumas, such as an experience of a car crash, are contrasted with complex ongoing traumas, and historical trauma that involves the displacement of communities over multiple generations. The sheer diversity of experiences can make it hard to find points of cohesion. For instance, how do you compare the experiences of First Nations communities in Canada, with the suffering of Palestinians, or how can memories of a concentration camp be interpreted alongside the experience of a child who has been molested by her parent? Or, how does a trafficked child's story intersect with an incarcerated person's experience of generational abuse and neglect? The list of questions goes on. It requires acknowledging the ambiguity, but also a search for points of intersection.

The first part of this book will look at how different theorists have tried to define just what this experience of trauma is. This means mapping out how the concept of trauma has evolved, conceptually and scientifically. Trauma, as a lived human experience, requires understanding how we, as humans, are *affected*, and then how we live out that *affect*. This means that we need to know something about the body. But it also requires looking at the different ways in which we try to share our bodied histories or hide them away. It asks us to listen to the soul and to explore consciousness and emotion. It presses us to understand the role of ritual and practice, of place and our interconnection with others. As we will see, each theory of trauma gives its own interpretation of what it means to be a human being in relationship with the world around us.

But for us to understand what it means to live trauma, and what it requires of us, we need to look at how specific experiences of suffering are *lived*. It requires defining the interdisciplinary discourse on health and trauma as a living dynamic experience of rupture and replacement between the psyche, the body and the relational self. Because trauma is a description of a specific kind of human experience, it is important to understand how different theories explain this experience. In Chapter 1, we will look at psychological accounts of trauma. Chapter 2 will assess body-based theories that start by reading the physical experience of the body and its response systems for signs. Chapter 3 will then engage with the tricky task of diagnosing and reading trauma through alternate modalities. Chapter 4 will end with an analysis of the limits of these models, suggesting that the story of trauma needs re-situating in a wider story of human relationship.

Amira's Story

The first time I met Amira was at a café in central London. I was working in a back corner, typing through a final draft of my PhD and she was having lunch with a friend. That was a few years ago. When I told her that I was writing a book on trauma, I felt somehow that I wanted her story to be included in it. I knew something of her context, coming to the United Kingdom as a political refugee from Palestine. I also felt like the research I was doing was taking me into an experience that needed me to connect it to someone I knew and trusted. As I sat down to hear her story, it opened my eyes to just how unique each experience is.

Amira was born during the First Intifada and the Gulf War. She shared with me her mixture of memories accumulated from growing up during that time. At age three, she remembers hiding out with nine other people in her little room. It was the safest room in the house, and all of the windows had been taped over. Amira remembers these early emotional cues vividly. Pat Ogden, Kekuni Minto and Clare Pain write that in traumatic situations, our emotions colour our thought processes, in order for us to direct our attention to specific cues (2006, p. 11). For Amira, she remembers feeling a constant fear of death, and realising early on that she was helpless to do anything about the violence that enveloped her neighbourhood.

Amira recalls the rhythmic sound of conflict and remembers once how her grandad untaped the window in the house to show her the fighter jets flying close outside. During the five years of the second Intifada, clashes flared up constantly until they built the West Bank wall around her house. During the first three months, the family went into hiding. But once they realised that the conflict was not going to stop, they tried to get about their business again. Amira remembers the fear, often of being shot or of seeing someone she loved shot. She lost a friend and a family member in the violence. She got used to seeing people dead and manoeuvring around the city to avoid the clashes and bullets. She felt it was a miracle that they didn't get hit.

For Amira and her family, this time meant living on high alert, in what she described as 'fight or flight mode'. Current research tells us that the fight or flight mode means that the body has shifted into instinctive hyperarousal response to a situation that continues to be dangerous, and from which a person cannot escape (Ogden et al. 2011, p. 33). Amira said that what compounded the challenges were that the culture around her was not forgiving either. The rest of Bethlehem had avoided some of the intense clashes that had surrounded the area of Rachel's tomb where her family lived. In the 40-day siege, they ran out of food. Her siblings were younger, and she felt a need to protect them, but she also realised that she was physically unable to do this by herself.

Amira remembered driving to school once with her dad and some other children. They saw a mysterious white truck and thought it would be fun to follow it. It reached the mall, and then the truck stopped. Men jumped out and started shooting at the air as people scurried in all directions. Her dad continued driving and the children all fell into hysterical laugher at the back of the car. They had been so scared that laughter had welled up inside them as a shock response.

Often, Amira would be evacuated in the middle of the night or spend days at home surrounded by machine-gun points. There was a military camp five minutes from the house and bullets were always firing. In the day, it was rubber bullets and gas bombs, and at night, there were always clashes. I asked Amira what she felt about the word *trauma* when she remembered her past.

She said that after being educated about what trauma was, that the term meant a lot to her. She took the term seriously because she could connect it to what had happened to her. She realised that whatever people have experienced leaves an impact that they need to work through. Of course, there are different kinds of traumas, she readily admitted, and different scales of traumatic intensity. She said she initially realised that trauma was related to war and refugees, death and attacks, to intense world events or intense events related to war. But she recognised later, when she heard about other people's experiences, that trauma can also be experienced by people who have been sex trafficked or in car accidents. Differing from other experiences of suffering, Amira thought that trauma was attached to multiple layers of experience, at a higher intensity.

Amira tied trauma to an existential questioning. She said that part of what makes trauma different from other experiences of suffering is that it can raise unanswerable questions and leaves people with unresolved feelings. In trauma, she realised that the more events and relationships involved in the experience, the more unresolved questions it would leave. There was that difficulty because you could not have resolution. You are left asking, what was the point of all this?

Amira recognised that she always knew she and her family were paying a price for two groups of people, so it was not just a straightforward division between what was good and what was bad. There were multiple contributors, rather than one perpetrator. For her, it was more nuanced. She had to understand and reconcile herself to her own trauma, but then she wanted to move on. She said, 'I find it hard to come to terms with being victim, unless it is that, yes, I have had trauma'. She said she felt there was a problem with taking the full identity of the victim and getting stuck there. Being a victim, as a complete identity, was different than unpacking the trauma. For her, the term victim can be all-consuming. She said:

> what drives me to see the perspective as objectively as possible is that I don't want to be labelled as a victim and I want to do something about it. Making a change would be rewarding and would be a part of healing my trauma,

> like initiating processes of preventing others from going through trauma – so healing is reciprocal. As I see people set free and protected, the more I am healed.

She said that, in going through these extreme experiences of conflict and rupture, she felt the need to engage in the opposite in order to heal. Advocating for other at-risk people groups has become a part of her journey of healing.

Amira referred to how events continued to influence her years after they had happened. Ogden et al. write that '[l]ong after the original traumatic events are over, many individuals find themselves compelled to anticipate, orient to, and react to stimuli that directly or indirectly resemble the original traumatic experience or its context' (2011, p. 65). I asked Amira about her physical experience of trauma, and how it had felt for her. She said that the first time that she noticed it was in a destabilising move to London where her pillars of healing had been taken away (she was referring to her home, education, friends and family). It was then that she realised something was not right in her body. She felt pain, and it was as if her body was speaking to her. At that point, her head was mostly clear from having done psychotherapy. She said in that context that her emotions just needed space to be heard.

But when Amira realised that the pain was still present in her body, she went to get diagnosed for post-traumatic stress disorder (PTSD). The trauma would appear as a physical symptom whenever she exercised or did intense activity, as a nerve flare-up on the left side of her body, in her face, sometimes it was in the lower neck, left arm and left leg, and most recently the right side too. Whenever she left London, it would almost disappear. At present, she does different things to heal, like yoga, and wants to explore more trauma healing methods 'to re-wire my brain a bit'. But she says, science aside, her instinct is that finding a safe and nurturing presence and place, and prayer, are keys to her healing.

Reading this Book

Spending time with Amira's story shed new light on my research on inter-relationality, or the relationships between experiences in trauma. I realised that trauma requires exploring how experience is impacted by the particularities of our suffering. This means that if we want to understand health, and how trauma can be healed, then we need to take time to unpack our definitions of what healing means, and how trauma affects the various interconnected parts of a person's life. Understood in this way, healing integrates the experiences of a whole life, in order for a cohesive sense of self to orient towards a future after trauma. However, as trauma can dominate an individual's sense of self, the experience needs to be understood, before it can be lived through. What I want to show here is that we need to have many different accounts, be it analytic, somatic, spiritual or political, to understand the ruptured relationships that constitute the trauma. Then we need to further these conversations, by exploring how our ideas of health can help us to heal trauma, or when our definitions of health require re-examination in order to hold what trauma shows us about being human.

These conversations will take place in four parts. The first part is entitled 'Critical Discourses on Embodied Trauma'. This part of the book will give us a broad overview of the history of trauma studies, and how different interpretations of what it means to 'be human' affect how theorists perceive trauma. Drawing on physiological research, Part I will examine how trauma affects the body, as developed in the theories of Peter Levine, Bessel van der Kolk and Stephen Porges' on polyvagal theory. Here, a dynamic mapping of trauma emerges through the exchange of the nervous system, the fight-or-flight responses and the interconnectivity of brain function. Part I will then develop how the effects of trauma on the body are experienced through relationship. More specifically, this means looking at how trauma is experienced through the rupture of relations of trust, the violence of social relations, and how this rupture manifests itself individually in the psyche of the self. This part will therefore set the context for the rest of the book, as it situates the interdisciplinary discourse on health and trauma as a living dynamic and rupture between the psyche, the body and the relational self.

Once we have a general understanding of how trauma has been organised as a 'kind' of disordered experience, we will turn to philosophy. I use philosophy as a way of understanding the subjective experience of an individual life, in order to explore how each person can experience trauma differently, through to one's interconnected experience of relationships. In Part II, 'Phenomenology and the Traumatised Subject', we will look at the rupture of relation as experienced in trauma through the language of philosophy. When I was in the midst of writing this book and I said that I was going to use philosophy to explore trauma, I initially received some strong reactions. Would it be clinically significant? Wouldn't philosophy be quite alienating and difficult to understand? Why make something that is already complicated even more so? As a practitioner involved in healing traumatised persons, this normative aspect of the work meant a lot to me.

I realised that to engage trauma and philosophy, I would need to work on two tasks at once. First, I would need to show how philosophy actually can help us to do 'better' interdisciplinary work, through clarifying our ambiguous perceptions. That is, I need to explain the relevance of philosophy in integrative discourses. Second, the philosophical theories that I am using need to be presented in a way that helps us, rather than hinders us with more obscure terminology and complex descriptions of simple things. This is why I decided to write the book as a series of interlinked philosophical reflections on concrete experiences of trauma. I also took care to use relevant philosophers who had written from their own experience of trauma.

In Part II, I introduce philosophy as a way of exploring the experience of trauma in the following ways. Using Emmanuel Lévinas' phenomenology to understand how the self exists as a relational subject, I will show how he helps us to connect responsibility to our agency. Also central to Lévinas is how our relationship to others is premised on our response to their suffering. Then, having that experience of a relational subject established, I consider how Paul Ricœur explores the subjective imagination. He uses the imagination specifically to understand suffering as a place of blame and lament, which is important in examining the complex relation between the victim and the perpetrator. Finally, I move to Maurice Merleau-Ponty's philosophy of the body. For Merleau-Ponty, the body as a site of meaning and exchange places a value on uncovering the complexity of embodied experience in a way that brings meaning and ethical illumination to relationships between the body structures and the world around us. Each philosopher provides phenomenological descriptions of the human experience that can enable a more detailed understanding of what trauma entails. From this understanding, the aim is then to develop a philosophical inquiry into how we understand health, through exploring bodies situated in relationship, with particular responsibilities and individualised instances of suffering that can help us to understand the interconnections found in traumatic experiences.

I use phenomenology existentially, as it is portrayed in the relational life of consciousness in Merleau-Ponty, Lévinas and Ricœur. I am taking the task of phenomenology to be mainly concerned with description, 'and not to explain or analyse', as Merleau-Ponty puts it (1962, pp. ii, viii). In this way, phenomenology helps us to hold together, connect and explore our 'life-world', and how our consciousness of these phenomena are 'consciousness *of* something' specific (Husserl 1931, p. 242; Cataldi and Hamrick 2007, p. 1, italics in the original). Exactly what it means to be conscious of something requires exploring not only what that phenomenon is, but also who we are, as subjects that perceive and interact and respond to that phenomenon.

The phenomenon that this book seeks to explore is, of course, trauma. By now we know that trauma can be organised in different ways: some focus on the role of the psyche, while others spend their time defending the experience of the body systems, or the encoding of memory. But what philosophy shows us is that each person, as a unique relational being, experiences life individually and interconnectedly. Subjective experience is comprised of the interwoven relationships of a life. In Part III, entitled 'Living Trauma in Relationship', I will build on the interdisciplinary trauma discourse of Part I, and the concept of subjectivity as experienced through relationship and responsibility in Part II. Here, I will explore the relation between mental health and experiences of conflict in more general terms. Drawing on sociological, anthropological and medical case studies of social conflict and the complex effects on mental health in wider populations, I will consider how the situation of social rupture plays out in the embodied psyche of the individual. This requires developing a framework of peacemaking, from political theory, political philosophy and human rights discourse. Trauma can, for instance, often be experienced as the rupture in the responsibility to uphold specific rights. This has ethical consequences, as it influences how the self relates to the other, and to what obligations of protection and freedom have been denied them. Leading into Part IV, I will suggest that health, as an exploration of a transformed experience of relationship, will require examining the wider issues of social well-being, as evidenced in situations of trauma.

In the last part, 'Living Trauma as Health', the aim is to bring our exploration of trauma into the wider field of healing. This is, after all, what most practitioners aim to foster. But as philosophy helps us to understand, healing is a complicated experience. Each trauma is unique. The interhuman relationship and relationship to one's place of origin'differ from person to person. Some can heal quickly. For others, it is a task of a lifetime. That means that exactly what we measure as 'healthy' needs to be thoroughly examined. We bring a lot of our own preconceived perceptions into what we want to see for the ones that we care for, and for ourselves. Here, we will place the theoretical conversations of Part III into practical application, by asking how communities attempt to heal trauma. This brings the trauma narrative into the embodied social relation of rupture, while also acknowledging the complex existential questions that arise. This means that any concept of health in trauma theory requires further developing concepts of political rights and responsibilities, as well as meta-ethical considerations of relationship between disciplines, which the health and medical humanities have long acknowledged. I will consider how this might be addressed in populations who have experienced widespread trauma, as, for instance, areas of the Israel-Palestine conflict, as well as in individual cases in which trauma causes alienation of self and self-narrative from wider relations, as, for example, in situations of human trafficking.

This book attempts to rethink how we experience trauma symptoms through our own unique relationship to the world. Trauma cannot fully be understood through the diagnostic criterion of post-traumatic stress. Rather, I am suggesting that the phenomenological tools that are used to explore the body can also be an effective way to discuss the physical and mental aspects of embodied trauma. I am particularly interested in the thinking of Ricœur, Lévinas and Merleau-Ponty, and their understanding of the embodied and relational subject. This offers a reading of embodied trauma that can connect it to wider conversations in psychological underpinnings of PTSD through Peter Levine's somatic research and Bessel van der Kolk's embodied remembering. It also helps us to tie the embodied experience of relation in trauma to the wider causal factors of social suffering and relational rupture, nurtured by the theological, political and psychological language undertones found in the thoughts of Ricœur, Merleau-Ponty and Lévinas. If, as Weil tells us, uprootedness is the deepest challenge of our time, then considering how these ruptures of relation contribute to our unique traumas is urgent and requires going beyond the usual tools of medicine and psychology to develop our conversations. It might also provide the keys required to open doors towards greater healing.

2

TRAUMA, EGO AND THE BODY

A couple of years ago, I was wandering through the streets of Jerusalem, trying to make sense of the different stories I was hearing during my travels. Having spent a bit of time in the West Bank, I had received first-hand accounts of the traumatic experiences of occupation. One of my friends told me about being held at gunpoint as a small child. For those who know about trauma, it would be quite understandable to conclude that these children would experience traumatic symptoms. But my friend did not grow up with the terminology for this. For her, as the years went on, she experienced unusual physiological responses from unknown causes. It was only when someone explained to her that she was suffering from the effects of trauma that she realised how the violent events had imprinted themselves on her life in a permanent way.

But at the same time as I had been hearing the stories about my friend and her family, I was also reading the accounts of people who had survived the Holocaust. Moving to Israel from war-torn Europe, they had settled in a turbulent landscape of ancient conflicting narratives and juxtaposed ethnic and religious identities. These new refugees held their own trauma, but they also bore the trauma of those who had not survived the war. Lévinas' writings point to those traumatised by the Holocaust who were not able to escape their suffering before their death. These names were the ones I saw commemorated at the Yad Vashem memorial. I realised that, in order to understand the trauma of Palestine and Israel, I would need to hold these two experiences of trauma that were being lived out at the same time, in this small geographical space.

Often trauma is described through concepts like rupture, suffering, displacement and loneliness. In the simplest terms, it is a continued experience of suffering instigated by a past event. Like many, my friend Amira lived her trauma both physiologically and psychologically. In his contemporary classic on trauma, *The Body Keeps*

DOI: 10.4324/9780367800017-3

the Score, Bessel van der Kolk suggests that trauma is an embodied situation of 'permanently unfinished tales' (2014, p. 195). van der Kolk writes that

> Being traumatised means continuing to organise your life as if the trauma was still going on—unchanged and immutable—as if every new encounter or event is contaminated by the past.
>
> *p. 53*

The unfinished tales are the experiences of suffering that ruptured a person's sense of predictability, trust and connection. At times, this story continues to be told by any means necessary for its expression. The memory can reveal itself in a domineering way, through nightmares, aggression or episodes of rage. In other instances, it shuts itself off from being told. The person dissociates or withdraws; the body is limp to touch.

Early Interpretations of Trauma's Psyche

Peter Levine goes as far to say that trauma has become so common in our time that it goes almost undetected. This statement garners support from the widening research on the diversity of trauma populations (2010). But the experience of trauma, though its organised psychological documentation is relatively recent, has been a part of the human condition since its recorded beginning. Ancient mentions of trauma come to us in the form of myth, plays and narratives, as well as historical accounts. For instance, in the Greco-Roman traditions, they range from portraying trauma mythically, in characters like Gorgon Medusa, whose victims transform to stone in her gaze, to detailed accounts of Homer's injured soldiers. Nikitas Nomikos references 178 cases of physical trauma in the Greek epics of Homer, suggesting that these are the first accounts of trauma in European writing. These Greek accounts are mainly found in the *Odyssey* and the *Iliad,* though trauma here refers to the physical wounds experienced in war, rather than psychological memory affect (2017).

More nuanced accounts of trauma are offered through the mythical characters of Philomela, who was raped by her sister's husband, King Tereus of Thrace. She is rendered speechless, and Nanette Auerhahn reads this account psychoanalytically, suggesting that the 'action in the story...is shown to be an apt metaphor for visceral affective knowing and for recruitment of the body in the metabolization of trauma' (2016, p. 78). Whatever the case, it shows an understanding of the interconnection between adverse experience and a change in how the body communicates. In these ancient narratives, physical trauma is recorded and recounted in a way that connects these ruptured body relations and speech acts to the horrific events that caused them.

It is, of course, not only the Greek texts that give insight into ancient experiences of trauma. In the ancient Hebraic texts, for instance, Abraham brings his nephew Lot and his family out of the city of Sodom and Gomorrah before it bursts into flame. Lot's wife turns into a pillar of salt as she looks back at the burning remnants of Sodom and Gomorrah, exhibiting what Levine will later on refer to in his work as bodily affect (2010, p. 31). Other accounts in the book of the Prophets, such as the one found in Isaiah 7, recount the traumatic events that surround the communal trauma of the people of Judah (Esterhuizen 2018, p. 524). Here, trauma is revealed through the prophetic text narrative, as a 'suffering that remains' in the narrative history of a people (Rambo 2010, ct. in Esterhuizen 2018, p. 524). This selection of ancient texts offers only a glimpse of the multiple interconnections identified between event and response, which we will return to and expand on throughout the rest of this book.

The more subtle, psychological description of trauma, as an ongoing psychic suffering, is however quite recent. In fact, with the exception of historically documented ancient accounts of war, the psychological mapping of trauma only really started to take place at the end of the nineteenth century, at the time when psychology was developing as a field of study. Despite the phenomenon of trauma being a central experience in sacred texts and ancient dramatic narratives, medicine only recently turned its critical attention to the mental aspects of trauma. It was only even later into the twentieth century that the term post-traumatic stress disorder (PTSD), emerging out of the generalised criterial for 'gross stress reaction' (GSR) and transient situational disturbances (TSD), and later coined by the APA in the Diagnostic and Statistical Manual III, began to be used as a way of connecting and treating the disparate experiences (DiMauro et al. 2014).

Early Analytic Accounts

At present, a person can be diagnosed with PTSD in 636,120 different ways, suggesting that trauma must be considered in light of the more specific life experiences of the individual (DiMauro et al. 2014). The first accounts of the systematic studying of memory in relation to trauma occur in the late nineteenth century. During this time, the nature of traumatic memory became a central topic of discussion as it pertained to the wider systematic study of mental health problems (van der Kolk 2014, p. 176). Particular attention was given to patients in England and France who showed loss of memory through a phenomenon known as 'railway spine' (p. 177). Individuals who had experienced train accidents were studied as doctors tried to connect the 'spinal symptoms' suffered with the 'nervous manifestations' that were present in the patients afterwards (Grant 1898, p. 956). However, it was not until Jean-Martin Charcot's study of hysteria that trauma was properly and formally developed through scientific study.

Charcot developed a comparative analysis between hysteria, which included mostly female patients, and the symptoms of railway accident victims, which were often male. He noticed that his patients with hysteria had similar symptoms to the 'post-traumatic symptoms found among the predominantly male population of workplace and railway accident victims' (Fletcher 2013, p. 21). Charcot, referred to later as the 'father of neurology' (van der Kolk 2014, p. 177), observed a behavioural likeness in the two populations. He realised that both populations showed traces of traumatic memory in the body and a loss of language function (ibid.). This led to Charcot's theory of *auto-suggestion*. Recording his findings, Charcot wrote

> That a vigorous artisan, well-built, not enervated by high culture, the stoker of an engine for example, not previously emotional...should after an accident to the train, by a collision or running off the rails, become hysterical for the same reason as a woman, is what surpasses our imagination.
>
> *Lecture XVIII, in Charcot 1889, p. 222, qt. in Fletcher 2013, p. 21*

The bodies of these individuals were somehow responding in a similar way to both events. For Charcot, auto-suggestion meant that a 'subjective impression or idea' could be experienced as if it was like an object or a thing, like a physical blow from a stick, acting on the subject. Studying this subjective experience of 'shock or fright', Charcot believed, took him to 'the very border between neurology and psychology' (Fletcher 2013, p. 21). It gave an early indication of just how our memory connects our psychological self to our physical body. For instance, in the case of Lelog, a patient who had been injured in a cart accident, the accident could not be recollected in memory: 'Instead of remembering the accident, he developed paralysis of his legs' (van der Kolk 2014, p. 178). What Charcot's auto-suggestion theory helps us to understand is that a subjective impression can express itself somatically as a bodily symptom.

Charcot situated the recreated event of trauma in the neurological centres. It was Pierre Janet who took this research further, collaborating with Charcot on systematic laboratory research centred on studying hysteria. In *L'automatisme psychologique*, Janet suggests that 'vehement emotions' that cause 'intense emotional arousal' are at the root of traumatic experience (Van der Hart and Rydberg 2019, p. 191). It was Janet who also first used the term *dissociation*, as he explored the way in which memory and retrieval of memory was affected by emotional states (Janet 1889/2018). The role of 'altered states of consciousness' in the understanding of trauma was later further developed and proven through laboratory work and David Spiegel's dissociation research with civilian disaster populations (Janet 1889/2018, p. 131), but it was Janet who first pioneered the connection between memory retrieval and trauma experience.

Janet's pathogenic study of patients with hysteria not only laid important groundwork for understanding dissociation. He was also able to show the interconnection in how trauma stores memory in a different way to regular experiences. Revealing the connection between broken narrative and trauma symptoms, Janet's work served as an important precursor to a variety of psychotherapeutic methods. For instance, Judith Herman shows that Janet importantly documented traumatic symptoms 'but also found that these symptoms resolved when the memories, with their accompanying intense affect, were reintegrated into the ongoing narrative of the patient's life' (2015, p. 133). Janet clearly outlines this novel and important interconnection between narrative and trauma symptoms.

This interconnection of trauma with its recollected narrative is critically important. Janet showed that psychological phenomenon is essentially an experience of action. So, memory, as a psychological phenomenon, is an expression of action as well: 'the action of telling a story...' The traumatic story lacks its completion, as it has not completed its full range of action and has not been integrated into the wider narrative. Janet suggests that this synthesis, or 'liquidation', cannot happen until a person has achieved an inward reaction, that is, an organisation of the words that a person uses to understand her story: 'the organisation of the recital of the events to others and to ourselves, and...the putting of this recital in its place as one of the chapters in our personal history' (Janet 1976/1919, p. 661).

Janet is connecting the body's untold story with trauma's recurring impact on memory. Interestingly here, we also see a precursor to somatic engagement with trauma, where the body itself becomes a player in completing the action that trauma requires of the body, thereby 'putting [the] recital in its place' (ibid.). This insightful exposition on memory, linking the narrative dimensions of pathology, as well as the body's reaction to, and processing of, 'vehement emotion', enabled theorists after Janet to connect the mysterious realms of trauma experience with new depth and clarity.

Freud, a contemporary of Charcot and Janet, became fascinated with the theory of *auto-suggestion*, having observed similarities mentioned in his own patients' cases of hysteria in Vienna. However, in Freud's analysis, developed in the essay 'On the Psychical Mechanism of Hysterical Phenomena' (1893), he expressed an explicit desire to 'exit from neurology... "onto psychological ground"' (p. 170, qt. in Fletcher 2013, p. 28). For him, it was important to clarify that traumatic events are not so much 'represented' in the neural cortex, as they are imprinted as mental representations. This means that the psychical trauma becomes 'a matter of affect' that reveals itself after the event, in a specific way, through the person's psychical experience (pp. 29, 38). For Freud, trauma is part of the developmental arch of the ego (Alford 2013) and the wider study of the experience of the self.

The interconnection between our past and our present features extensively in Freud's work, and trauma plays an important role in linking the two. Freud's structure of the personality hinges on the interaction between our conscious and unconscious psychic experiences. The ego, or the integrated self, contains elements of both of these. In trauma, Freud writes that the equilibrium of the ego floods the subconscious 'with the memory of the event, the trauma, which produced the paralysis' (Fletcher 2013, p. 172). The ego-personality that we experience now is therefore being affected by the unconscious past. This *affect,* understood psychologically, refers to the 'lived experience of traumatic memory'. More specifically, the re-told trauma narrative reveals a blurring of what we consider to be facts about our experience. We do not just recall the things that have happened to us chronologically or objectively. What is recalled is mainly 'the impact of those facts on victim's lives and about the painful continuities created by the violence in their lives' (Gobodo-Maikizelu, ct. in Stauffer 2015, p. 70). In contemporary discussions of this theory, Gobodo-Maikizelu goes on to clarify that this lived experience of traumatic memory becomes 'a touchstone for reality' (ct. in Stauffer 2015, p. 70). The memory interprets and lives through the traumatic experience as more than just 'facts' that have happened to us. This experience of affect is lived out in how the traumatised person understands and interprets her story.

Freud points to two driving forces that shape the construction of the ego. The formation of the ego is experienced as both the conflict between instinctive impulses, which Freud labels as *Eros* (the sex instinct) and *Thanatos* (the death instinct), and the repression of these instincts (1991). Freud thinks that this conflict between instinctive forces is central to constructing a healthy ego. However, traumatic repression is somewhat different. First, traumatic repression disrupts the neuropsychological equilibrium. Second, the way that the event has been placed in memory affects the verbal rendering of the events. For instance, in *Studies on Hysteria*, Freud and Breuer write that 'the symptom joins in the conversation', and 'the foreign body [or cause of trauma]...continues to operate unceasingly as a stimulating cause of illness until it is got rid of' (1895, pp. 39, 35). In order to rid the ego of this unwelcomed presence from the past, the traumatic event itself needs to be put into words. In this way, '[t]he patient's speech comes not from the present moment but from the traumatic experience in...its moment of origin' (p. 39). Freud therefore develops the nuance of traumatic engagement beyond neurology, locating the trauma narrative in the psyche, or the whole mind, as distinct from the physical body (APA 2013).

Trauma, in this understanding, affects the self-development of the ego, and, more specifically, how the ego will relate to the world through narrative. In this way, Freud shows us a type of historical understanding of trauma. Trauma, as an experience of loss, is located in the history of the self, and impacts how the self-forms relationships with the world. For Sara Beardsworth, Freud offers the beginnings of uncovering the connections between the 'bonds of the trials of separation' with the 'possibility of bonds with others and socialisation' (2009, p. 46). In this interpretation, Freud develops an account of trauma that ties the ego to mythical originals of the psyche. The ego is constituted as a 'myth with foundational properties' (p. 47). As, for instance, evidenced in the Oedipal complex, where Freud dramatises the development of the ego through his rendering of the Greek story centred on paternal jealousy and narcissism, Beardsworth notes how Freud's foundations of subjectivity rely on a generalised notion of trauma.

Because of Freud's reading of conflict, Beardsworth concludes that Freudian psychoanalysis actually makes trauma a point of origin for subjectivity. Trauma, interpreted in this way, becomes important in establishing separation from others, and experiencing the conflict of relationship, meaning that trauma itself can open up the possibility of a subject's 'futurity' (2009, p. 47). As the *Thanatos* impulse shows, the subject can emerge through its experience of death, or as *Eros* reveals, the repressed sexual conflict reveals the birthing of the ego. While the comprehensiveness of the theories put forward by Freud and his predecessors has been disputed (which we will look at in a moment), these early accounts reveal how outer events can have inner psychic consequences. Through studying the symptoms of their patients, these early analysts started to map out how the physiological and the psychical worlds interacted, and how symptoms such as dissociation, repression and other affects offered keys to exploring a human's hidden experience.

Post-Freudian Theory

For Freud, traumatic symptoms, such as dissociation, point to 'a splitting of the content of consciousness' (1893, ct. in Ringel and Brandell 2011, p. 2). But the act of 'splitting' is caused by something external to consciousness. So, for instance, a car crash might be the act that causes disequilibrium in the ego, resulting in a person experiencing nightmares long after the event. Freud's conflict theory shows how an external physical event can impact consciousness. It also shows the importance of the historical self, through connecting adult lived experience to childhood traumas.

However, Freud and his predecessors could not fully account for how traumatic experience connects us to each other. For Carl Jung, Freud's unconscious mind needed further expansion. Jung appealed to mysticism and to natural laws in order make sense of the human psyche. For Jung, our unique personality emerges as an inward psychic entity whose source is a collective unconscious reality. Jung mapped the psyche's interaction with the collective unconscious, through the personal psyche's unconscious desire to find balance in midst of the opposite states of nature (Kelland 2015).

Drawing on the psyche's interaction with collective unconscious archetypes that organise human personality, Jungian theory posits an interesting counterpoint to Freud's exposition of trauma and affect. Jung reads these human experiences as psychological complexes, in which experiences are clustered around a specific archetypal theme. Understanding trauma in this way can take different interpretations. For instance, looking at Jung's mapping of generic complexes, John Wilson suggests that it is possible to create a Trauma Complex. The Trauma Complex exhibits archetypal psychological processes, such as the 'Abyss Experience', and constructs a reading of experience that ties it to wider themes of self (2004, p. 43). Similarly, contemporary psychoanalyst Donald Kalsched suggests that in Jung's account, trauma can often be understood as a kind of spiritual crisis. Both accounts show how Jung's poetic structure of the mind connects the images of the mind to its common collective resource. It was these images that came to represent parts of the self.

Contrasting the objects-relations theorists Fairbairn and Winnicott, who suggest that psychic figures are conditioned by external objects, Jung proposes that the inner objects are brought forward by the unconscious itself. He writes that: 'If the unconscious figures are not acknowledged as spontaneous agents, we become victims of a one-sided belief in the power of consciousness' (1967, par. 299 and 62). This interplay between the unconscious and conscious realities is critical to the understanding of affect, which we see in traumatic cases. We note here the shift in language from the Freudian psyche. For Jung, this spiritual crisis would require accessing something beyond the ordinary means of coping with life alone; it requires the 'intervention of powerful archetypal forces from the unconscious' (2013, p. 21). Now, in Jung, as with Freud, we see a blurring of the mythic and the psychological. However, Jung uses myth almost spiritually, as a reconstruction of personality. Jung interprets archetypal powers as taking on the function of, what Kalsched refers to as a 'self-care system, whereby the "fugitive parts" of the self can find a framework for return' (p. 21). As with Freud, then, we see an emergence of the subject associated with the traumatic. However, we also see the reverse. It is the specific experiences of trauma that bring the ruptured, or traumatised self, into the light.

Jung writes that 'the essential basis of our personality is affectivity' (1960, par. 78). That is, who we experience ourselves to be is actually a compilation of our various interactions with the world, which are conscious and unconscious, individual and collective. But 'unbearable' affect is a sign of trauma, which possesses the force of dissociation (Kalsched 1998, p. 467). Kalsched's interpretation of Jung, drawing on research from Badenoch, suggests that *dissociation* can be understood as the psyche's response to trauma. In this instance, trauma can trigger anti-life forces that break a person's ability to feel their lived body experience. But these can also be helpful, because the body's experience is actually overwhelming. Badenoch writes that by fragmenting, dividing and encoding different aspects of the traumatic experience in the brain into compartments and segmented 'neural nets', it can protect the individual 'from the full impact of experience that is unbearable' (2008, p. 9). This segmentation restricts our sense-making and ability to recount our life-narrative cohesively. The ego tries to 'glue itself' back together through the use of different kinds of experiences, such as sensations, memories, images and feelings (Kalsched 1998).

This effort of the personality to preserve a sense of intactness is what Kalsched refers to as the ego's 'self-care system'. The 'self-care' system calls on the archetypal, or collective, forces in our subconscious as a way of protecting the self from its suffering. These forces, Kalsched suggests, are spiritual, or 'numinous'; they are manifest in dreams and the 'imaginative products of the human psyche', uncovered through psychotherapy (p. 24). However, whilst these powers have the ability to protect the self from trauma, they can also manifest as aggressive 'demonic voices' and unstable 'inner entities'. This can, for instance, be experienced in traumatic nightmares. These aggressive and impersonal, untransformed powers in the personality are almost 'mythological', reflecting what Winnicott and object theorists refer to as 'child omnipotence' (2013, p. 25). But they are also more than childhood models, Kalsched suggests. They are 'personified representatives' of 'universal archetypal forces' (ibid.). The universal forces become resource for those in trauma living without, or before, resource. The challenge, however, emerges when these representatives actually become a '*substitute* for reality', rather than as incorporated in a helpful, wider transitional experience.

Some critics of Jung have labelled his work 'sheer mysticism', and others have challenged his very particularised uses of folklore (Drake 1967, p. 321). Still others problematise the notion of a collective archetype that has any substantive unifying unconscious content (Neher 1996). In Kalsched's contemporary adaptation of Jungian trauma theory, he emphasises how Jungian analysis needs to avoid the pitfalls of disembodied theory.'Jungian analysis', he writes,'has been especially guilty of this ascent into mentalisation and the pursuit of intellectual meaning' (2013, p. 8). Aware of the limitations of Jungian analysis, however, he also suggests that it works well in partnership with contemporary somatic-based findings. What Jungian analysis offers is a narrative context that shows how trauma can impact the constitution of personality. Without understanding the inner event of trauma, beyond the dominant perspectives of neuroscience, the concept of *affect* loses its inner significance. So what this means is that the neuroscientific explanations, which we will turn to in a moment, somehow require a grounding beyond the seen experience: 'neuroscience will have to open to the fact that *for every self-other relational moment in psychotherapy, there is also an inner event*' (2013, p. 8, italics in the original). It is the inner event that Freud and his contemporaries tried to uncover, and it is the inner event that Jung is also interested in exploring.

That trauma can be understood as an inner event is important, because it challenges approaches to trauma that want to reduce it to a materialistic event alone (we will look at this more in a moment). Kalsched is careful to note that this 'inner event' is not 'the wiring and the sculpting of the brain', but rather 'the sculpting of the soul', which Jungians may call the ego-self relationship (2013, p. 8). Here Kalsched offers psychoanalytic insight into the philosophical problem of trauma phenomenology. Similar to Merleau-Ponty's problem with reading experience through science alone, Jung helps us to understand how trauma might interact with mysticism and a shared inner world. This could also give some insight into how trauma might have intergenerational affects, without having to reduce it to changes in DNA structures. Ascertaining the experience of trauma reaches beyond materialism, taking hold of the entire self, demanding that the self-confronts its subjectivity. The experience of affect can be as an infinite overwhelming, the experience of which requires both metaphor and philosophy.

For Jung, the self becomes itself through an interior relational movement, rather than a Freudian catharsis of ego. But he is not the only theorist who challenged Freud's concept of trauma. While Jung turns to the archetypal unconscious to understand the traumatised self, Winnicott theorises that the self is constituted from a responsive relationship to outer objects. Winnicott rejects the death instinct's primary function in Freudian theory, suggesting that personality develops though the subject's own experience of her environment. It is this dynamic experience that fundamentally impacts the emerging subject (Flynn 2019). The development of this rich inner life is the central concept of Winnicott's work. Winnicott's object relations theory suggests a social account of trauma, in which trauma is understood as 'the penetration of the self, and trauma as the erosion of the self' (Alford 2013, p. 264). His concept of the false self and the true self is particularly useful, as Winnicott's 'true self' connects the self in its narrative and embodied structures. This 'true self' is not so much a 'psychic structure', as it is 'a vital psychosomatic center, bound up with a feeling of bodily aliveness, and experienced most immediately in the spontaneous gesture' (p. 264). This contrasts with the false self, the gestures of which are 'reactive, compliant and lacking in spontaneity' (ibid.). What Winnicott is able to do quite carefully is to maintain the unconscious experience of self, with its embodied existence.

What we can start to piece together from Winnicott, as well as from Freud and Jung, is that trauma is constitutive of human experience, but also an individually lived experience. This means, if we look back at the introduction, that trauma has phenomenological value because it affects our experience of being in the world. In object relations theory, Winnicott explores this by pulling some of his ideas from Freud, and he expands, critiques and contextualises them in the infant-parent relationship. For instance, he illustrates ego formation in the infant though showing how the needs of the infant are similar to a satisfied id. However, if the ego is not able to include and synthesise the id-excitements, then they can be experienced traumatically: 'the id-excitements can be traumatic when the ego is not yet able to include them' (1965, p. 141). A false self then develops as a way of shielding the ego. Though in an initial way it can be perceived as taking care of the ego, shielding it from being overwhelmed, it actually hinders the person from fully integrating and living from their whole self. Reflecting on a patient that exhibited this false self, Winnicott wrote of her experience that she 'had the feeling all her life that she had not started to exist, and that she had always been looking for a means of getting to her True Self' (1965, p. 142).[1] Winnicott helps us to see how trauma can rupture the true self, or the ego, at a very early age. In these instances, the ego is formed as the infant learns what her needs are, and how to express them.

However, traumatic situations are different. The overwhelming circumstances a person faces coax out the reactivity of the false self. This reactivity breaks down the unity between the body and the mind and affects the core of the self (Alford 2013). Winnicott writes: 'The word psyche…means the *imaginative elaboration of somatic parts, feelings, and functions,* that is, of physical aliveness…' (1949, p. 244, ct. in Alford 2013, p. 265, italics in the original). It describes a 'live body', who, with its limits, its internal and external experiences, 'is *felt by the individual* to form the core for the imaginative self' (ibid., italics in the original). In trauma, and the symptomatic experiences of PTSD[2] in particular, the restricted affect is observed through the loss of vitality or dulled emotion. These symptoms are accompanied by exaggerated startle responses and hypervigilance, as the vulnerable self-experiences a fragmentation and disruption of who they are in relation to the world around them (p. 266). Winnicott summarises this in 'The Concept of Trauma', when he writes that 'trauma is the destruction of the purity of individual experience by a too sudden or unpredictable intrusion of actual fact' (1989, pp. 146–147).

Winnicott helps to show us how the external world helps to construct and destabilise the personality, developing and critiquing the experience of Freud and Jung through the language of true and false selves. While these theories refer to the relationships between people as impacting the formation of the self, it is usually as a secondary experience. The attachment relationship to others is prioritised below the primary motivations of hunger and sexuality. However, John Bowlby's theory of attachment, which has become central to trauma discourse, problematises this motivational priority. He asserts that an infant's need for love is just as strong as an infant's need for food (Lahousen et al. 2019). Bowlby's attachment theory suggests that the child self-internalises her caregiver interactions in memory. These relational memories of our attachment figures (AFs) are stored and become an 'internal working model' (IWM) that sets future expectation for relationship.

This attachment relationship then becomes the primary motivational system that helps the infant to mediate her engagement with the rest of the world (Lahousen et al. 2019). It shapes how the individual expects and responds to her 'requests for care and comfort' in the wider life contexts (Bowlby 1969/1982; Farina et al. 2019). Cassidy and Shaver (2008) go as far as to suggest that the relations formed with AFs may shape neuroanatomical structures central to the development of an individual's 'emotional, cognitive and meta-cognitive skills' (ct. in Farina et al. 2019, p. 4). Secure attachment develops a healthy and predictable set of expectations for a child. If she has a need, then the AF will respond. However, what can often happen in life is that children develop alternatives to healthy attachment: disorganised attachment, anxious-avoidant attachment or disoriented-disorganised attachment. Comfort is not extended from a caregiver, or maybe it is sporadic and chaotic, so the child does not know what reaction to expect. In this theory, trauma is read through the attachment style of this primary caregiver. The trauma develops as a result of this attachment relationship, and the satisfaction of the primary needs of a child feeling safe and provided for.

Attachment theory reveals why experiences such as child trauma affect the person in complicated and interconnected ways and situates this theory between psychoanalysis and psychobiology. For instances, some people may develop complex functional impairments as they evolve to cope with the suffering of neglect or violence (Gilbert et al. 2009; Fegbert and Stotzel 2016, ct. in Farina et al. 2019). This theory is particularly important in understanding trauma that has happened in early childhood. One recent epidemiological study conducted by Green et al. (2010) revealed that 'approximately 44% of mental disorders with onset in childhood and 30% of those with onset in adulthood are associated with childhood trauma' (Farina et al. 2019, p. 3). However, child trauma is incredibly complex. It reveals how our relational self is tied to the development of healthy attachment, because it is not merely emotional, sexual and physical abuse that constitutes trauma. According to Woller et al., neglect results in the greatest form of developmental traumatisation (2012). Neglect is not actively inflicted on the child; it is a withholding of provision. As such, attachment theory can show how both passive and active relationships to primary caregivers can be a source of trauma. This disconnection from the other can then become integrated in the disconnection from self, or, put in another way, the disconnection *of a self.*

Collected research on attachment theory shows just how interconnected we are. A caregiver's unresolved grief, or her own trauma, can provide a 'highly inconsistent, frightened or overtly threatening behaviour towards the child' (Liotti 2009, ct. in Farina et al. 2019, p. 4). Systems-oriented perspectives show how the well-being of families is interconnected. Cloitre et al. emphasise that the interpersonal context of trauma requires the healing of 'attachment-related injuries' that are found in the family (2009, p. 395). The dynamic family system reveals an interconnection of emotions and reactivity that link individuals to each other in a common 'perceptual field' through which the external world is interpreted and experienced (Papero 2017, p. 585). Attachment theory brings together the gaps in the relational models that previous theories passed over, showing how others affect the relational self in both active and passive ways.

In this section, we have looked at how psychology helps us to understand trauma through focusing on conscious experience. Freud and his contemporaries, Jung and Winnicott all refer to a conscious self when speaking about trauma. In Freud, the traumatic results in the unconscious asserting itself, requiring history to speak. In Jung, trauma is a way of understanding the spiritual crisis of the self, and how the collective archetypes can protect the self, or further the trauma. In Winnicott's analysis, the self is formed through the relations to the outside world, and trauma results in the true self regressing into the false self. Bowlby helps us to see just how particular attachment experiences between people can produce trauma and hurt our self. Each of these theories shows how relationship interacts with the formation of the personality.

Body-based Experiencing

Analytic interpretations of trauma show us that memories can affect us both consciously and unconsciously. They also reveal how our encounters with the physical world can have mystical consequences and are mapped in the wider stories of collective traumas and events that have happened earlier in our lives, whether we are conscious of them or not. The early analytic psychologists did an incredible work in forging unexplored terrain, and making links that prior to the late nineteenth century were in the realm of myth and mysticism.

What attachment theory also manages to do is to connect the contemporary research on neurobiology with a historical but also embodied relational self. Attachment is about the care for material bodies, not just about complicated narratives. This is particularly important, as sometimes we can find that readings of unconscious narratives can feel far from the often quite simple realities of the traumatised body. This complication between psychic and material interpretations of reality is what French philosopher Paul Ricœur picks up on. Ricœur suggests that Freudian analysis in particular needs to be able to maintain the unity between the psychical reality of the conscious and unconscious experience, and the physical reality of the events that happened to the person. He says that there needs to be a 'coherence' in narrative, differing from 'certain manifestations of the unconscious, which led thinkers such as Freud to speak of "psychical reality" in contrast to material reality' (2012, p. 16). Ricœur suggests that if we just read experience through our psychical reality, then we will not be able to get at the concrete events that actually happened to the person. In a psychical reality, the symptoms (say, for instance, of trauma), 'abstract from the object and thus renounce every relation with external reality' (Ricœur 1986, p. 368). In this reading, the affect is discontinuous. However, to maintain the continuity between psychic and material reality, the foreign intrusion of the trauma narrative needs to be translated through the material experience of the past.

Other thinkers pick up on the need for psychical and material unity in theories about consciousness. Gregg M. Horowitz writes that '[t]o the unending chagrin of its practitioners and proponents alike, psychoanalysis remains an incomplete unified discipline' (2009, p. 23). By this he means two things: first, the aim of psychoanalysis is to offer 'an integrative theory of the mind' (ibid.). In this way, it offers a metapsychology: the function of psychoanalysis is to show that empirical understanding of reality is not enough. This, however, differs from the second aim, which is that psychoanalysis needs to offer a therapeutic response. The aim of psychoanalysis is therefore not only to understand the experience beyond the appearance of material things, which gives it a distinct advantage over bodied accounts. It also needs to 'relieve disabling emotional and psychological distress' (2009, p. 24). So, responding to Ricœur's challenge, analysis needs to account for the connection between material and psychical reality. But further to that, it also needs to show how trauma is more than just a material experience of suffering while tending to the suffering person who they have been asked to treat.

Horowitz believes that the challenge for psychoanalysis emerges in holding together these 'two masters'. He writes that 'Sometimes...[in] psychoanalysis, two masters issue demands that are not merely refractory, but intractably incompatible' (2009, p. 24). Offering a classic example of Freud's interaction with his patient Dora,[3] Horowitz suggests that Freud's persistent authoritative insistence on the 'rightness' of his interpretation, which differed from the patient's perceived experience, resulted in a breakdown of relationship and a case of 'poor hearing'. Here, Horowitz shows how a person's demand for methodological correctness and 'metapsychological consistency', despite the patient's suffering contradiction, ends up resulting in the patient's inability to heal (p. 25). In other words, practically speaking, Freud's metapsychological analysis presented itself as therapeutic failure.

I would moderate Horowitz claims of therapeutic failure with the suggestion that the real problem lies in the fact that these certain instances of analysis do not present wholly embodied accounts of trauma. When my friend spoke about her experiences of reliving the trauma of the Intifadas, she realised that it had unconsciously worked itself into her present experience. But for her, this experience of trauma was primarily located in her body. Analysis presents us with an important way of contextualising and giving meaning to deeply ambiguous circumstances. It shows us that we cannot just seek material answers for the trauma, but that we need to interpret the unconscious interactions in a person's life. However, divorced from the materiality of the body, this reading of trauma does not account for how consciousness interacts with a specific, sensing and breathing person.

Horowitz's criticism of Freudian metapsychology is similar to how contemporary psychiatrist Bessel van der Kolk's challenges Freud's understanding of trauma. Freud suggests that the visceral memories associated with traumatic experiences are a 'compulsion to repeat'. This compulsion indicates that the individual wants to gain control and eventual mastery over a situation. But van der Kolk suggests that reliving the trauma in this way can actually reassert the powerful memory in the mind. Rather than acting cathartically as Freud believed, the repetition could instead sediment the memory in the neural pathways of the brain. That means that rather than achieving a narrative catharsis, what is needed is to integrate this embodied dominant memory. The dominant reactive memory needs help to find its place in the continuous unfolding of present and future experience (2014). So we see here that how we understand the traumatic interaction between memory and the brain not only affects how we can figure out how the memory is first encoded, but also how to distinguish between re-traumatising a person and healing them (something we will examine further at the end of the book).

Kalsched suggests that Jung's early understanding of dissociation can give clues as to why repeating the trauma narrative might re-traumatise the patient. This is because the memory, when it is articulated in language, can place the patient in a constant 'risk of being flooded with overwhelming unmodulated affect' (1999, p. 471). The result of relaying the traumatic narrative through analysis in this way, Jung realised, 'often leaves them feeling re-traumatized', and, in specific instances, this re-traumatisation in therapy may itself 'set off hallucination-like symptoms, flashbacks, sleep disturbances, nightmares or incursions of traumatic emotion' (ibid.). That is, the reflections of the analyst may invoke a traumatic transference that precipitates 'sudden splitting and regression' of personality (ibid.). So we can see that van der Kolk's concern about reading trauma as a psychic narrative divorced from the material body is further highlighted in Jung's observations.

Peter Levine prefers a body-based reading of trauma. He thinks that trauma needs to be able to be understood without an analyst. He writes that 'traumatised individuals are not made whole through the therapeutic relationship alone' (2010, p. 110). This is not just a critique of psychoanalytic method, but rather of understanding trauma without accounting for the significance of the body. Levine suggests trauma needs to be understood through how it affects our neurophysiology. He reads trauma as a somatic experience. The terms somatics, coined by Thomas Hanna in the 1970s, connects consciousness with muscle and nerve control, integrating into a state known as sensory-motor awareness (Hanna 2004). In essence, this is a theory of corporeal reflexivity (Maitland 2016). The body is maintained by biological systems that operate in integrated feedback loops. These systems then respond and adjust to fluctuations in order to bring the body back to homeostasis.

Fluctuations can be caused by endogenous or external experiences (Protevi 2009). Usually, the body returns to equilibrium, through these innate self-regulatory systems. However, if a change happens that pushes the system beyond its regulative threshold, the system will struggle to recuperate (ibid.). The somatic theory of trauma is premised on the idea that the body has not been able to complete the self-regulative return to homeostasis. Rather than being defined as a disease, it is a disrupted bodily process that is rooted in innate biological shock responses (Levine 2010). This view of trauma, as a series of neurophysiological effects that trap undesired tension in the body, is premised on Stephen Porge's trauma theory. Porge links trauma to the body's unfulfilled fight-or-flight response to a terrifying experience. When the traumatic event passes, the trauma is stored and relived, as the body stays stuck in an incomplete response (2017). An example of this would be when a person who has been in an accident freeze when they hear the sound of car breaks (immobilisation) or becomes unusually agitated when getting into a car again (sympathetic arousal). The body is telling the person that the memory of the trauma still lives on in the arousal systems of the autonomic nervous system (ANS) and the muscle memory.

Levine highlights that when the body is reacting to the current experience through its memory of a past trauma, it is difficult for the person to process critically. What Levine means is that it can be very difficult for a person to accurately verbalise and process the trauma, when the basic responses of the body systems are on high alert. Levine suggests that 'Unable to recognize caring feelings in the face and posture of others, such a client finds it extremely difficult to feel that anyone is safe or can really be trusted' (2010, p. 111). In this state, then, the embodied affect of fear can involuntarily lead to retreat in relationship, through projected statements of blame, as well as 'self-recrimination and shame' (ibid.). van der Kolk suggests that the person, having experienced a break in relationship to the outward world, and to other people, is continuing to respond to this break, involuntarily, and bodily, in the current experience. This inadvertently compromises all relationships, including the patient-therapist relation. But this is more about the body's unresolved response to trauma than it is about the effectiveness of the therapist. What this shows is not only how important addressing the basic responses of the body is to the clinical relationship, but, even before that, how important it is to understand how trauma compromises the body's response systems.

van der Kolk shows us that traumatic memory can be stored as an experience of helplessness. The memory is stored in the body 'as muscle tension or feelings of disintegration in the affected body areas' (2014, p. 265). This sensed experience then accompanies them in the present and can also be expressed through heart rate variability (HRV), where 'good heart rate variability is a measure of basic well-being' (p. 267). This is seen when the sympathetic nervous system (SNS) is stimulated by heightened arousal to raise the heart rate, and the parasympathetic nervous system (PNS) is activated to lower the heart rate, experienced, for instance, in dissociation (also known as flat affect) (pp. 266–267). When these two parts of the ANS are not exhibiting good patterns of variability, 'the lack of fluctuation in heart rate in response to breathing – not only has negative effects on thinking and feeling but also on how the body responds to stress', which is a symptom commonly experienced by traumatised individuals (p. 267).

For van der Kolk, this ruptured relation to the world constitutes trauma. He says that 'disassociation is the essence of trauma' (2014, p. 66). This is because, according to this body-based perspective, trauma is representing itself as an 'overwhelming experience' of being 'split off and fragmented' (ibid.). This means that the sounds, images, emotions, sensations and thoughts that are connected to the trauma can 'take on a life of their own', by intruding 'into the present, where they are literally relived' (p. 67). Understanding the interconnected phenomenon of bodily experience is therefore crucial to figuring out how this fragmented self can be restored to relationship with herself and with others. It is here that the disciplines of medicine, psychology and philosophy can illuminate one another.

Conclusion

In Amira's experience of trauma, she referred to living in a constant state of flight-or-flight response to events around her. During the sieges and intense fighting during the Intifadas, her family often needed to hide in a safe room, until the demands of life forced them out of isolation. Years later, she recounts the impact that these events had on her. She tells me that it was the physical experience of pain that told her that she was not fully well. She says that after some talk therapy, she has been able to clarify her thoughts, but that she still felt that her 'body was speaking'. Whenever she exercises or undergoes a physically intense experience, nerve pain flares up in the left side of her body, her 'face, sometimes lower neck, left arm and, more recently, my right side'. It was this continued pain that caused her to seek out a diagnosis.

Amira's story shows how the body encodes the trauma in complex ways. The experience of the body is tied to a wider network of relations between the self and others. It also connects us to our experiences of value, our beliefs about the world around us and about ourselves. This is where interdisciplinary conversations are particularly important. Given the complexity of trauma, it requires that 'metaphor, emotion and spiritual and existential dimensions' are studied as 'central parts of the experience of the patient', despite not being 'part of the language of the clinic' (Carel and McNaughton 2016, p. 295). But this is not just a matter of psychical representation; trauma must also consider that an individual person experiences her body in a particular way. Without this account, the individual body cannot find its cohesion, which is central to an experience of health. A person is never a 'neutral object' that we can understand through 'objective measures'. The experience of being our body is therefore 'filtered' through prior, and often unseen, influences, such as our relations to the wider world and to our value structures (p. 297).

Trauma is trickier to locate than other physical states, which means that discourses on health need to account for this ambiguity. It requires that we understand how our body and minds are affected by memory and by different forms of relationship. Trauma shows us that how we experience the disordered present is as a result, not of some physical presence in the body now, but as the embodied hostile memory still working itself out in present experience. In experiences of dissociation and immobilisation, which are the symptoms of trauma, van der Kolk asks, 'How can traumatised people learn to integrate ordinary sensory experiences so that they can live with the natural flow of feeling and feel secure in their bodies?' (2014, p. 127).

According to van der Kolk and Levine, trauma understood as a situation of isolated suffering requires examining the rupture of embodied relation.

Notes

1 This notion of false and true self somewhat overlaps with the Internal Family systems theory, which we will look at later on.
2 We will look at this diagnostic definition in Chapter 3.
3 From 'Fragment of an Analysis of a Case of Hysteria' (1925).

3

LABELLING TRAUMATIC AMBIGUITY

So far, Part I has done a great deal of meandering through theoretical interpretations of trauma. We looked at a few ancient examples, followed by analytic accounts that ask us to verbalise unsaid terrors and piece together broken stories. Then we saw how somatic and body-based theories try to veer away from the delicate interpretative relationship between the analyst and patient in order to focus on understanding the role of the material body. In this interpretation, trauma is more of an incomplete response than an archetypal self-care system.

But we still have not touched on the basic tool for interpreting traumatic experience. The *Diagnostic and Statistical Manual* (DSM) is a handbook of diagnostic criteria, compiled by the American Psychological Association. Read through this guide, the trauma criteria enable us to put a label on the traumatic experience that helps get support, money and medication to treat it. The DSM interpretation has received substantial criticism and requires that we read trauma through a set of its symptoms. Whether mental disorders be classified as 'discreet clinical conditions', or how arbitrary the distinctions between conditions are has followed the discourse on categorical models of disorders since the beginning of its compilation (Widiger and Samuel 2005). Nevertheless, the DSM enables clinicians to recognise particular dimensions of classifications that can enable them to treat their patients in a unified manner.

The Diagnostic Criterion for Trauma

Here again we see the tenuous link. Does all trauma need to be diagnosed in order to be understood? Very few traumas are the simple kind. The role of the diagnostic tools is to clarify the complex situation, to give language to ambiguity, which helps to provide concrete next steps. This is not a matter of sticking a label on some symptoms. For instance, cumulative relational trauma, referred to as 'complex

DOI: 10.4324/9780367800017-4

PTSD' (post-traumatic stress disorder), rather than situating itself in one event, shows how different relationships overlap one another (Herman 1992; Sar 2011). In other conversations, it has been suggested that the complex trauma of children and adolescents be referred to as 'developmental trauma disorder' (van der Kolk 2014). The original intention behind the DSM, according to van der Kolk, was to gather symptoms of trauma-related experiences, rather than serve as a diagnostic toolkit (van der Kolk 2020). The PTSD diagnosis needs to be open to complex interpretation and sub-categorisation. This means that seeing the DSM as a diagnostic source is complicated by an ambiguous interconnection between being a source of prescription and diagnosis and being a resource for classifying symptoms of mental health disorders.

It is in the DSM-III that one first comes across the diagnosis for PTSD (DiMauro et al. 2014). When I was speaking to Amira about her experiences of trauma growing up during the Intifadas, she told me that connecting her pain symptoms to the events that she had experienced prompted her to get tested for PTSD. In its simplest form, PTSD, as it is interpreted in the DSM, presents a medicalised account of trauma that quite practically helps identify and treat people with symptoms of trauma.

The stories for the emergence of this diagnosis are varied, combining the narratives of Vietnam War veterans coming home with anti-war protests to the advances in the medical sciences that wanted to push away from moral explanations of medical experiences. PTSD emerged as a cluster of disorders. From that point, the history of this diagnosis has been marked by considerable disagreement and converging medical advancements. In order to treat patients, however, clinicians require a robust understanding of trauma experience. This means extending beyond narrow definitions of trauma, which include definitions confined to single generations and to specific, unified contexts.

It is important to have a nuanced understanding of the history, sociological structures and biological adaptation that we know constitute each individualised traumatic experience. However, this differs from extending definitions of PTSD to everything: as psychiatrist Lynne Jones puts it when reflecting on her work in the Bosnian War in the 1990s, not every wound is PTSD, and 'not all suffering is mental illness' (Jones 2014, 'Each Scar is Different'). Using particular tools to therefore evaluate and understand the experience, such as the Traumatic Life Event Questionnaire and the PTSD Checklist, offers ways of quantifying traumatic experience so that individuals can receive the help that they need in experiences of overwhelming suffering. But quantification and definition come at a cost. Exactly what is 'in', and what is 'out'? Furthermore, what do we do with the experiences that are not deemed 'quantifiable' in these models of understanding?

Another challenge concerning the DSM is that it presents a very particular view of the subject. Gaines (1992) suggests that it shows a 'cultural ideal of the normative personality', which is predominantly a white Protestant male of European ancestry, whose emotive state is regulated by rationalism. This dualistic interpretation reveals that the emotive self (affect) needs to be regulated by the cognitive (rational) self, in order to be measured as a balanced, healthy person. So, what it is essentially promoting, Plotkin Amrami et al. suggest, is an 'autotelic' subject, whose ability to govern himself enables him to stay 'resilient' in traumatic situations, to reflect the 'natural' potential of the human being (2016, pp. 2, 4). But this is obviously a problem when we consider that the traumatised subject does not often fit into this narrow definition. A broader understanding of the subject, promoted through the DSM, then could be a personality that is constructed based on a symptomatic deviation from the 'normal', which means that figuring out what these definitions entail in terms of subjectivity is crucial.

Attempts to redefine and extend the understanding of trauma experience, particularly in diagnostic accounts of PTSD, can be found in the work of Levine and van der Kolk. But there are others who want to diversify diagnostic definitions. For instance, a movement towards placing the diagnosis in a wider biological history is reflected when Bracha and Maser suggest that new DSM definitions take into account 'empirical studies and/or theories that place psychopathology in an evolutionary context' (2008, ct. in Levine 2010, p. 29). They suggest that this extension will show the interconnectedness between trauma and wider human and animal experiences. They write that the trauma field will then be able to connect 'to broader issues in biology' and that psychopathological data can then be placed in a 'widely accepted concept' that can enable clinicians to possibly develop 'more effective behavioural treatments' (2008, ct. in Levine 2010, p. 29). Levine suggests that the original diagnostic literature on PTSD 'pigeonholed trauma as a reified and incurable disease' (2010, p. 28). The instinctive elements of trauma, as Levine illustrates in his body-based approach, seemed to be avoided in the earlier editions of PTSD, along with specific mechanisms that explain the interaction between the brain and the body (2010).

Emil Kraepelin's early diagnosis of trauma emerged after Freud in 1909, as a 'fright neurosis' in which the body responds to overstimulation and overwhelming stress. Levine suggests this significance is due to the recognition that the role of fright has in the traumatic experience, 'although the word "neurosis" has pejorative associations' (2010, p. 32). Writings about symptoms of shell shock in the soldiers returning from First World War alongside accounts of 'battle fatigue' and 'war neurosis' in Second World War gave evidence for widespread symptoms of war trauma (2010, p. 33). The problem was, and often is, not so much the definition itself, as how the definition paints a picture that society, and clinicians in particular, then respond to. For instance, defining trauma as a neurosis, and 'shell shock', contains ethical and emotive responses. Levine writes that the trauma response thereby implied 'that a soldier's "shell shock" was somehow due to a "character defect" or a nagging personal weakness' (2010, p. 33). The response to 'stiff upper lip' could cover a multitude of nuanced problematic engagement.

The Ambiguity of Diagnosis

In the mental health literature, we see a widespread move away from moralistic and reductive accounts of wellness, from medicalised models seeking clinically assessed and systematic approaches, to compassionate engagement that avoids the stigma of these reductive labels (see, for instance, Arboleda-Flórez and Stuart 2012). van der Kolk writes how PTSD emerged as a means of classifying the wide variety of responses that returning Vietnam War veterans were exhibiting (2014). Whatever the primary motivator was the result of the systematisation of accounts led to the development of the PTSD diagnosis, which was included in the *DSM-III* in 1980. This diagnostic tool then led to the development of treatments that included not only war veterans but also those who had experienced traumatic events such as car accidents, sexual assault and rape (van der Kolk 2014). PTSD offers a helpful reading of experience that enables people to seek help. It addresses problematic moral prejudices and allows access to resources that alleviate painful symptoms. However, it also contains the lived experience of an individual to a set of criteria that not all will share.

According to the DSM-5, the 'bible of mental disorders', the disorder that results from trauma, is classified as PTSD, more specifically grouped as trauma- and stressor-related disorders. The classification contains, for instance, the following:

> A. The person was exposed to: death, threatened death, actual or threatened serious injury, or actual or threatened sexual violence; B. Intrusion symptoms; C. Persistent avoidance of stimuli associated with the trauma; D. Negative alterations in cognitions and mood that are associated with the traumatic event; E. Alterations in arousal and reactivity that are associated with the traumatic event.
>
> *DSM-5*

It encompasses, as Levine puts it, 'frightening and bizarre symptoms', which include

> flashbacks, anxiety, panic attacks, insomnia, depression, psychosomatic complaints, lack of openness, violent unprovoked rage attacks, and repetitive destructive behaviours.
>
> *1997, p. 41*

This list of traits gives us some indication of what might be classified as trauma. Rather than experiencing the natural cycle of growth and consolidation of experience in the body, the traumatised person becomes 'stuck', unable to integrate the present experiences into what has happened previously in her life story (2015).[1] Understood in this way, the disintegration results in traumatic symptoms.

The interaction between traumatic experiences and PTSD diagnosis is complex. To reduce trauma to PTSD would be to greatly misread the countless other experiences that trauma contains and causes. For instance, J. Irene Harris et al. write in their report on trauma outcomes that 'decades of clinical and research findings suggest that trauma is associated with diverse outcomes', which range from healthy and 'normal' experiences of mental health functioning 'to severe psychiatric symptoms such as PTSD, depression and alcohol abuse' (Kessler et al. 1995; Brewin et al. 2000; Ozer et al. 2003, ct. in Harris et al. 2011, p. 17; Bonanno 2004).

Given this, understanding PTSD offers one way of reading a specific expression of an experience of trauma. Yet how PTSD developed as a diagnostic experience is important as it enables clinicians to understand what 'kind' of experiences the diagnosis describes. It requires assessing the standard for a healthy individual, as well as confirming that the qualitative experiences of trauma actually can be quantitatively measured and diagnosed. Most of this section will focus on the development of the *DSM* definition of disorder. However, it is important to note the other widespread classification found in the *International Classification of Disease*, now in its eleventh edition (ICD-11), where PTSD is included, along with its subtypes (WHO 2018).

In the previous definitions of PTSD, such as the one found in DSM-III, Levine writes that the 'official definition that psychologists and psychiatrists use to diagnose trauma is that it is caused by a stressful occurrence "that is outside the range of usual human experience, and that would be markedly distressing to almost anyone"' (DSM-III 1993, ct. in Levine, p. 24). The diagnostic classification of trauma in the form of PTSD has been particularly effective in initiating pharmacological responses to mediate trauma symptoms, such as hyperarousal and sleep disturbances. Pharmacological interventions can include targeting amygdala over-reactivity and gamma-Aminobutyric acid (GABA) and corticotrophin-releasing factors (CRF) (Stamatakos and Campo 2010).[2] According to Stamatakos and Campo's report in 2010, approximately 95% of physicians who treat PTSD in paediatric populations use pharmacological interventions, showing the significant link between this specific intervention and the development of a diagnostic criterion (ibid.).

Michael Lambek notes that little philosophical reflection has been done to understand the complex relation between pharmacological treatments and trauma, as the philosophical discourse has traditionally favoured interaction with psychoanalytic approaches (2013).[3] However, Herman shows the considerable benefits of developing diagnostic definitions for trauma. That trauma is the 'result of "intense fear, helplessness, loss of control and threat of annihilation"' (Sadock, Alcott Sadock, and Ruiz 2009, ct. in Brown Golden and Bergo 2009, p. 10) supports the diagnostic language of the DSM-IV. Herman shows that scientific research on memory indicates the emergence of paradoxical patterns. Traumatic memories are both 'indelibly imprinted' (Lifton 1980, pp. 113–126) *and* often 'inaccessible to ordinary memory' (Herman 2013, p. 130). The result, Herman suggests, is that there is an authoritative trend to ignore the details that do not suit the overarching theory (similar to the critique Horowitz offers of Freud's psychoanalytic understanding of the Dora case). Yet the unifying paradox of memory requires sticking close to the facts.

Herman suggests that the tension can be resolved through two kinds of theoretical constructs. She writes that 'The first [theoretical construct] is the concept of state-dependent learning; the second is the distinction between storage and retrieval of memory' (2013, p. 130). The first construct references how the brain encodes memory differently depending on the biological state. This is mediated through the experience that the individual undergoes. The unifying experience in Herman's definition of trauma is terror (which she draws from the fourth edition of the *Comprehensive Textbook of Psychiatry*), which is defined as the experience of a traumatic event experienced as a loss of control and fear of destruction (Herman 2013, p. 130). This means that the mediating event of terror, as it is experienced in the body, will also have biological impact. In the case of trauma, the traumatic memory becomes a stumbling block for living the present reality because of how it is coded in the body and in memory. The 'biological state of hyperarousal' has overconsolidated the memories of a particular time (2013, p. 130). It is not just another event.

Herman's ability to bring together both the biological and the narrative concepts of trauma through the experience of terror is significant. She not only validates the story of trauma but she also shows how diagnosis works to reveal an embodied encoding of experience. The limitation of this theory is that it relies on defining trauma through an experience of 'terror'. This has ramifications particularly on the DSM's definition of trauma, as experienced through PTSD; a definition that critics suggest reflects a specific Western and individualised experience of trauma. As we saw in attachment theory, childhood trauma encompasses both active experiences such as assault and passive experiences of neglect.

Extending this problematisation, Stephanie Craps highlights the discordance in trauma definitions when she writes that founding trauma texts fail to account for social and non-Western traumas. She suggests that the diagnostic tests have a tendency to marginalise, or ignore, traumatic experiences of non-Western or minority cultures' (ct. in Andermahr 2016, pp. 500–505), because they have a tendency of universalising the validity of definitions of trauma and recovery, derived from the modern West. This is particularly relevant when accounting for systematic and transgenerational abuses of racism and colonisation, in which trauma's 'frightening event' takes on an existentially normative problematic. Recognising the historic and social elements of trauma requires understanding how traumatic events that 'cause catastrophic upheaval' might also manifest as biological states of hyperarousal. Walters et al. suggest that historical trauma studies need to problematise simplistic definitions of trauma and assess 'how historical processes and contexts become embodied' (2011, p. 179).

Trauma experience reveals a delicate connection between psyche, history, narratives and biology that requires constant attention. This is also interesting when we consider the contemporary widespread experiences of coronavirus disease 2019 (COVID-19). Whilst not necessarily fitting Herman's criterion of 'terror', aspects of the virus experience have been referred to as 'traumatic'. In a recent article written for the *New York Times*, psychologist Daphne de Marneffe references the trauma experienced by the current effects of COVID-19. She writes that

> [p]eople often think of trauma as a discrete event – a fire, getting mugged… But what it's really about is helplessness, about being on the receiving end of forces you can't control. Which is what we have now…No one knows when the pain will stop.
>
> *ct. in Senior 2020*

Reading trauma through its symptoms gives some indication of what is to be expected in instances of suffering and upheaval. However, it does not give an indication as to why this is. In Amira's case, she mentions that the ongoing experience of hiding away, feeling herself activated into fight-or-flight mode and helplessness in a situation of ongoing violence shows why she considers the experience traumatic. But she also reminds me that she learned about other experiences of trauma, car accidents and deaths. As experts try to refine the definition of trauma, saying too much is just as problematic as saying too little.[4]

It is important to consider whether simplistic definitions might omit important parts of traumatic experience. But Herman, van der Kolk and the historical overview of trauma show that theorists and practitioners have always struggled to define the ambiguous experiences that lead to something being 'traumatic'. Having a definition like PTSD in order to facilitate therapeutic and hands-on care seems to be an important first step if we want to care for a large population of traumatised persons. However, it is equally important to continue to assess what this definition might be missing.

Discrepancies and Critiques

An example of how interpreting trauma diagnostically might vary across sources is shown in the distinctions made between the DSM and the ICD. Specific alterations that classify 'complex PTSD' have been included in the *ICD-11* (WHO 2018), but not in the latest *DSM-V* (APA 2013). The *DSM-V* does, however, explore the subcategory of a dissociative subtype (Farina et al. 2019, p. 933). Farina notes that researchers have also 'argued that the conception of a dissociative subtype leads to a false dichotomy' (ibid.), as dissociative symptoms are often present in those who are non-dissociative. Reflecting on several studies that demonstrate the presence of dissociative symptoms in each patient diagnosed with PTSD, they notice that symptoms exist 'along a continuum rather than being a categorical variable characterizing a small subset of individuals' (Van Huijstee and Vermetten 2018, ct. in ibid.).

These subtle differences are important. As symptoms are studied, the cumulative histories of trauma start to show us this interrelationality between the body and the mind, while also revealing the complexities of our social histories. Though the *DSM-V* falls short in outlining the whole story, Choi et al. suggest that the changes that have been made in this recent edition reflect 'the growing evidence base demonstrating that trauma, dissociation, and posttraumatic stress frequently co-occur in survivors of maltreatment' (2017, p. 1062). The DSM-V, for instance, draws further attention to the behaviour symptoms that accompany trauma, attributing four distinct clusters: 're-experiencing, avoidance, negative cognitions and mood, [and] arousals' (APA 2013). This seems an important step in understanding aspects of relationship in the experience of trauma.

Levine shows us that traumatised peoples' experiences are reflected physiologically. These experiences include symptoms of 'flashbacks, anxiety, panic attacks, insomnia, psychosomatic complaints, lack of openness, violent unprovoked rage attacks, and repetitive destructive behaviours' (1997, p. 41). In the most recent *DSM-V*, the eight criteria include stressors, intrusion symptoms, avoidance, negative alterations in cognitions and mood, alterations in arousal and reactivity, duration, functional significance and exclusion. Stressors may range from direct exposure of death to 'indirect exposure to aversive details' (APA 2013), while intrusion symptoms encode the traumatic event in persistent symptoms, including physical reaction and nightmares. Avoidance symptoms might include evading stimuli related to the trauma and the negative alterations in cognitions and mood, which can encompass a broken recall of the event, as well as dullness of emotion as evidenced in negative affect. But this is an interpretation of experience that is primarily physiological.

In this interpretation, trauma is experienced through PTSD symptoms. To be diagnosed, the symptoms must be strong enough to cause impairment and last for longer than one month. Alterations in arousal include irritability and difficulty sleeping. The current changes in the DSM-V have allowed for two specifications. The first, dissociative specification, includes depersonalisation, which is the sense of being other/outside of one's own body, and derealisation, or an experience of the unreal. The second specification is 'delayed specification', in which partial symptoms might emerge and only later be followed by the full source of diagnostic symptoms (APA 2013). Significantly, the DSM-V presents PTSD as a new chapter, under 'trauma- and stressor-related disorders', providing a distinct category of reference from the DSM-IV, which previously examined PTSD under the wider umbrella of 'anxiety disorders' (APA 2013). Complicated in this symptomatology is (1) the role of cause and effect, (2) the specific subjective readings of experience and (3) wider influencers, whose roles require ethical and sociocultural analysis (see Parts III and IV of this book for further analysis of these interconnected conversations).

This section has used PTSD as a way of understanding trauma. But Murphy (ct. Burke and Neimeyer 2012) suggests that emphasis on diagnosis unfortunately still offers a limited understanding of the experience. It can lead to a 'paternalistic[5] policy of coerced treatment because the state [carer, etc.] is actually saving sick people from themselves' (Murphy 2015, p. 47). Levine critiques the PTSD diagnosis, which he suggests aims to interpret trauma as an experience that is 'fully sanitised as a medical "disorder"' (p. 33). I would suggest that this critique does not take into account the limitations that the DSM admits of itself (see 'Introduction', DSM-V), and the strengths that it has offered in developing a systematic approach to engaging with trauma. However, I fully agree with Levine that any definition that limits human experience according to a specific set of criteria will be problematic. As studies on historical trauma illustrate, it is crucial to carefully assess the myths and stigmas that accompany our ways of classifying experience. For instance, the victim – perpetrator model is complex; the role of the soldier, as both undergoing and instigating trauma, requires further analysis when used as the population basis for a generalised diagnosis.

Defining the 'Traumatic'

Examining the ways in which we understand and prioritise certain experiences is essential when we determine what should be defined as 'traumatic'. For instance, if we go by a definition of trauma as 'a frightful event outside of human experience' (Herman 1992, p. 172), we need to make sure that it is workable for individuals outside of our own contexts. As Sonya Andermahr notes in *Decolonising Trauma Studies*,[6] in experiences of racism, the traumatic experience needs to address historical narratives of suffering that are rooted in 'global systems of trauma' (2016, p. 502). This trauma is ongoing and intergenerational; it is not just about 'one overwhelming event' (p. 502). She further suggests that this means documenting and assessing multidirectional narratives and memories.

Andermahr cites Rothberg's analysis of trauma studies in which he challenges both hierarchical and exclusivist approaches to diagnosis and readings of trauma that present 'either mine or yours' (2008, ct. in Andermahr 2016, pp. 2–3). The 'problem' with trauma is its fundamental ambiguity. In trauma, 'collective memories of seemingly distinct histories – such as those of slavery, the Holocaust and colonisation – are not easily separable' (ibid.). Too much separation and quantification render the experience unrecognisable. In Feinstein's account of trauma in war journalists, he summarises the experience in overlapping and ambiguous terms: 'nightmares, alcohol, cannabis, and cocaine to still the dreams, a diagnosis of PTSD, a failure to follow through with therapy, an inability to tolerate the smell of a morgue' (2006, p. 28). Trauma lives itself through the particularities of a specific life, while it simultaneously jumbles the individual experience into pieces of a larger enigmatic puzzle.

Trauma, as a particular experience of suffering, casts its shadows from a variety of experiential sources. For instance, while sexual, physical and emotional abuse, situational conflict, the death of a loved one or natural disasters might account for most of the experience that we think of as traumatic, Levine suggests that there are others. Even experiences of hospitalisation and birth can be trauma-inducing, according to Levine. In this interpretation, then, it could be that we see widespread trauma in populations as a result of COVID-19. The challenge of trauma, Levine argues, is not in maintaining a clear causal narrative, but rather in understanding the impact of an experience on a 'cellular level'. He writes that 'Intellectually, we may believe in an operation, but on a primal level, our bodies do not' (1997, p. 54), outlining that trauma corresponds to 'the perception of the instinctual nervous system' (p. 54). While this situates the experience primarily in the body, more analytic accounts also take into consideration the impact of an experience *by a particular individual*. For Gabor Mate, trauma is related to the *way in which* we experience the event, and the story that we tell about it. Two people will experience one event in different ways. The same is the case with potentially traumatic experiences. For my friend Amira, she only started to experience the symptoms of trauma after she moved to the United Kingdom, as she left the known relationships of family and her homeland, despite it being the site of the violence. It is the experiencing self that undergoes the trauma, in unique relationship to a context.

While we have been able to map out a general conversation about trauma in this part of the book, we have opened up a series of philosophical problems. The relationships in these ambiguous experiences are both individualised and complex. Little has been said about the interrelation between cause and effect. Symptomatology, as the lens for diagnosis, is inherently limited, especially if it only offers us a material explanation for experience. However, as we have manoeuvred through the various accounts, we see that there is still a shape that is emerging in the ambiguity. There are common aspects of the experience that define it – though it is still quite shallow and somewhat broad.

To delineate trauma in a meaningful way requires understanding how it connects to this wider discourse of relational embodiment. Just reading trauma through its symptoms leaves us with many unanswered questions. For instance, in accounts of childhood trauma, we can see how the biological and narrative selves interact in the experience of events. Adriano Schimmenti writes that 'childhood trauma and related attachment disturbances may interact with inborn genetic vulnerabilities, which account for about 50% variance in psychopathic traits' (Blonigen et al. 2003, ct. in Schimmenti 2020, p. 220). This, he suggests 'may foster alterations in the development of brain regions that have been associated with psychopathic behaviours' (2020, p. 220). Such alterations in brain structures include disturbances in decision-making, via the orbitofrontal cortex, as well as the emotional regulatory and learning systems of the limbic system, and particularly the amygdala (Carré et al. 2013, ct. in Schimmenti 2020, p. 220). An epigenetic understanding enables us to trace the conversation of psychopathology back to the ambiguous interconnections of traumatic experiences.

Schimmenti further explores how the history of psychopathology mirrors the work in trauma. He suggests that early psychopathic research revealed 'a positive relationship between relational adversities in childhood and the development of psychopathic traits' (2020, p. 221). He cites Partridge's early study in 1928, where 12 adolescents with observed psychopathic traits had also experienced clear parental rejection. Further studies by Field in 1940 revealed psychopathic traits connected to early childhood rejection by the mother, and McCord and McCord's work in 1956 with boys displaying psychopathic traits, whilst having experienced 'parental neglect, psychological abuse, rejection, [and] inconsistent discipline' (pp. 220–221). This, Schimmenti suggests, clearly reveals how a kind of 'secondary' psychopathology can emerge out of a childhood of abuse and rejection. This is, in itself, a traumatic situation in which extreme feelings of hatred and hostility towards others can be fostered (as, for instance, seen in Karpman's theory [1941]) (p. 221).

This is furthermore supported in current research between attachment discourse and experiences of trauma. Carr et al. developed a systematic review of 44 articles, through which they 'reported that the subtypes of childhood trauma (especially physical neglect) can predict the development of psychopathology in adults' (2013, ct. in Farina et al. 2019, p. 933). The relation between trauma and other disorders is, of course, nuanced, and saying too much here can be as unhelpful as not saying anything at all. However, an increasing body of research now links the role of developmental trauma to correlational attachment experiences, as well as the difficulties of diagnostic systems in understanding the trauma experience (Farina et al. 2019).

Further Discussion on Trauma and Relationship

In Part I of this book, we have tried to understand what contemporary discourses can tell us about trauma. Moving from analysis to somatic work and through the challenges of finding a consensus of human trauma experience, we quickly realise that there are multiple factors that we need to consider. Relationships, individual bodies, the unconscious storing of events and contexts that we find ourselves in all become important factors in shaping our unique trauma stories. But outside of these classical examples of trauma, there are other ways of understanding trauma that situate it in literature, myth and religious scriptures. Here, we see how trauma affects the interrelational structures of communities and histories, as well as individuals.

In Chapters 1 and 2, we have looked at how conversations on trauma have shifted from ancient narratives through to early analytic theory. We then explored how contemporary theorists have reasserted the role of the body in trauma experience, which is then taken up in the third discussion on quantifying what constitutes the traumatic experience. In those chapters, it was mostly about opening up the conversation between therapeutic modalities that address trauma. However, the aim of this book is to also speak into the existential and phenomenological experience of trauma, as a way of connecting the different disciplines together into one conversation. Exploring this lived experience of trauma requires us to reach beyond therapeutic models alone. Understanding and healing are interconnected, but the need to understand is the philosopher's primary task, and, hopefully, the more we understand, the more we heal.

Auerhahn and Laub propose that trauma cannot be clearly represented, which means that it cannot just be changed by our interpretation, because we can never represent it fully. For them, then, 'what is required initially in the therapy is not elucidation of psychic conflict but [that] the self and other must be rebuilt' (1993, p. 392). Traumatic experience is the experience of a self in the world. This self is not isolated, but continuously relating to others. It requires understanding who this traumatised self is. It also requires examining how the self relates to others, and whether, or how, the ruptured relationship between the traumatised person and the world can ever be restored.

Mythical Trauma Narratives

Trauma studies have long recognised this interconnection between different disciplines. Visser writes that if trauma theory makes connection with other fields of study, such as sociology and anthropology, then 'trauma would not only be a coherent of cause and effect, but it may affirm a sense of belonging, kinship and mutual trust for the individual and community' (2015, p. 15). This book is specifically interested in how the phenomenon of trauma connects the various relations of human experience. It reveals how the experience of trauma is essentially relational. Trauma, as a particular experience of suffering, as an experience of being in the world, requires understanding *how* we are in this world.

An example of the relational aspects of trauma, or the *living* of it, is illustrated in the Greek myth about Philoctetes, which Sophocles adapts as a play. I have found this description of trauma particularly interesting, first, because it is written as a piece of art, rather than as scientific evidence of behaviours, and second, because it references the interpersonal space that trauma creates between the self and the other, and the sense of isolation that is suffered in the experience. In this play recounted by Sophocles, the protagonist Philoctetes, once a member of Odysseus' party, is left alone on the Greek island of Lemnos, after a snake bites him.

The narrative of the play shows a character whose physical trauma, the bite of a snake, causes profound emotional and psychological disturbance. The wound cannot heal, and the agony of the wound provokes such distress that his screams cause his crew to abandon him, claiming that it disturbs their offering to the gods (Lloyd 1998), p. 1). Philoctetes' cry sounds like 'animal groans', and he exhibits the 'unsleeping sleep of all men who are sick'. However, it is later revealed when they return to land without him that it is the bow of Philoctetes, rather than the strength of the armies, that contains the key to winning the Trojan War. As a result, Neoptolemus is sent by Odysseus to retrieve the bow. Lloyd, in his translation of Sophocles, thereby extends the classical narrative to show how healing the trauma of Philoctetes is interconnected with the political success of the victory for the Greek army.

Sophocles' ancient account becomes important to our trauma discourse for three reasons. First, it shows the relation between a material, or somatic, experience of trauma and the traumatic symptoms of incommunicability and sleeplessness, which we will encounter later in this chapter. David Soskin writes that 'Even to Neoptolemus, Philoctetes is unreachable through language' (2013, p. 215), making his entrapment on the island a truly existential event. Second, in the relationship between Philoctetes and Neoptolemus, we see a relation between the traumatised self and the other, premised on vulnerability and compassion, which will be explored in Parts II and III of the book. Philoctetes reveals his loneliness when he recounts seeing the crew leave him behind on the island: 'How I wept, how I cried out in distress...with no one else to help, no one to soothe the ache of my disease. I looked everywhere, but all I found around me was my pain' (lines 330–335). Third, Sophocles' use of myth motions to the profound interconnections between political, social and traumatic healing, which we will explore later in Parts III and IV.

Soskin summarises this interconnection of communicability, somatic experiencing and the interrelational aspect of trauma – the three conversational cornerstones of this book – when he suggests that the tragedy of Philoctetes happens even before the play has a chance to begin. The tragedy is a result of 'the effects of Philoctetes' wound, his abandonment at Lemnos, and the failure of the Greeks to palliate or tolerate his pain' (2013, p. 215). The traumatised self is isolated from the other in the physical distancing from the island, but also in the inability to understand, heal or hold his suffering. Soskin writes that this breakdown in communicability is important to the play, as well as to the experience of traumatic isolation. He states that because of Philoctetes' screams, they are unable to make their usual offerings to the gods. They decide to leave him on the island as a result 'because these rituals imbued with iterative prayers represent the highest form of communication for the Greeks'. This isolation means that Philoctetes is 'displaced' from the process of human communication because of the pain of his wound, which renders his language into 'animal groans', which 'repel' the other humans around him (2013, p. 215).

But this isolation of incommunicability is bridged, in part, when Neoptolemus experiences the suffering of Philoctetes. We see here how the bodily representation of suffering, the somatic experience, imprints itself on Neoptolemus, allowing him to somehow connect with, and feel compassion for the isolated trauma of Philoctetes. Soskin shows that 'Neoptolemus can translate [the] limbic language', which then enables Neoptolemus to listen to Philoctetes, which, Soskin remarks, 'is first a process of feeling, not thinking – a process Philoctetes attributes to Neoptolemus as the palpable expression of "being pained by my suffering"' (2013, p. 215). This ancient account of trauma therefore helps us to situate three key aspects of the lived trauma: how trauma is experienced (subjective and somatic experience), how trauma is expressed (communication) and how others interact with the traumatised self (interrelation).

Sophocles' reading of Philoctetes does not just give us a good story and tell us a bit about ancient culture. It can also help us to understand trauma phenomenologically. First, it shows the traumatised subject's complex relation with the world, as revealed through suffering's silence and lament. We will unpack experience of the suffering subject in Part II of this book. Second, it establishes the phenomenological relationship between the traumatised self and the other. The relational aspects of traumatic experience will be introduced in Part III. Third, Sophocles motions to the profound interconnection between political- and land-based experiences of trauma and healing. The political and environmental 'living' of these experiences will be developed further in Part IV.

In this section, however, we will explore the meta-ideas that frame these conversations. In order to develop the nuances of subjective traumatic experience, it is important to have a holistic perception of what we are talking about. This requires taking what we have learned about the history and modalities of trauma therapy and extending our vision to examine the interrelation between trauma and the experience of suffering, and the lived trauma narrative. To grasp the lived experience in this way, however, we first need to situate the self as a unified embodied being; that is, we need to re-body the traumatised person.

The Traumatised Subjects

Understanding trauma in a way that respects the integration of consciousness and the body requires taking time to look at the presuppositions that we have about subjectivity. In his book *Trauma and the Ontology of the Modern Subject,* John Roberts writes that

> Trauma is precisely that psychological and cultural architecture that allows us to understand how events of both formative and intervening intensity may dislocate our sense of who we are, and how pathogenic memories form.
>
> *2018, pp. 1–2*

Previously, I have extended this concept from a being a distortion of the mind to understanding it as an embodied continuous experience, as actual re-*living* of trauma. I would also extend this 'existential phenomenological architecture' to include our relationships to institutions (politics) and place (environment).

We have read the story of trauma through classical psychological- and body-based theories, as well as seen how myth can help us to think through the problem differently. What we are left with is How do we answer what distinguishes living trauma from living other experiences? This requires addressing the wider meta-relations that are touched in a person's experience. Psychiatrist David Soskin, reflecting on Sophocles' *Philoctetes*, provides profound insight into how we might listen to and learn how to understand trauma. For him, medical models ('with their clinical vernacular and resolute human boundaries'), literary and spiritual models ('with their semiotic and sweeping pathways to the imagination') can both be fundamentally inadequate in 'contacting' the 'experience of "sickness"' (2013, p. 215). This is because they 'fail to live through it, to convey the guttural insides of the disease', and thereby they fail 'to inhabit the isolation of being a patient' (2013, p. 215).

It is no surprise that considerable effort is spent on deciphering the ambiguous yet omnipresent connection between suffering and trauma. That trauma remains ambiguously elusive is due to the complex outworking of how we individually, and collectively, live out our various sufferings. Trauma has been referred to a 'suffering that remains' (Rambo 2010, in Esterhuizen 2018, p. 524). Elsewhere, as for instance, in Helen Luke, it assumes a moralistic undertone: 'True suffering belongs to innocence, not guilt', she writes (1995, ct. in Kalsched 2013, p. 214). This differs from Melanie Klein, where trauma is a basic part of life: the infant starts life in the 'destructive phantasies deriving from the death instinct' (1940, ct. in Kalsched 2013, p. 214). Suffering, as the interlocutor of trauma, manifests itself in multiple readings and diverse interpretations, in a mixture of complex moral, philosophical, political, theological and psychological musings. This chapter asks us to consider how these various interpretations of suffering impact the multiple readings of trauma that we will explore throughout the book.

Eric Cassell defines embodied suffering as 'a state of severe distress associated with events that threaten the intactness of the person' (1991, p. 32). Trauma can be explained in similar language. The 'at-homeness' of the body is now experienced as 'unhomelike' (Svenaeus 2017, p. 216), and the meaning-patterns of this experience require consideration in the attempt to understand what it is to 'live' trauma. A further difficulty in understanding trauma is that the suffering is not seen. This presents what Carel and McNaughton refer to as the 'invisibility' challenge, which can heighten the sense of a person's helplessness (2016, p. 299). I will therefore suggest that reading trauma, as an outworking of self-relations (relationships between the self and her world), requires reading embodied consciousness as the site of rupture.

We have previously seen that Freud has located Charcot's neurological affect in the psyche of the self, suggesting that speaking the narrative might bring cohesion to restore the ego's equilibrium. This situation centralises the role of the self-narrative that is ruptured in the experience of trauma. In *On Psychoanalysis*, Ricœur explores narrative focus through the work of Freud. He writes that Freud's psychoanalytical method becomes a context in which the traumatised narrative is worked through, in order to bring this isolated event into 'meaningful sequences and ordered connections' (2012). Freudian theory spends a considerable amount of time to painstakingly develop how the conscious and unconscious self work in bringing these memories into the present narrative. This is particularly important in the events that do not 'conform to the linear determinism that would place the present in the first grasp of the past in a univocal fashion' (2012, p. 21). Trying to situate new events in light of a ruptured linear narrative requires a reimagining, or re-enacting, of the narrative.

First, I have suggested that suffering can be understood as having a role in defining trauma, through the experience of rupture. However, suffering's ambiguity extends further than this reading. Horowitz, for instance, suggests that 'suffering already conceived is…suffering evaded' (2009, p. 28). This is of critical importance. To suggest that suffering can be understood, is, as we will see in the work of Lévinas, philosophically, if not therapeutically reductive. There is no 'one way' of understanding suffering, which is why the focus of this book is on the experience of how it might be uniquely *lived*. The problem here is that we can then make suffering so complicated that we end up misinterpreting the simple relations that are right under our nose. As Horowitz writes, in an exposition on Freud, 'there need be nothing deep about the incomprehensible' (p. 29). What we do not want to do is complicate simple things. But what we do want to do is understand what the experience of trauma is really telling us.

A key idea to this whole book is that relationship takes trauma's centre stage. Another is that trauma affects our basic relationships with the world around us. It is important not to overly romanticise trauma when speaking about its ambiguity, as I find myself so often doing. For instance, I have found that I have a tendency to overemphasise particular emotive experiences of people that I work with, to the exclusion of other, more simple and common behaviours. It is important to remember that something can be incomprehensible while also being a part of many peoples' human experience. When Horowitz states that '[t]he source of our suffering…is not a complicated desire but rather a wishful, and therefore complicated, relation to a simple desire' (p. 29), he is telling us something very important. The complicated suffering of a child cut-off from his mother can be simplified to a desire for connection. It is how this suffering is worked out in us and in our multiple relationships with the world that brings it into incomprehensibility: 'The measure of the grandeur of the gods to whom we bow down is the sacrifices they demand of us' (p. 31), or to quote Freud's account of dreamwork: 'At bottom, dreams are nothing other than a particular *form* of thinking, made possible by the conditions of the state of sleep' (1925 footnote, ct. in Horowitz 2009, p. 30). Horowitz, and anyone studying the body's experience of living trauma, needs to go beyond Freud's theory of smokescreens.

Trauma is not merely a particular form of a mirage, or a measure of idolisation. Rather, it is suffering's marker of an 'undead past' (Horowitz 2009, p. 33), or rather, the persistent living of suffering: 'the continuing force of the past in the present, the past's power to persist in and as fresh experience' (p. 32). It is here that the second exploration of suffering reveals itself in trauma, not merely as rupture, but as a dysmorphism of time and place: 'The past is patently all over the place' (p. 33). We can see this in the writing of Catherine Bjørnholt Michaelsen, who suggests that, since Freud, trauma has been understood as becoming 'a trauma belatedly, or *after its own fact*' (2015, p. 43, italics in the original), as trauma is made manifest by the traces it leaves after it withdraws, 'that is, by its aftermath and its effects of repetition and deferral' (ibid.). Here, an absence leaves a mark on the present. The absence, however, is also experienced as an ongoing lived rupture, continuing to unsettle present, despite having been left behind long ago in a linear understanding of time. It is these tales of trauma that we will see emerge through the narratives of the next few chapters, varying from the colonisation of First Nations people in North America, to the sexual exploitation of female sex workers trafficked to the United Kingdom from Eastern Europe.

This ongoing lived rupture can, for instance, be seen in accounts of First Nations trauma. Here the language of trauma, tied to generations of familial and land displacement, rape and loss of language, is more authentically read through concepts of 'soul wound, collected unresolved grief, collective trauma, intergenerational trauma and intergenerational PTSD' (Palacios and Portillo 2009, ct. in Walters et al. 2011, p. 156). Interestingly, as exemplified in other traditions, such as the Jewish rituals outlined in their holy texts, we see in First Nations populations that communal ritualistic and spiritual practices, as well as understandings of collective identity, contain their own sites of resistance. However, we will spend more time on these examples later.

Living the Trauma Narrative

Understanding what it means to live trauma, through connecting it to our individual sufferings, involves engaging both with the ambiguity of rupture and an 'undead' past. In his work with traumatised war journalists, Feinstein suggests that talking about the trauma that they have experienced feels like a crucial part of maintaining a sense of self. But it does not mean that the trauma is 'cured' by talking about it, or even understood (2003, p. 28). Contemporary theory has showed us how there are many ways of trying to understand trauma, from the retelling of story and recounting dreams, to studying transference between patient and analyst. It also advocates for the centrality of the body's experience. This shows how bodywork theorists, psychiatrists, psychologists, philosophers and practitioners have asserted the central role of the material body in interpreting trauma experience.

We have looked at how the trauma interacts with the body, through physiological and neurobiological discourses. However, philosophy offers another way of reading this embodied experience. Philosopher Kristen Brown Golden writes that '[f]or Merleau-Ponty, the body exists as communication' (Brown Golden and Bergo 2009, p. 87). The suggestion that the body is not merely a passive recipient of external forces, but rather serves as a lived interface of human experience moves theory away from a predominant focus on spoken narrative, and involves studying the body itself, as a communicator and interpreter of experience.

We have seen how van der Kolk offers a neurobiological approach to trauma, which explains the encoding of memory in the brain as 'imagistic, iconic, [and] sensory'. These 'extremely accurate, close to camera-like images', Alford writes, become difficult to integrate into the narrative, or 'signifying', mind (2013, p. 261). But these iconic images are not to be confused with symbol: they 'stand in opposition to verbal images' (ibid.). It is this final point that Alford wrestles with, suggesting that this visual image seems to stand in contrast to verbal images, where language and form speak together. 'For example', Alford writes, 'good writing uses words to conjure images, and images can almost always be described in words...or what is poetry for?' (ibid.). This makes it about a problem of witnessing, Alford suggests, because the witness cannot create a narrative for the images that she has seen. While this imagistic approach seems to bring out elements of van der Kolk's theory, however, it diverges from the methods that he suggests, which include the use of narrative through dramatisation, as a means of embodying what it feels like to be someone else (van der Kolk 2020). Maybe the challenge remains; the witness is mute but needs to bear the experience of another.

The withdrawal of presence reveals a suffering that passively acts on the other to overwhelm her present experience. The challenge is that, according to Porge's theory of trauma (introduced earlier with Levine), this withdrawal response comes as a result of a rupture in the relation between the self and the other. Usually, according to this theory, when a person feels threatened they first appeal to the other for help (social engagement). This is where the subject might respond. But the problem is that, here, in this traumatic moment, no one does respond. Thus, the second turn is to fight or flee the situation (an act of protective violence). However, if this does not secure the self, she then freezes or collapses.

The body displays the symptoms of immobilisation, resulting in an 'extreme disconnection from the body' (van der Kolk 2014, p. 84). For instance, in the examples of traumatised migrants, Fleury and Mahmoud-Shwana write, 'their identities are broken into a thousand pieces that are scattered like the pieces of a jigsaw' (2010, pp. 98–99). Each piece of the jigsaw repeats the same scene, replicating the cells of their human bodies: the patterned memory of the traumatic events. Kalsched goes as far as to say 'that the post traumatic psyche includes a *violent pathological (anti life)* force that becomes resistance to healing' (2013, p. 81, italics in the original), or a permanent self 'exile by defensive processes and the anti-life forces that get established in the psyche' (p. 85). So somehow this relation between the person and the body needs to be safely phenomenologically reconstituted as a self, before the other can reveal herself to the other. The reasons for exile need to be understood before the person can come back safely.

We need, for instance, to look at how a self can be understood as many experiences at once: Ricœur shows in his distinction between *idem* and *ipse*. *Idem* constitutes the qualities that we share with others and reveals who we are to the world, such as our body. These include features of permanence and sameness, regardless of the space or time we are in (Ericson and Kjellander 2018). Really, objects and persons can both be distinguished by *idem* identity. This differs from *ipse* or the self-understanding being (Glas 2003). *Ipse* reveals the selfhood 'in the sense of change and interrupted continuity' (Ericson and Kjellander 2018, p. 205). Narrative identity brings these two together in the development of character and story that shows how a person relates to a plot in a unified way and what that person's reactions and behaviours tells us about what the person values (Glas 2003). The narrative self also plays a part in this subjectivity, but each experience of self needs to be explored in order to develop a unified self (as he writes in *Oneself as Another*). Glas writes that, given this explanation of identity, the challenge of psychopathology is not so much that there is a 'breakdown' in the narrative of the self, as it is that the self-relational breakdown, which differs from the *idem*, is not generally observable to the outside world.

However, it is this self- referential capacity that creates the conditions to form a responsible and autonomously choosing subject (Glas 2003). Psychoanalyst Marilyn Charles suggests that reflective capacity, or the 'ability to know oneself in relation to others who may be both similar or different' (2019, p. 5), is critical to understanding ourselves in the world. The common transformational process of becoming an adult self requires moving from an 'object position', where the self understands herself through how she is acted upon, to the 'subject position', where the self extends her self-knowledge to the world, through articulating her values, goals and needs to the other. For Charles, an 'encounter with otherness' enables us to translate between 'the concrete realm of words as things' into meaning-making communication and engagement that uses the 'symbolic functions of words' to construct meaning that is complex and responsive (ibid.). Charles shows that this encounter with the world is gradual and relational, requiring 'sufficient experiences to invite persistence' in the more difficult instances of life that we might face.

The reflective capacity emerges in this subject position, where we recognise ourselves in the world, engaging and responding to it. However, in trauma, this reflective capacity is assaulted. We are acted upon. The other is a threat to our sense of self-integrity. This destabilises our very ability to reflect on the world as a subject. Learning the connection between *who someone is*, from *who she says she is*, requires a certain understanding of language, which we will look at further in Part II of this book. It is this ability to translate the language of interior's ambiguity that is at the heart of the psychoanalytic process, where the nuanced overlapping and entanglement of meaning is caught up in both conscious and unconscious forces (Charles 2019). However, language presents a challenge because it often masks what is actually going on. This leads Charles to suggest that 'we learn more from the way people *are*, than from what they *say*' (2019, p. 5). In van der Kolk and Charles' discussion of trauma, the ability to self-reflect is critical to mending the 'derailed' narrative.

For both Charles and van der Kolk, it is examining who the person is, prior to what she says about who she is, that is key to situating the self in trauma. The behaviour of the person therefore becomes key to reading and interpreting the language of the person. According to Charles, it is the ability 'to insist that human behaviour must make sense even when we don't know the story well enough to make sense of it' that enables us to ask the wrong questions in a way that can get us closer to asking the right ones (2019, p. 6). Ascertaining the 'right questions' requires assessing the embodied experience, the person as she presents herself. The body itself keeps the score, insofar as the self-reflection cannot occur prior to a re-recognition of self as embodied and present.

van der Kolk problematises using 'talk therapy' as a central interpreter of trauma and advocates for body-based approaches prior to resituating language. Charles, however, speaks about embodiment from the psychoanalytic tradition. Charles maintains that central to psychoanalysis, 'as a clinical enterprise', lies a hope to help the person 'ungrounded in their internal experience to find sufficient safety in relationship' (p. 6). This safe relationship enables the building of what Winnicott refers to as 'the capacity to play, with feelings, ideas and one another' (ibid.). So, while van der Kolk suggests that body-based work diverges from psychoanalysis, I would suggest that Charles' interpretation of Winnicott shows just how the psychoanalytic perspective can open up to a relational experience of play that, in many ways, parallels van der Kolk's clinical use of yoga to resituate the self in the body, in this present, prior to engaging in self-reflection. This, I would suggest, bears similarities to Winnicott's exploration of early negotiation, or '*the capacity to use an object*, to recognise the separateness and interdependence of each person on others' (Winnicott 1971, ct. in Charles 2019, p. 6, italics added by Charles). Examined living, if this is the goal of analysis, requires both the analytic examination of conscious and unconscious forces, as well as the simultaneous living, or indwelling, of experience. To separate one from the other reduces either.

However, in *The Body Keeps Score*, van der Kolk is emphatic that treating trauma cannot be contained to tending to the mind's narrative. He responds to Freud's emphasis on traumatic re-enactment, or 'the compulsion to repeat', writing that: 'He and many of his followers believed that re-enactments were an unconscious attempt to gain mastery over the painful situation' (2014, p. 31), though there seems to be no evidence for this. Rather, van der Kolk appeals to the embodied absorption and re-networking of the brain that makes the imaginative narration ineffective without the centrality of tending to the body.

Conclusion

Discussions on trauma have been so vast that it is difficult to get a good grip on all that has been said in one section. The aim of this book is not to do that. Instead, the intention is to give enough of an overview for us to take into a philosophical discussion that can help us to connect the various experiences of what living trauma might mean. This requires understanding the nuanced relation between trauma and human history. In exploring trauma, we cannot just examine the 'victim' or 'patient' in isolation. In a way, this has already been done and would not help to deepen our understanding. But seeing how people and place connect, beyond reductive labels – that is, truly making space for the interconnection of the human story, socially and morally situated in embodied communities of people, and imperfect histories of humanity – requires finding out more about the relationships that extend beyond the individual subject.

Understanding trauma requires attunement to the wider relationships. This is a world where the victim and the perpetrator constantly brush up against each other, and in which the perpetrator herself may contain traces of victimhood. Exploring the moral discourse of justice is paramount to establishing a relation of healing, as we will see in Parts III and IV of this book. Interpreting trauma through the social justice discourse also connects the histories of trauma, to wider attachment relationships and experiences of violence. While none of these conversations will try to say 'everything', they aim to show how these correlational experiences, and their roots in attachment, are a central part to understanding the trauma framework. It is through recognising the role of relationships in the experience of trauma that we can get closer to understanding how health might be restored. Drawing on sociological theory that points to the crucial importance of relationship in its affect on health behaviour (Umberson et al. 2010), this piece of philosophical work further developed in Part II can help us to describe trauma in a way that provides a context for relationship to be examined more clearly.

Notes

1 van der Kolk suggests that this is due to the survivor's energy being used to control the internal chaos of a re-directed central nervous system, an activity that takes up a considerable amount of conscious and unconscious experience that may otherwise be directed at re-situating the traumatic narrative in the wider life experience. But whilst we have contemporary diagnostic models that focus on the physical symptoms of the body, it has not always been so.

2 I will not spend more time on the pharmacological treatments of trauma here, as it pertains specifically to the *healing* of symptoms of trauma, as a neurobiological disorder. That this model offers a neurobiological reading of trauma is significant, however, I will treat this reading as linking to the body-based readings of Bessel van der Kolk.

3 While thinkers such as Andrew Lakoff (1993) and Tanya Luhrmann (2000) offer critical insights into philosophical issues in rising use of pharmacological interventions, these do not specifically focus on PTSD. This thin reflective engagement is similarly mirrored in body-based approaches to trauma, which is a specific emphasis of this text.
4 More of this discussion will emerge in Part IV of the book.
5 Where I broadly understand paternalism as an expression of moralism.
6 For more on postcolonial accounts of trauma, see Part III of this book.

PART II

Phenomenology and the Traumatised Subject

4

THE PHENOMENOLOGY OF LÉVINAS

When Amira told me about her experiences of growing up in conflict, and her subsequent journey to the United Kingdom, I was struck by how clearly she was able to see the connections between different circumstances that led her to where she is now. She said that, for her, it was a matter of 'understanding and coming to terms with being traumatised, and reaching out'. What she was able to get me to see is how each of the experiences she had gone through weaved together into the whole; how she experienced the pain in her body, the violence surrounding her neighbourhood, and the relationships between family, civilians and political powers. Amira showed me just how important these interconnected points are in *living* trauma.

Introducing Phenomenology

Trauma remains a complicated and, at times, an ambiguous experience. So it is important to try and clarify it as precisely as possible so that the trauma can be healed. Psychopathology is not just about material relations. As Giovanni Stanghellini et al. write, 'it requires investigating the exchange between the classifications of psychiatric disorders, research on the brain and the complex web of individualised subjective experiences' (2019). Philosophy, and phenomenology in particular, has a unique ability to go beyond discipline-specific sets of language and methods of practice to imagine ways in which experiences might connect together. This book is really about re-perception – how it is that we can understand all of these interrelated parts of the experience, how trauma is *lived*, and then later, how we might use this to re-perceive a transformed experience, which is simply *healing*. In Part II of this book, we will explore the lived experience of trauma, through the phenomenology of Emmanuel Lévinas, Paul Ricœur and Maurice Merleau-Ponty.

DOI: 10.4324/9780367800017-6

Using their ideas about subjectivity, we will then see how this might benefit a re-perceived reading of trauma.

The philosophers that I am using each has a very personal experience of trauma. These three philosophers each emerged around a similar point in the history of French phenomenology, during and after the Second World War. Lévinas and Ricœur were both interned at prisoner of war camps, and many of Lévinas' works are dedicated to his Jewish community lost in the concentration camps. Merleau-Ponty was active in the French Resistance and served as a Lieutenant in the French Army. As such, it is perhaps obvious that the role of the suffering body and the connection between ethics and experience figure centrally in their works. Though their different backgrounds and approaches provide unique insights, these three accounts have specific elements in common.

Each of the philosophers has somehow lived through their own experience of trauma. Emerging through this, both Lévinas and Ricœur astutely explore relationship with other people in their accounts of suffering. They also discuss the notion of hope and justice, which figures centrally in our later discussions about healing. In this discussion, Ricœur is also able to point out some of the challenges that emerge when we only read experience through psychoanalysis. Merleau-Ponty is able to offer a phenomenology of the body that helps us to understand and contrast the corporeal references in Lévinas and our previous conversations about somatic therapy in Part I. The main question that this chapter is interested in asking is how phenomenology can help us to answer what it is like to live trauma.

Simon Critchley once wrote that phenomenology is the 'sciences de naivitées' (2002, p. 7), whose main aim is to examine experiences that are often already assumed to be understood or are easily brushed over. This task is often existential, as it involves examining relationships: as Merleau-Ponty puts it, not extrapolating a world based on 'solitary thought but through the experience of concrete situations and in a living dialogue with others' (1990, p. 94). As a way of understanding experience, phenomenology can help to clarify the particular pieces of the puzzle that we might miss and offer a way of re-perceiving a situation. One such challenge is the role of memory in re-presenting trauma (as seen in Herman 2015; Bloom 2009). Another challenge we confront is how to account for a psychological experience existing simultaneously to a physiological experience, as shown through the work of van der Kolk.

Living Trauma

For van der Kolk, living trauma involves the whole lived self. It is a particular way of experiencing ourselves as living creatures, because, unlike the 'normal' experiences of sense-making and order that we generally encounter, traumatic experience ruptures this lived framework and leaves us searching for ways to recuperate the pieces. van der Kolk writes that what constitutes trauma is that 'it is overwhelming, unbelievable and unbearable' (2014, p. 195). He advocates that meeting each patient requires suspending our conceptualisations of 'normal' and accepts the dual reality that trauma brings: 'the reality of a relatively secure and predictable present that lives side by side with a ruinous, ever-present past' (ibid.). Here van der Kolk motions to the interesting experience of time and a-temporality that trauma brings. He is also interested in how the traumatic experience differs from our experience of something that is defined as 'normal'. For example, in someone who has not experienced trauma, life has a general sense of predictable linearity. But in a traumatised person, the events of the past can continue to interfere with the present. So how experience is lived is, in these ways, very different.

In this chapter, we are not interested so much in the essence of *what trauma is*, as we are in *how trauma is lived*. So, the living of trauma involves assessing how the experience of this kind of suffering affects our relation to time. It also, perhaps, puts into question how 'normal' experience actually differs from living trauma, and how our language can fail to give an account for what is happening to the body as it undergoes trauma. This chapter uses phenomenology as its method, seeking to existentially engage with how trauma is lived. Existential phenomenology, as it is used here, concerns itself with the life of consciousness (Brown Golden and Bergo 2009). This is particularly effective for this discourse because it helps us to move away from the challenges of precise diagnostic definitions and therapeutic 'workability' and use the ambiguity of trauma as a phenomenon to explore what it reveals about the human experience. Often, when read solely through the lens of particular theories, the nuance and the paradox of trauma are reduced, making the theory say more or less than it intended to say.

Phenomenology dances through these shadow spaces, opening them up to the light of experience without reducing them to moralistic or therapeutic conclusions. In the last part of the book, we were introduced to Levine, whose account of hyperarousal, through the language of somatic experience provides important insight that can be read phenomenologically. For Levine, 'trauma is not a disease... but rather a human experience rooted in survival instincts' ('Introduction', Gabor Mate, in Levine 2010, p. xiii). Levine connects trauma to the wider picture of what it means to be human. For him, it constitutes a part of our experience as an animal self. He writes that 'Humans...*reterrorize themselves out of their (misplaced) fear of their own intense sensations and emotions*' (2010, pp. 62, italics in the original). Here, he is connecting a specific experience in the body (what he unpacks as the fight or flight experience) to the flooding of an emotional experience, associated with trauma.

The somatic view of experience is decidedly materialistic, if we are to read the transfer of energy states according to biofeedback systems only. According to Protevi, this affective science posits that cognition has to go beyond the 'processing of representations', to formulate a self that is responding as an organism to 'real-time' events around and within ourselves (2009, p. 25). Subjectivity, in this somatic reading, needs to account for how we are affected and respond to the world through biological feedback, as organisms (ibid.). It is helpful to see how the body and memory connects in this way, but it also leaves many unanswered questions. How is the body being perceived by the world, and how does the body perceive itself? What does this experience reveal about the ongoing suffering, as it constitutes a person's subjectivity? Why are particular experiences interpreted in this way? Not all of these will be answered here, but those that are will require the tools that existential phenomenology brings; namely, 'how we are formed as selves', as Jill Stauffer describes in *Ethical Loneliness* (2015, p. 25). This definition points not only to the narrowing of human experience as the task of this interdisciplinary work, but also to a permissive 'looseness' that involves exploring just what is meant by forming a self.

In the introduction of her book, Stauffer explores the situation that trauma leaves behind, a sort of 'ethical loneliness'. This is through the loneliness of violation brought about from an experience of abandonment by humanity (2015). For instance, she suggests that there are many who experience this phenomenon of loneliness, not only because of oppression and abandonment, 'but also the failure of just-minded people to hear well – from those who have suffered – what recovery or reconciliation…would require' (2015, p. 16). Stauffer situates her discourse in the wider conversations of political reconciliation, but her work has ramifications for anyone interested in understanding how suffering is experienced, and, the second task of this book, how we can conceptualise any conversation of meaningful healing. For her, we must address how a self is formed, and the intersubjective experience of how we listen to the traumatised self.

An Introduction to Lévinas

Lévinas was born into a Jewish family in Lithuania, which was at that time still under the Russian Empire. He later moved to France, where he pursued his philosophical studies at the University of Strasbourg and University of Paris. When the Second World War broke out, Lévinas was arrested and placed in a prisoner of war camp, where his early phenomenological thoughts started to take shape. These early writings show the first traces of the important role of the face (*visage*) and the connection between the physical body (*le corps*) and ethics *(la transcendence)* (Richter 2014). In these writings, he starts to connect the experience of subjectivity as being-for-another, which becomes the central phenomenological experience of his ethics.

For Lévinas, we exist as relational beings. Lévinas places the experience of the other person at the centre of the phenomenology of the self. He suggests that we are formed as subjects by our encounter with another person, which he refers to as the other. He writes, 'The word *I* means *here I am,* answering for everything and everyone' (ct. in Stauffer 2015, p. 7, italics in the original [Lévinas 1998b]). According to Lévinas, the experience of being is a unique experience. The I is me – there is no one else who can represent me. But this I is constantly being called to, beyond itself, by another person. So, who I am, as a subject, is one that responds to the other. This is the relationship of revelation, which he starts to develop in his later works. As we will see, Lévinas wants to weave together the language of different traditions to account for this experience. His phenomenology is a philosophy of the Torah, as well as an ethical plea to respond to the suffering of the unique other.

There is so much that could be said, and has been said, about Lévinasian readings of trauma. In this section, I wish to focus on two things specifically. First, we will look at Lévinas' critique of Being, suggesting that his account can give insight into how we understand trauma theory. Second, we will assess the role of trauma as the constitution of subjectivity and explore how suffering can be read as both an experience of uselessness and usefulness.

Subjectivity and the Limits of Being

Lévinas' early writing starts from the phenomenology of satisfaction with autonomous existence: the ego exists for-itself. For Lévinas, we become a subject when the other ruptures our enclosed ego with their plea for help. In other accounts, the ego opens itself in hospitality to the 'destitute' other, which becomes the emergence of subjectivity (Capili 2011, p. 677). Lévinas is referencing the human other here. The face of another person acts as a kind of 'provocation', that reveals our responsibility (2015, p. 152). Lévinas wants to show how our subjectivity requires a relationship of response to the other, who transcends our ability to comprehend her. This is alluded to in his Jewish writings, where he writes:

> In the Torah itself which remains, for a Jew, more intimate than his or her own inner self, there is a propensity for the outside: a remarkable requirement to enter into relations with all the nations, all the families of humankind.
>
> *1994, p. 86*

Lévinas cites this propensity for the outside, not only in the teachings of the Torah, but also in the phenomenology of the subject.

For Lévinas, the 'multiplicity of expressions' is not only the essence of the holy, but also the ethical relationship between humans (Guy 2009, p. 661). This ethical relationship is, however, situated in the context of human bodies. In his publications penned during his time in captivity, Lévinas writes, '*Le mot n'est pas séparable du sens*' (The word is not separate from the sensible, trans. mine, italics in the original) (1990b, p. 86). He goes on to suggest that this 'materiality' that the word takes on, through its particular definition, acts as a sort of signification for what it expresses. What we see here is a brief overview of what will take shape throughout Lévinas' writings. For Lévinas, our relation to the other is a bodied relationship, which opens us to someone who is unlike any other we have ever met.

When considering what it means to live trauma, Lévinas can show us how the body features in our relation to the other without reducing the other's experience to something that we have experienced before. First, there are no general experiences in Lévinas. But the person who reveals herself also hides herself from us at the same time. As Zimmerman writes, 'The face is both negation and affirmation' (2015, p. 153). This is what Lévinas is talking about when he refers to revelation. Second, Lévinas often references the experience of enclosure and rupture in his writings. For Lévinas, subjectivity interacts to break through the experience of being 'shut off' from the world. Both of these experiences tie together, as the face of the other breaks into our experience of ego enclosure, and we are asked to break into the enclosure of another person's experience of suffering.

Now in Levine's account of trauma, he suggests that the body experiences a kind of enclosure. In his study of the body's incomplete response to fear, he shows how the freedom of the body compromises itself, as it turns on and traps the self. 'Fear,' he writes, 'both greatly enhances and extends mobility and *also makes the process of exiting immobility fearful and potentially violent*' (2010, p. 62, italics in the original). The traumatised self, he suggests, lives through different experiences in the body. In some instances, it reveals itself in an immobilised state, whereas, on other occasions, the individual might act out violently. He recounts a story of a young boy in 1945, documented by David Levy, who studied the traumatic experiences of hospitalised children.

> The doctor tells me that everything is okay. The knee is fine, but everything is not okay for the boy waking up in a drug-induced nightmare, thrashing around on his hospital bed – a sweet boy who never hurt anybody, staring out from his anesthetic haze with the eyes of a wild animal, screaming, "Am I alive?".
>
> *ct. in Levine 2010, p. 63*

This child experiences first, an immobilisation, that is, loss of physical freedom through undergoing the procedure and then, he mobilises, reasserting his movement through 'thrashing around'. However, neither are completed and natural somatic states. The child's violent outbreak is just as 'unfree' as the immobilisation that he experienced during his medical procedure.

Levine provides a biological reading of the experience. He writes that 'Biologically [trauma] victims...are reacting like wild animals fighting for their life after being frightened or captured' (2010, p. 64). But humans are not the same as animals; many of the experiences differ. So, 'In humans, such violence...[can produce] tragic consequences to the individual and society' (ibid.). Levine is using biological language to develop this account, but it reveals two things that have phenomenological import: (1) trauma implicates the experience of freedom that an individual has, and (2) as humans living the traumatic experience, it necessarily connects us to other people as well. Trauma is not an isolated event, and it puts into question basic experiences of freedom.

Lévinas is also concerned with these two phenomena. The notion of freedom is one that he will return to time and time again in his writing. For him, the complexity of freedom is not adequately described by modern philosophy, and it goes beyond Levine's description of material freedom (that is, freedom of physical responses). Modern philosophy, Lévinas suggests, is preoccupied with freedom of the self. This self is conceived as unified and self-contained, akin to what he earlier on references as the ego. He writes that 'The simplicity of the subject lies beyond the struggles that tear it apart and that, within man, set the "I" [*moi*] against the "non-I" [*non-moi*]' ('On Escape', p. 49). Here, Lévinas is referring to the modern Western subject as one that is simple, self-contained, existing separately to others. In modern thought, the confrontation of the other comes from this self-enclosure: the struggle between myself and another person does not 'break up the unity of the "I"' (2003, p. 49). This 'I' unity that Lévinas referring to 'is given to peace with itself, completes itself, closes on and rests upon itself' (ibid.), that is, it is self-enclosed.

Thus, the experience of a being, unified, is a being at peace with itself. It is a being that is free to act on behalf of itself, as a unified being. This means that a confrontation with being, as self-enclosed and complete, also becomes a confrontation of freedom, because the very expression of being is in its enclosed state of freedom. Lévinas is critical of this enclosed experience of the ego. Not only does it place the individual into a general category of Being, but it also places Being in a problematic relationship with other people. Here, rather than responding to the other person, the task of the individual in this experience of Being is 'to loosen the grasp of the foreign reality [*réalité étrangere*] that chokes it, but this is in order to assure the full flowering of its own reality' (2003, pp. 49–50). The struggle becomes an account of the 'heroism of the individual', played out in his encounter with the stranger [*l'étranger*] (ibid.).

This reading of idealist philosophical theories of self is particularly interesting when assessed alongside Levine's account above. Lévinas suggests that there is a challenge of freedom, fear of the other, which seeks to rupture the 'peace' of the self, which consequently causes the disorder between selves. The experience of immobilisation leads to an experience, which cuts us off from fully expressing ourselves, but also from connecting to other people, and new emotions that might arise.

This means that for Levine as well as philosophical idealism, it is the loosening from the immobilisation that is required for freedom of the self. But whereas for Levine, who recognises that this will have a cost on the relation between the self and the other, eighteenth-century philosophy suggests that it is the struggle towards the other that becomes the source of a free heroism. Lévinas writes that the modern subject 'admits no inner division [*déchirement intérieur*]', and that the subject 'would be ashamed to lack confidence in himself' (p. 50). However, this is not just the experience of the self in the present, but what the self wants to secure for his future. If who the self is, is this free and unified being, then the reality of herself in the future is constituted on maintaining that integrated self-project. Thus, Lévinas says that the modern self concerns itself with 'reality and the future', because these two aspects pose the threat of breaking up the 'uncontested equilibrium of the present', which the individual possesses as its own (*ou il possede*) (ibid.) Lévinas suggests that it is this 'instinct of possession', and 'imperialistic' integration that comes from a 'search for security': The modern Western subject 'would like to cast the white mantle of his "internal peace" over the antagonism that opposes him to the world' (ibid.). In this imperialistic search for the possession of peace, this concern for the unified and free self not only becomes the conditions that regulate our engagement with other people but is also used to figure out how we will 'possess' our future.

This search for appropriated peace then becomes a task of violence, for in assuming our self-stability, we must make the other the same.

Lévinas thereby raises the issue which comes back repeatedly in his work regarding the violence of bringing the self under a universal vision of 'the same'. In problematising the reduction of the other to the same as an act of violence, Lévinas raises two interesting philosophical considerations that are important in this trauma discourse. First, do we, in our zeal to understand trauma, use theory a way of bypassing the individual experience? That is, as a means of comprehending the self, to restore the ego to its 'self-sufficiency'? Second, does the priority of freedom limit our ability to explore other aspects of the trauma experience? In both questions, Lévinasian philosophy motions to a problematic understanding of our encounter with otherness, which I would suggest has deep implications for how we interpret trauma and how we heal it.

Trauma, as Levine points out, jeopardises both the straightforward priority of freedom and unified 'project' of the self. Modern philosophy confronts the project of perfecting the Being of idealism and rational self-sufficiency. But in this confrontation, the modern subject abandons absolute notions of self. This 'abandonment of the transcendence project' opens up what Lévinas calls the experienced need of escape. It is a 'world-weariness, the disorder of our time [*mal du siècle*]' (2003, p. 52). In needing to escape the burden of existence, which is the freedom of the individual, there is language that can help us to understand trauma. Levine's interpretation of trauma is that the hyperarousal, which is caused by an inability to flee or fight in dangerous situations, is constantly activated. As a result, even when the dangerous situation has abated, the person is still in need of escaping the memory of the event in her body. Like the modern subject, the traumatised person is 'bound to a burden', to use the words of Leonard Cohen, even after being 'taken out of Egypt' (2018, p. 138). To use Lévinas' example, the autonomous self 'feels liable to be mobilised – in every sense of the term' (2003, p. 52). She belongs to herself, and the conquered terrain of selfhood takes on 'the inexpressible flavour of the absolute' (p. 52). The free self, choosing herself, is completely mobile – and in this becomes bound to the signification of her individual temporal existence.

Lévinas likens this modern experience of *enchainement* to an experience of suffering. For him, the I [*moi*] is revealed as enchainment: it is an identity of one that suffers and is inviting escape. In this way, Lévinas' subject is birthed through this desire to get out of the confines of oneself, that is, the confines of suffering: '*to break the most radical and unalterably binding of chains, the fact that the I [moi] is oneself [soi-même]*' (2003, p. 55, italics in the original). In this escape, the ethical subject is born, as being-for-the-other. For Lévinas, our experience of subjectivity does not rest in our ability to choose ourselves according to an ideal integration, or to know ourselves in light of any kind of abstract Being. Rather, subjectivity rests solely in the prior relation where the other reveals herself to me and calls me out of my enclosed ego.

Lévinas suggests that, in this need to escape the suffering of the I, a primordial reorientation of philosophy is required: 'It is a matter of getting out of being by a new path, at the risk of overturning certain notions that to common sense and the wisdom of the nations seemed the most evident' (2003, p. 73). The 'chains' of being are ruptured by the call of the other outside of myself. In this speaking, I both affirm the other, and I confirm the separation that exists between us (Zimmerman 2015, p. 153). Our subjectivity is experienced through affect; as subject, I am the one who is *affected by*, and thereby *responsible for*, the other. This affectivity, suggests Anderson, reveals that my vulnerability shows 'my own connectedness with the world that I want to believe I have mastery over or can escape' (2016, p. 58). The pain of affect shows that I am not alone, and that 'the world is *not* in my control' (ibid.). But this revelation is itself a form of mastery; it is the very constitution of responsible consciousness.

Extended in this critique of being is the notion of revelation. The other ruptures the enclosed ego, calling out the self as a subject. John Heaton, in his analysis of Lévinas and psychotherapy, reminds us that the other remains completely other to us. This confrontation between the self and the other is not a confrontation of the same; rather, it breaks totalising ways of knowing the other from the outside and requires the other to speak on her behalf. Heaton writes that 'the Other cannot be subsumed in a system and cannot be reached by a method however dedicated one is to it' (1988, p. 5). So for example, in the case of trauma, if a practitioner understands her patient through the DSM's criterion for PTSD without asking the patient to explore the nuances of their individual experience, then the practitioner can miss particular elements about how trauma is lived. The alterity of the other cannot be understood as just being like us. We respond to the other without being able to think the other out beforehand. This ruptures both reason and system; the relation to the other as revelation is prior to any systematisation of 'what' the other is.

One can also put Lévinas' critique of systematisation another way. The philosophical challenge of approaching the other through totality is also a critique of ontology's totalisation of Being. O'Connor writes 'For the ontological model of essential humanity Lévinas… substitute[s] an analysis of relationships – which are nonsynchronisable in a unitary mind or consciousness' (p. 58). I cannot possess the other, as a language of totality might have us believe, just as we cannot 'know' the other from the outside. The face actually speaks for itself: the body is taken up in both the communicating and living the experience through sensation (Zimmerman 2015). It is this body that is also capable of being hurt and in pain. This is the same for the other. Zimmerman suggests that the other's body is the source of 'all that constitutes the self', that is, 'language, sense, signification, meaning, responsibility and reason' (2015, p. 15). This is significant to how we understand trauma, because it presses against any systematised reading of experience.

While Lévinas wants to avoid normative application of his work, scholars have suggested that his reading of ethical primacy has practical implications in how we understand experience. For instance, this critique of totality then connects to Heaton's analysis of Lévinas in relation to psychotherapy. This is significant because trauma can be understood through therapeutic systems. But trauma, according to

Lévinas, constitutes a part of subjectivity, and this implicates a reading concerning systems that try to comprehend subjectivity from the outside. Heaton draws on this when writing that the 'problem of the Other', which is so important to psychotherapy, is often overshadowed by theoretical writings that see treatment as a pathological cure. As a result, the psychotherapeutic texts often replicate a theoretical system whose 'concept is cure and its methods of obtaining that cure are subsumed under the system' (1988, p. 5). What Lévinas wants to resist is exactly this systematic approach to the other. The other is radically different to the self. The other approaches us in saying (*le dire*), rather than being comprehended through her past, that is, through the said (*le dit*). The relation between the self and the other 'cuts through relations of power as possession' (O'Connor 1988, p. 58). We cannot possess the other, because the other 'transcends' me at all times (Lévinas 1961; 1978; 1998).

Heaton clarifies the repercussions of this understanding of cure and health for therapeutic relationships. Theoretically, there emerges a correlation between the 'cured individual' and 'the psychotherapeutic system':

> The system defines what cure is – integration and individuation, attainment of the depressive position, the ability to carry on one's own self-analysis, and so on – and the cure occurs because of the correct application of the method of cure generated by the system.
>
> *1988, p. 5*

Lévinas shirks any straightforward approach of the other that seeks to comprehend her, which can be understood as a position of power. We see this earlier in his work on *enchainement*. This interpretation by Lévinas is particularly important when we are trying to understand what it means to live trauma. For instance, in Amira's experience, the trauma could only be understood in the context of her whole story of growing up through the Intifadas as a minority, and then having to leave her homeland, and how her body experienced it was unique to her (the pain in the left side of her body). Similarly, rather than looking for a generic way of describing being, Lévinas seeks the revelation of the other. Ingrid Anderson writes that Lévinas sees humanity 'as *not* fundamentally for-himself, but as for-the-other, and *not* driven toward homogeneous, but desirous of the other as not-I, or heterogeneity' (2016, p. 57, italics in the original). The revelation of the other actually constitutes the very basis of our experience of consciousness.

What is important to take away from Heaton's critique is the problematisation of theory, rather than the suggestion that Lévinas criticises forms of helping the other. For Lévinas, the suffering of the other is our primary concern. The body is construed as 'vulnerable' (O'Connor 1988, p. 58), and it is this vulnerability that makes possession of the other so problematic: it has a particular and lived presence (Zimmerman 2015). The body that is vulnerable is the body that suffers. Here, then, we reach Lévinas' second contribution to our discourse, which is how suffering helps us to understand trauma experience.

Useful and Useless Suffering

For Lévinas, the un-assumability of the other is clearly revealed in suffering. While suffering can never be reduced to a moral system of interpretation, it can assume 'usefulness' when I take on suffering for the other. This, Lévinas reveals, is the ethical task that connects our subjectivity to the vulnerable face of the other. Trauma, then, becomes the experience through which subjectivity is constituted, without reducing it to something that can be understood or measured.

In his essay 'Useless Suffering', Lévinas explores the experience of suffering through a phenomenological encounter with otherness. He writes that suffering is un-assumable, incomprehensible, because the experience cannot be quantified. It is not 'excessive intensity of sensation', as somatic theory might purport; however, it is 'inscribed in sensorial content' (1988, p. 156). Lévinas shows us the value of his phenomenological treatment in that sentence – the experience of consciousness cannot be reduced to its 'felt' experience (i.e. its somatic presence), but it most certainly is connected to it. The person, living the suffering, is a body, which means that the vulnerably body is intimately connected to suffering, without us having to say that suffering can only be understood through studying the body. So, for instance, the suffering of a person who has been sexually abused will be experienced as a trauma done to the body, but it can also be an experience of betrayal, or of fear and vulnerability, as well as a breakdown of trust in relationship. This is important in linking the theoretical insights in the Chapter 3 while moving beyond theoretical accounts and into the connections between experiences.

Lévinas suggests that suffering distorts both time and freedom. It acts like 'a backward consciousness, "operating" not as "grasp" but as revulsion' (1988, p. 156). Trauma, we saw in the last chapter, is ambiguously categorised between the event(s) that happened to us, and the experience of the body in the living out of the aftermath. Lévinas interprets suffering similarly. In *Totality and Infinity*, he writes that 'Suffering remains ambiguous; it is already the present of the pain acting on the for-itself of the will, but as consciousness the pain is always yet to come...' (1969, p. 238). This concept of 'backward consciousness', alongside the 'consciousness [of] pain that is always yet to come' can help us to understand how trauma resists linear time, as well as how it is experienced both in the mind and the body of the person.

But this consciousness is passive; it is not 'doing' anything. The person is always undergoing, overwhelmed. Suffering is not 'because of' anything. Its uselessness is essential to Lévinas' resistance of accounts that seek to understand and undermine the suffering person. It is not a part of a project of a 'greater whole', or a Jungian spiritual journey; yet, it is also primary to an understanding of subjectivity, if looked at in another way. So, Lévinas says that 'suffering...in its own phenomenality, intrinsically, it is useless, "for nothing"' (1988, p. 158). As experienced in instances of pain, suffering is a 'basic senselessness', which has no deeper meaning, but rather exists so loudly that it has the capacity to isolate 'itself in consciousness, or absorbs the rest of consciousness' (ibid.). Lévinas maintains the empirical dimension of the pain experience in his phenomenology, showing how it isolates the self from others through its eclipsing affect on experience. Not assigned to any morally esteemed category, the suffering person just *is* in her vulnerability, suffering. Here, we see how Lévinas reads the human experience through the sensible, rather than through reason (Anderson 2016). The sensible experience of suffering therefore has the capacity to form the basic experiences of consciousness.

Suffering has the ability to turn the ego into a subject, through the sensible experience of consciousness. It is at this point that we can connect the revelation of subjectivity which we have referenced earlier to this experience of suffering. We have seen how suffering, as undergoing, is useless. It does not serve any wider purpose, it is 'extreme passivity, impotence, abandonment and solitude' (Lévinas 1988, p. 158). This resonates with the psychological and biological accounts explored earlier. However, for Lévinas, this 'un-assumable' suffering of the other, the experience that defies our theorisation, also contains a possibility of relation. Lévinas writes that 'wherever a moan, a cry, a groan or a sigh happens there is the original call for aid, for curative help' (ibid.). The interesting thing here is that phenomenologically, the other is not using precise language. The experience is still, in some way, unsayable (an idea that we will return to in the next part).

But this embodied expression, the 'cry' or 'groan' reveals 'the original call for aid, for curative help, for help from the other ego whose alterity, whose exteriority promises salvation' (1988, p. 158), that is, an exit out of the suffering totality. The responding subject thereby assumes the suffering other and concerns herself with it. This is where Lévinas writes that 'For pure suffering, which is intrinsically meaningless and condemned to itself without exit, a beyond takes shape in the inter-human' (p. 158). This inter-human perspective reveals the experience of suffering as 'meaningful in me, useless in the other' (p. 164), and the response becomes the grounding of Lévinasian consciousness.

That suffering can play this dual role is fascinating and illuminates the nuance of its ambiguity. In *Totality and Infinity*, Lévinas writes that the experience of suffering, as 'ultimate passivity', in this experience of response 'desperately turns into action and into hope' (1969, p. 238). This experience of hope, revealed through the intersubjective, is premised on an experience of 'patience – the passivity of undergoing and yet mastery itself' (p. 238). Suffering is phenomenologically transformed here into an experience of hope, not because it is fully explained or because it fully disappears. Anderson writes that this transformation of 'suffering into empathy, and empathy into shared responsibility for the other' is tied to the initial grounds of subjective consciousness, which is the 'shock of the pre-reflective discovery of one's own alterity' (2016, pp. 4–5). For her, this suffering is a call to action, before feeling 'free to do so' (p. 58). In suffering, a person can try to distance herself from her experience whilst still experiencing pain. It is paradoxically also a call to hope through despair: 'I hope the pain will end, and I hope that then I will be freed. I am patient because I have to be. In addition, I master the pain because I integrate that pain into my sense of self and world' (ibid.). In this paradoxical patient transformation, the experience of suffering still contains its sensible paradox. It cannot be comprehended from outside or explained through cause-and-effect. It is experienced in sensing bodies but cannot be interpreted through psychological or biological accounts alone. Furthermore, as it serves to reveal the other to me, it calls out the relationship between others and myself, which is at the very core of what it is to be human.

Conclusion

The implications of this relation to suffering for trauma discourse are quite profound because it reasserts the experience of relationship as prior to any real understanding of what trauma is about. We cannot 'read' the person through the theory; we can only grapple with understanding the other's face as it reveals itself to us. This is also important to an exploration of how trauma can be integrated in health discourse. Lévinas offers up a notion of hope, as expressed through the experience of suffering on behalf of the other. He obliterates the theoretical accounts of theodicy that equate suffering to punishment or growth while maintaining that suffering constitutes the grounds of our subjectivity. This problematises theories of measurable 'post-traumatic growth', whilst also suggesting that there is a role of trauma in our experience of self, and the wider experience of health. It is not about hiding ourselves away, and securing our borders. But it is never, in itself, something that has 'use' unless taken up on behalf of the other.

5

RICŒUR ON NARRATIVE EXPERIENCES

In Chapter 4, Lévinas shows how we can explore the ambiguity of suffering consciousness through his philosophy of subjectivity and responsibility. Lévinas challenges totalising accounts of experience and suggests that the uselessness of suffering can open a space for responsible and revelatory relationship. Lévinas appeals to the experience of the body, which we will look at later in Merleau-Ponty's writings. Lévinas also introduces us to the complexity of relationship: he shows us how the other reveals herself to us, and that she also evades us at the same time. Similarly, he situates our experience in relationship and defines subjectivity in relation to our responsibility for the other. In his Talmudic writings, he references how translation can be experienced as 'linguistic hospitality' (1994). Though he is careful to separate his philosophical writings from his Jewish themes (Nicholson-Weir and Hill 2008), this relation of hospitality provides a central theme for his philosophy. Reading a text through one's own perspective, without giving account for the unique attributes of the original language and meaning amount to an experience of egoistic totalisation (Davidson 2012). The original text has to speak for itself, rather than be reduced to the meaning of the translator.

Paul Ricœur picks up on these threads of linguistic communication and justice in his phenomenological writing. As with Lévinas, Ricœur had first-hand experience of trauma, though he was not Jewish but a Christian. His father was killed in the First World War when he was two years old, and then, in 1940, he was held prisoner by the German army as a French prisoner of war (Davis 2018). For Ricœur, the ability to tell one's story became central to his understanding of subjectivity. In the midst of the ruptures and unimaginable outcomes of life events, he argued that we need to be able to plot our experiences to give them meaning (*la mise en intrigue*). Ricœur acknowledges that '[e]xperience is confused, ambiguous, maybe even wordless' (Ricœur 1983, p. 13; Davis 2018, p. 120), which requires us to piece it together into meaningful stories.

DOI: 10.4324/9780367800017-7

As a result, it is problematic to conceive of reality in terms of things either being true or false, because the narrative that we 'plot' does not exist as some objective kind of experience 'out there' in the world. But, as Davis shows us, Ricœur's emplotment also helps us to bring a 'restoration of referentiality, because the stories we tell about our lives nevertheless tie them back to the real people we really are' (2018, p. 120). In this understanding, then, experience becomes a work of sense-making in the midst of chaos. This narrative phenomenology has particular implications for trauma in two ways. Ricœur offers a problematisation of how Freud reads experience, in a way that can help us to expand our understanding of how trauma is interpreted. This problematisation confers an ambiguity on straightforward notions of blame and punishment, which will help us in furthering Lévinas' suggestion that suffering is an absence of justice.

Critiquing Freudian Analysis

Ricœur is interested in how consciousness understands itself. In other words, how is it that we act and think, as individuals? But he is also, particularly in his later thought, interested in the subtle interpretations that we have to make of our experiences. Ricœur wanted reflexive consciousness to be hermeneutically interpretive. This unique phenomenology is particularly seen through his work on psychoanalysis. In his book *On Psychoanalysis*, Ricœur spends considerable time understanding the phenomenological reconstruction of psychoanalysis. As we saw in Part I, Freudian theory has shown a particular way of interpreting the traumatic experience, through the relationship of transference between patient and practitioner. There are two ways in which Ricœur challenges readings of experience in psychoanalysis, which will benefit our understanding of trauma. First, Ricœur shows how Freud develops a problematic account of communicating the unconscious experience. Second, Ricœur challenges Freudian subjectivity by placing it in a context of relationship, in keeping with a more bodied relational account of trauma.

In the first instance, Ricœur shows how the analytic relationship is constructed 'as a speech relation' (2012, pp. 95–96). Analysis makes 'the desire speak', which the unconscious is trying to communicate. This presses the desire 'through the defilement of words', which means that the analysand becomes capable of speaking about their experience through the presence of the other (pp. 96–97). For analysis, to speak about oneself actually becomes the very act that brings the unspoken, unintelligible into the intelligibility of narrative. So this means that in analysis, 'to speak of oneself is to move from an unintelligible to an intelligible narrative' (p. 97). One can see the appeal of this for Ricœur, whose plotting of narrative is of central importance to the experience of the self. For Ricœur, psychoanalysis does just this: it places the experience of a person in relation to her context and text. It is a 'labour of decontextualising and recontextualising', the narrative structures of the personal experience (ibid.).

This means that analysis becomes a matter of 'narrative analysis', and the experience of trauma is an experience of language interpretation, or a 'semiotics of symptoms', as Ricœur puts it (2012, p. 99). Symptoms are interpreted as 'another discourse', and the 'unconscious is structured like a language, to the degree that it may be understood as another kind of discourse' (p. 98). This is where one can see a convergence of Ricœur's phenomenology. Suddenly psychoanalysis takes on a hermeneutical dimension. Psychoanalysis asks that we translate experience in a similar way to the manner in which one translates a text from one language to another, or from one speaker to another. Ricœur describes this process as the dialectic of fidelity and betrayal, in which the translation of what is meant to be said gives up elements of itself to reach a 'relative equivalence' (Davison 2012, p. 4). Acknowledged in this is that there are often multiple meanings to one word: 'something is preserved but something is lost, something transferred but something blocked, something is understood but misunderstood' (ibid.). Ricœur suggests that there is the possibility of a 'happy' translation when the original text is perceived as being adequate, as opposed to equivalent. Adequation here means a sense of cohesion 'between a thought or word and what it represents' (ibid.). This 'relative equivalence' of a happy interlinguistic translation then becomes a way in which he interprets other inter- and intrahuman exchanges, with ourselves and with other people (2012, p. 5).

The limitation found in interpreting trauma through language alone is that Freud also needs to account for the experience of force, so we cannot just equate the two as one. As contemporary science shows us, trauma actually maps itself on the body as well as in psychic narrative. Freud is interested in interpreting a 'psychical reality', rather than a material reality, even though the psychical reality can be interpreted through both textual ('translation, substitution') and energy metaphor ('condensation, displacement, repression') (Ricœur 2012, p. 68). The mixed metaphors converge to create a psyche capable of two experiences: 'interpretation of meaning', like a text, and the 'handling of resistances' (ibid.).[1] Meaning and force are interpreted through one analytic experience. This challenges the action theory that philosophy of language proposes, which is that there are two different kinds of grammar: one is used to govern physical concepts (force, energy, movement). The other is used to govern the grammar of syntax. So, for instance, when you are speaking about a motive (the reason) for action, it will be different to the cause of the action. If considering trauma, the motive for dissociation (e.g. presence of perpetrator) differs from the cause of dissociation (e.g. activation of sympathetic-adrenal nervous system, see Morris 1969). When the language narrative is interpreted as the experience itself, a linguistic reformulation becomes a substitution for the experience itself.[2]

In this Freudian reading of reality, there is a 'tenacious dichotomy between the imaginary and the real' (2012, p. 17). The challenge of psychoanalysis is then a matter of phenomenological representation. Somehow the psychical unconscious needs to be transmitted into language and then be both accurately told by the traumatised person and analysed by the clinician. But the idea that an experience can be felt and then encoded in our subconscious, only to be perfectly retrieved and articulated seems to place a lot of confidence on the translation between psychical and material phenomenon. Ricœur suggests that 'psychoanalysis deals only with the psychical reality and not with the material reality' (ibid.). So here the reality criterion is not one that is observable; it even resists the observable reality. Reality therefore becomes a play of substitution. Psychoanalysis develops the fantastical as the 'paradigm of what represents psychical reality' (2012, p. 19), without confusing it with the real.

For Freud, then, language becomes 'the privileged instrument of efficacy', but for Ricœur, that does not prove that the actual experience (in this case, the trauma) 'is or must belong to language'. Instead, he argues for the opposite:

> On the contrary, it is because the level of interpretative expression proper to the unconscious is not language that the work of interpretation is difficult and constitutes a veritable linguistic promotion.
>
> *2012, p. 109*

Ricœur shows us that, phenomenologically speaking, experience is not just read like language. Though we operate narratively, this experience goes beyond language to communicate and translate embodied experiences. This makes sense when we consider the inexplicability of symptoms that are present, even after the work on the mind has been done. For instance, when Amira experienced the feelings of pain in the left side of the body, it was after she had made sense of the mental narratives with her psychologist. I would argue that this is because Amira's trauma not only resided in her consciousness, but also in the autonomic nervous system that regulated her experience of pain. In a way, Ricœur's idea of finding a translation for how trauma is lived into our 'own language', even when it omits something of the 'ideal and perfect' experience (Davidson 2012, p. 5), is one of the aims of book.

What we know about trauma is revealed in the traces that it leaves behind. So this idea that we look at how the memory of trauma is distorted and translated and stored in memory is not a problem; this is part of trauma's phenomenology. However, what Ricœur finds problematic is that the unconscious memories that are put into language are held to be the equivalent of facts. This means that it is 'not clinically relevant whether the…scenes are true or false' (2012, p. 17). What Ricœur is picking up on here is that the experience that is put into language and analysed may, or may not, have happened exactly as it has been stored in memory. That is, the psychical reality might not actually be representing a material reality. One could read Ricœur as overly critical of psychoanalysis. But this is not what Ricœur is interested in. He wants to clarify what psychoanalysis is, and what it is not. When psychoanalysis is asked to be what it is not, it loses the specific and uniquely critical analytic insights of the discipline. Does having a discipline that encompasses everything make it a better discipline? Or do the limitations enable us to seek dialogue partners that can fill the holes that we leave behind?

This section critiques a straightforward reading of analysis theory. First, Ricœur shows how Freud is unable to account for the problematic projected reading of reality. This, for Ricœur, becomes a phenomenological challenge to Freudian analysis. Second, van der Kolk and Levine suggest that trauma affect needs to be understood in relation to the embodied memory's effect on the body itself, in the experience of trauma. For Jonathan Lear, psychoanalysis problematically 'betrays its promise' through its paternalistic methodology: 'as doctrine and method that can authoritatively bring to conscious awareness all the determining forces of character' (1998, ct. in Horowitz 2009, p. 26). The strength of the discipline lies in, and indeed requires, both the metapsychological theorising that goes beyond mere body-based accounts, and the clinical therapeutic outworking of it in the lived body of the patient. It is the latter that both Levine and van der Kolk's work develops. However, before we move to these theories, we have further aspects of trauma history to uncover.

We will see this connection between the body and consciousness again as we turn to Ricœur's second challenge. In the second instance, Ricœur connects the ego's relationship to herself through a wider relationship to the world. Ricœur also develops experience narratively. However, he objects to particular abstract relationships that psychoanalysis constructs. For Ricœur, the Freudian 'topography' is abstract, because it is not able to give an account for 'the intersubjective nature of the dramas forming its main theme' (2012, p. 61). In both the unconscious dramas of the parental relationships that clients bring for analysis and the therapeutic relationship itself, where the drama is brought into speech, the analysis is nourished by a 'debate between consciousnesses' (ibid.). But this Freudian systematisation of events can create a solipsism that is hard to avoid, that differs from the analysis of actual situations and relations that are intersubjective (ibid.). For Ricœur, there is a problem in Freud's solipsistic reading of the ego experience. As we saw previously, reading trauma through its effect on the ego offers a way of exploring how traumatic memory is stored in the unconscious but breaks into consciousness through symptoms.

Reading trauma through the ego has helped to explore how memory affects our current experience of consciousness. However, as we see in the contemporary research of psychiatrist van der Kolk and psychologist Levine, trauma is not just a matter of understanding solipsistic consciousness, expressed as narrative that experiences the duality of forces towards death and life, as Ricœur summarises in *Freud and Philosophy*. Rather, contemporary trauma theory requires further understanding the self in relation to itself and others, as an intersubjective embodied consciousness.

Ricœur's phenomenological discourse in conversation with contemporary embodied trauma discourse links the embodied situation of healing to the relation of the body and lamentation practices, as a re-situation of ruptured relation. This, I will suggest, unpacks Freud's initial insight on rupture and re-situation while developing the insights gained from van der Kolk's research on how the physical body itself becomes the holding place of memory. The phenomenological exploration of rupture is further developed by Ricœur's concept of lament, as the spontaneous expressive search for relation beyond the silencing of trauma.

The phenomenological tradition that Ricœur inherits and responds to is constructed through the philosophy of Edmund Husserl. Husserl develops a phenomenological *epoché*, a suspension of set beliefs and assumptions, that 'lays open... an infinite realm of being of a new kind...transcendental experience' (Husserl 1999, p. 27, ct. in Kenaan and Ferber 2011, p. 5). This happens through '"the philosophically reflective Ego's abstention from position-takings, his depriving them of acceptance" that thereby modifies the given into a "mere phenomenon" (Husserl 1999, p. 20)' (Kenaan and Ferber 2011, p. 5). But in the writing of Jean Paul Sartre, reflected in Ricœur, there emerges a criticism of a transcendental reading of consciousness. Husserl, they suggest, blurs 'the existential motivations pulsating in the *epoché*' (p. 6).

Even Martin Heidegger, in his reading of *Dasein*, or being, as belonging to the World, the 'human realm of meaningfulness that precedes the distinction between the subjective and the objective' (Kenaan and Ferber 2011, pp. 4–5),[3] does not manage to attach it to a particularised existential body. But Ricœur, rather than reading experience transcendentally, suggests that phenomenon is experienced in lived and embodied consciousness. In Ricœur, '...the *epoché's* radical transformation of experience calls for a more coherent explanation – on that emerges from his analysis of the relationship between consciousness and Ego' (p. 6). That the relation between consciousness and its ego forms the reading of the lived experience, outside of its therapeutic treatment, is how I will choose to read trauma through the work of Ricœur.

A Phenomenological Reading of Embodied Trauma

The experience of embodied trauma therefore benefits from this phenomenological reading. I will suggest that this particular experience of ongoing suffering breaks with the at-homeness (Sveneaus 2000) of the lived body. Francois Fleury and Shadman Mahmoud-Shwana give an account of people traumatised by torture, through the structure of narrative. What distinguishes these stories is that they end 'in a state of post-traumatic stress' (2010, p. 97). However, this is not just the case for those who have lived the traumatic experience, but even those how have been 'in proximity' to it, or have witnessed it in some way. This state is a shattering of 'inner integrity', they suggest. For a person whose story ends in this state '*are homeless in terms of their deepest sense of protection*' (2010, p. 97).

The narrative is a lived experience. Here, the integrated experience of consciousness, the at-homeness of the lived experience, is ruptured. This is experienced internally, in terms of the self-identity of the person, as well as externally, through how the person relates to the world around her. This two-fold phenomenon therefore requires considering the relational meaning-making structures of the person. For instance, understanding the lived trauma means assessing how the trauma implicated the person's relationships to their home, to their sense of time and experience of value etc.

In its efforts to re-examine the limits of modern medicine, the medical sciences can therefore use philosophy to understand the patient and the caregiver in a relation of wholeness. Narrative language has long been used in exploring the experiences of the body. Through narrative, the somewhat ambiguous feelings of suffering reveal themselves as concrete experiences. For instance, in Langer's account of trauma, he uses metaphor to incline the reader towards the experience of trauma. He writes: 'Who can find a proper grave for such damaged mosaics of the mind, where they may rest in peace?' (1991, p. 34). For a traumatised person, life continues to move on, but its temporality is split between the movement into a future, and a future that is constantly gripped by 'a memory laden in grief' (ibid.). It is in this metaphor of the mind that Langer can show the temporal split between the past and future: a rupture that is not easily recollected, though time continues. Rita Charon emphasises the embodied encounter of the suffering person as one enriched by the language of values, an account that enables contemporary medicine to grapple with the depth of situations of suffering, as experienced in embodied trauma.

Using the philosophy of Ricœur, the subject is understood as an embodied subject-in-relation. In *Freud and Philosophy*, Ricœur references Freud's duality of forces that work in the life of the self, towards life and death. Traumatic experience reveals the dominance of the death instinct as a permanent and isolating presence in the self (1977, p. 93). Ricœur writes that trauma reveals the death and life instinct in battle, whereby 'Freud speaks of the death instinct as a "mute" energy, in contradistinction to the "clamour" of life. Death works in silence...' (p. 294). For Ricœur, this is a materialistic and reductive understanding of the hermeneutics of the self that is 'opposed to a nonreductive and restorative hermeneutics' (p. 59). This means showing how our narrative can open up to a future, taking account of the rupture we experience, and reorienting ourselves in the midst of it ('seule l'interprétation est le "remede" a la faiblesse du discours que son auteur ne peut plus "sauver"') (Ricœur 1998, p. 188).

This situation of embodied trauma not only reveals the body's central role in relation but also how the situation of suffering ties both victim and perpetrator together. Ricœur's phenomenological exposition[4] opens up a preliminary grappling with the subject as embodied. He shows how the body is central to the experience of selfhood. Posing the question that van der Kolk probes his reader, Ricœur asks: 'What mode of being, then, belongs to the self, what sort of being or entity is it?' (1994, p. 297). This is the challenge, van der Kolk, has suggested – the ontology of being intersects with the phenomenology of experience, revealing the self as irreducible to either material or disembodied consciousness. 'One's own body', Ricœur says, 'is the very place—in the strong sense of the term—of...belonging, thanks to which the self can place its mark on those events that are its actions' (p. 319). It is this embodied consciousness that has 'been subjected to the violence of fear, of its passage and its touch' (Fleury and Mahmoud-Shwana 2010, p. 99).

Previously, we have looked at how existential phenomenology, through the work of Ricœur, might provide a rich exploratory context for the rupture of relation that takes place in trauma. In this exploration, we saw how contemporary trauma theorists choose to connect the body to the narrative – the narrative, as consciousness in form, speaking and interpreting herself. The way that Ricœur can connect the traumatised body of the past to the hope of a future (thick) 'goodness', without a reductive utopic vision, is revealed through his treatment of lament.

In the account of trauma experienced by torture victims, Fleury and Mahmoud-Shwana write that: 'The lack of being as the suffering is prolonged, and the confused and complex sensations experienced, render the person both mute and without witness' (2010, p. 101). The suggestion that the self, because of the rupture of trauma, is rendered both mute and without witness is important. There is no narrative that can be spoken – the body cannot speak for itself. There is also no one to listen, so the self-other relation is absent as well. They write that their patients perceived going through a 'time of "voicelessness"... Their identity was frozen at some point in time and they see this as being irreversible' (p. 107). This means that in some instances, 'it took more than nine months to say just a few words' (pp. 101–102). In order to explore a self beyond rupture, a narrative also requires that the body is taken up in the act of saying, in order for it to be an experiential self-relation. But it also needs a relation, another person as listener and witness, in order that the self can experience this subjective re-formation. Fleury and Mahmoud-Shwana expand on this in the cases of migrant trauma when they suggest that the 'neo-formation of the self' cannot happen unless there is a partial or full destruction of the old self. For them, the new self cannot emerge from the old self. The new self is, rather, formed from the elementary fragments that are the 'products of [the] destruction' (p. 104).

Levine and van der Kolk emphasise that the body itself needs to process the rupture of trauma. What Fleury and Mahmoud-Shwana note is that trauma can actually destroy our original self-construct. They suggest that the traumatised self is often caught in the schism of narrative played out in the body – it is stuck in the fragments of the old self-experience. For Fleury and Mahmoud-Shwana, the repetitive playback of traumatic events releases an 'emotional discharge' that is the body's attempt to 'reconstruct itself', which happens in the presence of a stressor: 'The identity is returned, in a final effort and in the shape of a sacrificial victim, to its existential cry' (2010, p. 104). Here, the self-experiences an embodied expression of self-fragmentation, or 'non-exit', to use the words of Lévinas in 'Useless Suffering' (1988). The self is stuck in the phenomenological experience of rupture that separates the self from the other. But at the same time as the body feels this, the verbal narrative of the person's story is also experienced in fragments. The body itself echoes the schism of the opening towards the future.

How the subject can be reconnected to her own experience, both in terms of conscious narrative and material, bodied experience then becomes a central task for those who work with traumatised people. Connecting the fragmented self to the wider self story, both of one's own life, and one's relation to the rest of the world, can be seen in the psychoanalytic work of Carl Jung on the imagination. For instance, Schore, Wilkinson and others in this tradition suggest that 'affects-in-the-body', which are encoded through implicit memories occasioned by early trauma, are often more easily accessed through 'the mytho-poetic image-language of *dreams, metaphor, and poetry* than the rational-interpretive language of insight' (Kalshed 2013, p. 117). As such, the development of the trauma narrative is one that involves 'mytho-poetic language' that they suggest 'taps a *daimonic* or *collective* stratum of the psyche' (ibid.). But, while referencing the body abstractly, this narrative seems to base itself in a transcendental story that lacks the clear reference to the material body, which is part of the phenomenological experience that we want to address.

The Ambiguity of Trauma

Ricœur's contributions on the ambiguity of language are particularly helpful in considering trauma. Ricœur engages with narrative reconstruction through the lens of phenomenology. He is interested in plotting the experience of the self, through an interpretation of reality that avoids the fallacies of objective experiences. This becomes particularly important when addressing the ethical challenges that Lévinas poses in his account of suffering. For Ricœur, the concept of guilt and blame often overlap in the ambiguity of experience. However, reading trauma in this way does not mean that this ambiguity always exists. Often, there are clear examples in which a person has been traumatised, and there is a clear sense of moral guilt, or direct known cause of a single episode. The challenge is that trauma often is constituted by overlapping experiences. As an example of this, we could look at prison populations. Studies on this population show that rates of physical, emotional and sexual trauma in inmate populations can range up to 44.7% (Wolff and Shi 2012). The traumatiser is often (though, of course, not always) the traumatised. These figures, as well as meta-analyses of intersecting traumatised populations in conflict areas, make it important to account for the overlapping of traumatic and traumatising experiences. There is an ambiguity to the relationships between ourselves and the world that all form part of the traumatic experience.

As we saw in his interpretation of translation and psychoanalysis, Ricœur is interested in interpreting narrative as a 'threshold of fact and fiction'. According to psychiatrist and philosopher Gerrit Glas, Ricœur's narrative interpretation helps psychopathology by providing a 'large laboratory for moral thought experiment and the imaginary trying out of alternate life scenarios' (2003, p. 349). One way that this laboratory of thought is helpful for us is when trying to understand the experience of suffering in trauma. Trauma combines a complex array of experiences and interpretations of the world, and this is particularly revealed through the experience of suffering. Reading suffering through materialistic accounts alone does not give justice to the depth of interconnection between experiences and the moral as well as imaginative dimensions of trauma. One way that Ricœur wants to account for multiple interpretations of experience is through myth. In *The Symbolism of Evil*, Ricœur writes that mythical imagination, in the modern sense, is 'not a false explanation by means of images and fables, but a traditional narration which relates to events that happened at the beginning of time…' (1967, p. 5). In this way, it acts to establish ways of acting and thinking that enable humans to understand themselves in relation to the world (ibid.).

Because we cannot connect myth to a concrete linear history or geographical place per se, myth evades the confines of neat explanations. Ricœur is adamant that human experience involves confusion and ambiguities. Experience is even, at times, 'wordless' (Davis 2018, p. 120). What myth does do is open up the space of meaning making. In its use of symbols and metaphors (its 'symbolic function'), it reveals 'the bond between man and what he considers sacred', which helps to connect the individual story to a wider meta-narrative (1986, p. 5). So, for instance, the story of my suffering, which has left me wondering how to order my life, can receive a kind of emplotment through the mythical symbol of evil that shows how a person has suffered and the narrative reasoning behind the experience (such as, the gods showcasing their anger, or the person experiencing the curse of the Fall).

But Ricœur suggests that myth itself cannot adequately account for the ambiguity of suffering. Myth acts as a kind of intermediary of experience, which allows experience to have a place in a wider story arch. This view of myth is similar to Jung's account of archetypal narratives in our unconscious. However, differing from Jung, Ricœur's self has to account for *idem* and *ipse* identity as well. One way in which Ricœur engages with myth is through interpreting human suffering as an experience of evil. He writes that evil enigmatically encompasses diverse phenomena of 'sin, suffering and death' (1995, p. 250). In this way, the experience of suffering is explored as a situation of moral relationship, of vulnerable bodies, of textual significance and as acts of consciousness. For instance, the moral experience of evil might account for trauma through the experience of justice. Evil can refer to a wrongdoing, in the sense of a perpetration of justice. If we read trauma through this lens, we can see how the 'evil' of trauma can account for the widespread experiences of abuse that some prison inmates are said to live through prior to their acts of violence (Harlow 1999). This cycle of re-victimisation is a breakdown of relationship that then facilitates an experience of both victimisation and perpetration. The blamed perpetrator violates another, and the act is associated with guilt and punishment (we will return to this later in the book).

But interpreting suffering as evil through Ricœur's phenomenology also means that we need to account for the lived body. In this experience of evil, the sufferer is in pain because of an infliction to the vulnerable body. In this interpretation, evil assumes itself on multiple kinds of human experiences. For instance, when the suffering person articulates this evil, she invokes the language of lament. This connects the moral, material and narrative aspects of a person's experience. In this mythic laboratory, Ricœur is able to fine-tune how we understand human experience. He shows, for example, that the moral and the bodied experience of trauma requires a different interpretation of language: 'Lament occurs as the opposite of blame; whereas blame makes culprits of us, lament reveals us as victims' (1995, p. 250). In interpreting experience through myth, the phenomenology of trauma can show its complex interconnectivity. Trauma involves the experiences of both perpetrator and victim. To do harm involves making someone else suffer, whereas to experience the harm means that the embodied self is the one that suffers. The *poena* – pain or punishment – is different to each but is experienced in both. This means that though what happen in the two experiences are very different, the boundary between them is blurred. Caught up as oppositions, blame and lament,[5] guilt and victimisation present suffering's enigma. It also directs us to the call for justice. I would argue that we can interpret trauma in a similar manner. A rupture and a reperceiving of the self-other relation needs to be re-situated, or transformed, in order for us to be able to re-engage with the self and the other, which echoes profoundly with both van der Kolk and Levine's current trauma theory discourse.

But Ricœur problematises the notion of staying in the realm of myth. For Ricœur, the history of philosophy, developed through the suspicion of Freud, Marx and Nietzsche, breaks down the naïve assumptions about the assumed structures of life that myth inhabits. However, breaking away from this 'School of Suspicion', Ricœur also problematises a fundamentally suspicious approach to experience. For him, we can still understand our experience, even though it has to be continuously reassessed and critically revised. So experience has to be understood beyond myth but still requires emplotment to a whole life. Ricœur moves from myth to narrative. The challenge with suffering is that it often breaks apart the experience of a narrative self: trauma particularly can put into question all of our basic trust in the world and our relationship to it. Suffering connects us to a wide variety of relationships, and our experience of it needs to take these relationships into account. This leads Ricœur to choosing different interlocutors for his phenomenological discussion.

If we take the experience of suffering, this narrative 'plotting' will resist any attempts to read narratives as the same as each other. Ricœur is similar to Lévinas in this way. But he also wants to show how the narrative structures help us to explore and give shape to our experiences of the world. So for him, the experience of lament becomes central to the experience of suffering. Richard Hughes writes that for Ricœur, 'Myth is a form of symbolic totalisation, an explanation of primal origins, which lament challenges, undermines and rejects' (2006, pp. 6–7). Ricœur's philosophy pushes us beyond myth, into the embodied expression – the interconnected self in relation to the other in the form of lament, because it both moves the self towards a future and grapples with the complex overlapping experiences of suffering. He not only looks at suffering as an experience of physical pain and facelessness but also through the phenomenon of evil that links both perpetrator and victim. Myth helps make the connection to the moral experience and the language that it articulates, but one needs to move beyond myth in order to do something about this problem concretely and individually.

In Ricœur's account of suffering, he connects the suffering past with the possibility of the future through invoking the imagination's role in lament. Here he distinguishes between the harm done in violence to the victim and the suffering received. The invocation of suffering in phenomenology, echoing contemporary Lévinas, is through the ambiguous language of evil. Kearney reflects that Ricœur's phenomenology of evil cannot adequately be dealt with through the 'intentional consciousness', or a kind of moral violation, because in this experience, people find 'themselves estranged from themselves, divided within' (2006, p. 197). This 'limit-situation' that Kearney presents is one that can shatter the illusions of the self, as autonomous and sovereign. It exposes the self to the anxiety of one's fallible finitude (ibid.).

Ricœur wants to reclaim the ambiguity of suffering experience, as an experience that has the capacity to shatter our previous understanding of self. The narrative that we hold about how the world operates, how people are trustworthy, or how I am valued is ruptured in complex, interconnected experiences. It can affect our understanding of theology, or our mental wellbeing. It can even disrupt our politics.[6]

Mythical narratives only go so far in helping to attune us to our wider system of relations that trauma disrupts. The rupture is lived out in conscious bodies. As van der Kolk writes, the 'traumatised people feel chronically unsafe inside their bodies: the past is alive in the form of...interior discomfort' (2014, p. 96). It is not merely a matter of interpreting and sewing together the psychic pieces. We need to connect with another person who is able to be present to our suffering. Ricœur also views the subject relationally. For him, who we are is directly tied to our relation to the other. But this relationship is not just symbolic: it is lived experience of relationship that Ricœur wants all of this to point to (Dierckxsens 2017, p. 1). This relational, bodied consciousness counters the experience of rupture; this belonging both as a body at-home with itself and as a person in relation to others is situated against the traumatic relation of either asserted violence or absence of relation. As such, it requires engaging with the paradox of orienting towards response and relationship when human relationship has proven hostile. In this rupture of narrative that suffering can bring, embodying this response-ability requires tools that extend beyond the ambiguity and rupture of the situation. It calls for us to re-situate the relation in which we can respond, not out of hostility or anxiety but out of an act of hope, where the plenitude of being develops a relation of future-oriented response.

This is particularly interesting, as we have just shown how this implicates our understanding of evil, and particularly experiences of suffering. However, what we are mainly interested in is how this contributes to what we know about trauma. If we are to take contemporary phenomenological interpretations of illness, which 'disturbs meaning processes of being-in-the-world' (Sveneaus 2012, p. 212), and in which 'metaphor, emotion and spiritual and existential dimensions are...central to the experience of the patient' (Carel and McNaughton 2016, p. 296), then the role of myth in transitioning the experience from disorder into a language, from dysrelation to relation (justice), without reducing its enigma, might very well play an important role. The point is not to replace a biomedical definition of health and mental illness. However, it is important that this concept is placed in conversation with the wider experiences of lived consciousness that constitute the disorder. For trauma, we need to look at how the whole experience is lived.

Conclusion

If, as Lévinas suggests, the subject is one who is oriented towards the other, then the phenomenology of trauma will require addressing the relation of justice. Justice will also be a key consideration in the wider conversation of health, as it restores the interrelationality between people and institutions. Ricœur helps us to see how the ambiguity of trauma interrupts our normal plotting of narrative. He also shows how we can appeal to different aspects of relationality, through symbolism and myth, which help us to make sense of challenging concepts such as how the experiences of the perpetrator and the victim can overlap, through the phenomenon of evil. In this Ricoeurian interpretation, understanding the narrative self that is ruptured through trauma requires looking at the semantic structures and the translation of physical experience into language, as developed through psychoanalytic accounts. It also means that we see how language permeates our experience of being in the world, without directly accounting for all parts of the experience. Discourses on health and healing, then, as we will see, also require identifying something beyond the biochemical and biomedical models that are offered – engaging with and moving beyond the totalising accounts of universal collective narratives of beginning and end (Ricœur 1986, p. 144). These are phenomena which bring the person out of isolation and situate the self in a context of meaning, without reducing the situation to a moral, and thereby reductive, formula.

Notes

1 Similarly, Ricœur notes that for Freud, 'language functions at a pictoral level that brings it into the neighbourhood of the visual' (pp. 111–112), but this means translating it into a different experiential phenomena.
2 Arguably, a similar, but reversed, substitution occurs when body-based practices explain trauma using only materialism. This is why I argue that phenomenology can help make sense of how these two interpretations can be re-perceived as one lived experience.
3 Heidegger, Kenaan and Ferber remind us, interprets the world through Dasein, or Being that reveals itself to consciousness. They write that 'for Heidegger… Dasein always belongs to a world; but this world is neither the totality of objective facts nor a merely subjective experience' (2011, p. 4). For Heidegger the world is represented as the human realm of meaningfulness' that goes before any distinctions between the objective and subjective. This means that our 'embeddedness' in this world is predicated on attachment to meaning, which is then expressed through how we experience the world – namely, 'as that which matters to us' (p. 5).
4 This time referencing the self in *Oneself as Another.*
5 I want to explore this experience of lament in the final part of this book, but introduce it here as an example of how the ambiguous experience of suffering can connect different parts of the experience together.
6 As Ricœur himself felt when he confronted his Pacifism during the widespread suffering of Europe in the Second World War (Davis 2017).

6

MERLEAU-PONTY ON EMBODIMENT

We have previously relied on the philosophy of Ricœur and Lévinas to highlight areas of conversation that help us to explore the ambiguities of trauma. However, they still lacked a full account of how the body itself is re-perceived through traumatic experience. Ricœur's phenomenology challenges straightforward interpretations of language and agency through analysing myth and narrative emplotment. In Merleau-Ponty, we see how there is a distinction between the role of language and perception of bodied experience (Brown Golden 2009 p. 5). For Merleau-Ponty, to be in the world means to be a part of the continuous perceptual exchange of touching and being touched by the world. Furthermore, while Lévinas places our subjectivity in the exchange between faces, his approach might benefit from the writings of Merleau-Ponty, who accounts for how the material body interacts with the world.

In *Phenomenology of Perception*, Merleau-Ponty writes, 'We are caught in the world and we do not succeed in extricating ourselves from in order to achieve consciousness of the world' (1962, p. 5). For Merleau-Ponty, the body is immersed in an experience of symbols and signs that connect consciousness and language in the 'embodied experience of knowledge' (Zimmerman 2015, p. 155). This interconnection of experience reveals what MaryCatherine McDonald terms Merleau-Ponty's 'prism' approach to existence; each part of experience intersects to form what we understand to be real. In order to fully grasp an experience phenomenologically, we have to look at how it is lived, through the interaction of consciousness with that particular phenomenon. The parts come together into a unified and continuous expression, which takes up the body and consciousness and all of the other life 'stuffs'. In this chapter, we will look at how Merleau-Ponty's understanding of phenomenology can help us to understand how we 'live' trauma as bodied consciousness. This requires first looking at his definition of phenomenology. Second, we will explore how this prismatic approach can shape our engagement

DOI: 10.4324/9780367800017-8

with contemporary trauma theory in a way that gives a unified account of the individual's lived experience.

Merleau-Ponty Defines Phenomenology

In the previous sections on Lévinas and Ricœur, we examined how each philosopher contributes to our understanding of subjectivity. Each is a phenomenologist, but the particular way in which they define and use their phenomenological method offers different ways of accounting for life experience. Of course, if we want to know how Merleau-Ponty would address trauma, then we need to know what kind of phenomenology he was interested in and why. Through this, we can then see how phenomenology might serve as a tool to further understand trauma as it is lived in human experience.

Merleau-Ponty writes that 'True philosophy consists in re-learning to look at the world' (1962, p. xx). This ability to re-learn how we look at the world is actually the real strength of philosophy, because it requires that we face our preconceptions and takes us back to our points of origin. The philosopher, in attempting to discern just 'what' something really is, in that basic baby step, is therefore 'a perpetual beginning', which means that a philosopher is not able to take anything for granted (p. xiv). All that we believe we know about ourselves and the world we inhabit, we are asked to re-examine. For Merleau-Ponty, this has a specific meaning, because it requires examining perception itself. This is really going back to basics! For Merleau-Ponty, we actually need to reassess how we perceive our own existence in the world.

He suggests that philosophy has done a good job in analysing parts of life, but it has done quite a poor job in unifying existence. We judge specifics, such as whether our ethical action fits Kant's deontological formulation of the Categorical Imperative, whereby the good is measured through doing the same in the particular as in the universal context, but Merleau-Ponty is interested in how our whole perception connects. In the Preface to *Phenomenology of Perception*, he writes that '[t]he real is a closely woven fabric. It does not await our judgment before incorporating the most surprising phenomena, or before rejecting the most plausible figments of our imagination' (1962, p. xi). Reality, as our lived experience, is a unity of various threads. While much of philosophy and other disciplines have relied on critically judging bits of this reality, it seems to forget that the reality is itself a whole. Rather than going from the parts to the whole, we are actually always starting from a whole. It is not about constructing a world from fragments and various bits of proof; 'the world is what we perceive', as a whole and living experience (p. xvi). For Merleau-Ponty, the world is not like a person or an 'empirical subject', but rather 'that thing of which we form a representation', as if we all exist as 'one light and participate in the One without destroying its unity' (p. xii). This phenomenology of perception reveals us to ourselves and the selves we are as we perceive the whole.

There is an intuitive appeal to this thought, but it requires some effort to figure out what it actually means, and how it can help us to better understand trauma.

McDonald suggests that Merleau-Ponty's return to origin means looking at phenomenology as 'the first-personal perspective *as it is lived*' (2019, p. 187). He makes a distinction between scientism, which approaches experience from generalised theory, from 'above', and the 'there is which precedes it; to the site, the soil of the sensible and humanly modified world' (Merleau-Ponty 1964, p. 160). The goal is not to catalogue and analyse symptoms or ways of being human, but rather understanding from the inside how the person perceives their world as a living being (McDonald 2019, p. 210). The lived experience is not a string of causal explanations, but rather a sort of prism in which multiple parts of existence constantly interact and fuse together (p. 239).

Merleau-Ponty's phenomenology of perception requires that we recognise the connections between phenomena. To put it another way, we need to distinguish between perceiving others as truly other, rather than as 'universal subjects' (Cataldi and Hamrick 2007, p. 12), and part of this means understanding how Merleau-Ponty's world is one of 'intercorporeality', that is, an interweaving of living bodies (2007, p. 13). This world is not one that we think out, 'but what I live through' (Merleau-Ponty 2002, p. xxviii). This means that our experiences intersect to form our whole lived experience of the world. It is not just my experiences but those of others around me that intersect in this way, engage with 'each other like gears' (1962, p. xx, ct. in Dunphy-Blomfield 2007, p. 219). The world of Merleau-Ponty is conceptually unified, as a lived experience of interconnected relationships. The unifier is found in our embodiment because it is the body that acts as the vehicle of our perception of the world (ibid.).

This phenomenological exploration of the body is interpreted through Merleau-Ponty's central notion of flesh, which we will reference throughout the book. For Merleau-Ponty, the intercorporeality of the life-world requires assigning a specific phenomenological descriptor to the flesh (or *la chair*). Flesh, rather than constituting a specific body or material, is a 'general thing, midway between the spatio-temporal individual and the idea' (1969, pp. 183–184). The flesh constitutes both my own flesh that senses itself and the 'flesh of the world' that exists outside of me, and yet it is perceived and taken up by me.

Flesh, in Merleau-Ponty's later phenomenology, explains how we live as bodies, and how my lived body intertwines with the other's lived body (Cataldi and Hamrick 2007, p. 4). It is through this lived flesh that the body is explored and understood. Contained in Merleau-Ponty's understanding of the body is a duality of perception. In *Phenomenology of Perception*, he writes that the duality of perception means that the body has 'two faces or two "sides"' (p. 129, ct. in Dunphy-Blomfield 2007, p. 222). The body 'is a sensible, and it is the "sensing"; it can be seen and it can see itself; it can be touched and it can touch itself' (ibid.). In this way, it is the body that embraces the 'philosophy of flesh', through making visible what is invisible (ibid.) The body then also contains the duality of conscious and material life, which connects humans not only to each other but also to the material and conscious natural world around us.

The unified lived self therefore originates in and through the body of the individual. But this corporeity is not as concerned with the theoretical function of specific parts as it is with the interconnection of the living whole. This embodied 'form' is not a presented given 'thing' that we can use for understanding and analysis; rather, it is a living 'existential value of manifestation, of presentation' (Merleau-Ponty 2003, p. 188). The self is always communicating itself through its interweaving and adapting to the relations of her experience. The 'objective mode of inquiry' that Merleau-Ponty is critiquing in his predecessors (Edwards 2011, p. 38) means that the bodied experience is always being mediated. This is so important when we consider trauma, because we are primarily concerned with how trauma is lived in its intersection of life experiences. The idea that we can have one specific way of living trauma is highly problematic when considering the varying causes and symptoms, the ways of interpreting the experience and the relationships that the person finds themselves in.

This definition of phenomenology is important to us because it shows how Merleau-Ponty explores human experience. We are interested in understanding trauma as a particular human experience, which means that what Merleau-Ponty has said about phenomenology can help us to read how trauma might be *lived.* Merleau-Ponty emphasises that human experience must be read as lived; we need to account for the whole experience, rather than for parts of it abstracted out from the whole. For this, he sets himself apart from Descartes' distinction between the mind and the body. The suggestion that most of the human experience 'happens above the neck', in the mind, is altogether problematic because it makes false distinctions between the mind and the body (Brown Golden 2009, p. 71). In order to understand this whole and integrated experience, Merleau-Ponty emphasises the role of the body. In fact, it is through the body that communication and any kind of higher-order abstraction can occur. Merleau-Ponty's perceptual whole starts from corporeity, and it is the corporeity that 'exists as a structure that mediates all structures' (p. 73).

Part of what is challenging about trauma is how it reveals itself outside of a linear interpretation of time. The memory of a past event is breaking into the present, but in a different way than when it was experienced in the past. In Merleau-Ponty's later works, we see a movement towards a theory of time, explored as 'mythic time'. Mauro Carbone explains that it is 'a time of half sleep', that is 'properly Merleau-Pontian' because it is explored as an 'existential eternity' (Carbone 2004, p. 12). This contrasts classic understanding of time as serial, continuous, or discontinuous, such that the mythical time 'presents a synthesis of events both distant and present' (p. 39). This means that we are always arriving at 'the first day' because there are no linear 'previous days' (Carbone 2004, 12, ct. in Edwards 2011, p. 39). It makes sense when you explore Merleau-Ponty's phenomenology to arrive at this notion of living through time; the synthesis of these events is not an active one undertaken by reason, but rather a passive kind of synthesis in which 'the present and the past are simultaneous' (Edwards 2011, p. 39).

Edwards suggests that this idea of time is found germinating in *Phenomenology of Perception,* as a rejection of any reflective theory that posits a chain of straightforward causation. Edwards shows how Merleau-Ponty's use of mythic time explores and moves out of his earlier notion of prismatic experience, 'limiting the phenomenon to a reflective explanation of causality and description [that] fails to capture the essentially open nature of the phenomenon itself' (p. 40). It is the open nature of the phenomenon that gives an event its 'irreducibility' and maintains its 'indefinite'-ness. The indefinite, Edwards reads, is 'unable to be said entirely' (ibid.).

This phenomenology of mythic time works with Merleau-Ponty's earlier exploration of embodiment in rich ways, particularly as it applies to reading trauma. As we explored in the previous section on Ricœur, the mythic allows for an overlay of readings of experience to bring the phenomenon of the present into a whole. But both Ricœur and Merleau-Ponty present different readings of the mythic. For Ricœur, it has to do with primarily situating the narrative self. For Merleau-Ponty, the mythic concerns philosophy in that it 'gives this world other depths' (Mazis 2016, p. 202). It enables the person to experience a kind of 'oneness' with the world and 'overwhelming proximity of the object', which he suggests is repressed, rather than abolished, by objective thought and everyday perception of the world, and which is philosophy's task of rediscovering (p. 201).

The mythic is not the same as the 'ordinary' experience of perception. An example of this is how Merleau-Ponty uses the mythic in his reading of schizophrenia (Mazis 2016). This patient, he suggests, no longer 'inhabits the common space'. She has rather retreated into a 'second space' that dissociates itself from the world (Merleau-Ponty 1962). This 'second space' of the hallucinatory and imaginal also has the shared attribute of shrinking and overwhelming the experienced space and is separated off from the communal space. But it is also less flat, and less distanced than the ordinary space. The patient has dissociated from the interplay of all of the facets, or what McDonald has termed the 'prismic' quality of experience. For Merleau-Ponty, this presents a way of encountering the world through the imaginative and the mythic. This means that what we experience as 'real' must have the capacity to contain this experiential and interconnected ambiguity of experience. For Merleau-Ponty, then, 'the spaces of the real and apparent – and the realms of perception, imagination, myth, childhood – are interwoven, and none are absolutely foundational' (2016, p. 201). The lived experience maintains an openness to its own ambiguity as these planes overlap to create our perception of living.

In this section, we have explored aspects of Merleau-Ponty's phenomenology. We have seen how he relates the prismic qualities of experience, as it is lived, through reference to our embodiment and experience of the mythic. These concepts not only frame a philosophical outlook on lived experience but also critique some of the most commonly held suppositions of Western thought, as it pertains to how we understand experience. Like Lévinas and Ricœur, Merleau-Ponty asks us to go back to our primary soil, examining the suppositions that we hold. In so doing, he suggests, we can avoid the errors that have been caused by saying too much too soon.

The Phenomenology of Trauma

Merleau-Ponty's return to origin and his emphasis on the openness of the lived space provide a thought-provoking context for discussing trauma. In approaching phenomenology through 'the first-personal perspective *as it is lived*' (McDonald 2019, Loc. 187), he shows us that our experiences take place over a plethora of planes. Our bodies live the experience; our communication is not just a stream of thoughts, but rather movements and perceptions of existence. This section looks at what this might mean for our understanding of trauma. Merleau-Ponty allows us to bring together not only the diverging conversations between psychoanalysis and bodied approaches to trauma but also the wider converging conversations on how health and illness are lived.

First, we will look at what it might mean to read an experience as *lived*. For this, it is helpful to draw on how this lived experience is connected to illness. Contemporary phenomenologists have problematised reading illness as symptoms and classifications of mental disorders. For instance, Sigurdson suggests that illness is 'a radical change in how I relate to myself and my body, to other people and the world' (Sigurdson 2019, p. 31). When read in this way, Carel shows how illness colours the total experience of the person. This means that whereas a healthy body can take for granted the contributions of each functioning, silent part, 'in illness the body comes to the fore and its pain and incapacity directly affect the agency of the person' (Carel 2008, p. 73). This shift in relational perception marks the difference between the lived experiences of health and illness.

In illness, the general structure of the body and its cognitive function can remain relatively stable and the social exchanges between people along with the moral landscape that we occupy might stay relatively consistent. However, the person who lives illness is also at the same time experiencing that these relations are affected because of something that is happening in her body. It is not a different experiential structure per se. What is different is that the living of the experience is filtered through a variety of planes that are affected by the illness. For instance, Carel and Macnaughton use the example of the symptom of breathlessness to show the interaction between different experiences of the world. Stating that 'The invisibility of breathlessness has a social element but is also political and economic in the clinical context' (2016, p. 298), they show how this embodied lived experience takes up a history of socioeconomic relations, public prioritisations and educational background. The experience of breathlessness therefore is a phenomenon with existential value (as well as ethical ramifications).

Exploring illness this way is helpful when considering what contribution Merleau-Ponty can make to trauma. Carel shows us that the phenomenology of *living* illness invokes a range of different ways of experiencing ourselves in the world. If we apply this to trauma, the symptoms take on their own phenomenological significance. Trauma is not like cancer or heart disease because we cannot really locate it in a specific region of the body. We might experience bodily symptoms, but even the most materialistic explanations need to connect this to how an event is being remembered by consciousness. As such, the integration between the mind and the body, to form the whole experience of the person, is essential.

In *Phenomenology of Perception,* Merleau-Ponty is concerned with the Cartesian dualisation of identity. To separate the 'apparent self' from 'body and nature' becomes a philosophical problem. This problem is particularly revealed in communication (Brown Golden 2009, pp. 86–87). When we are communicating with others, it is the body that moves, the vocal cords that vibrate, the lungs that fill with air, as the thoughts translate to words that are then expressed to the other. So our 'animal corporeality' is part (constitutive) of what we need to communicate. Brown Golden shows that 'communication is rooted in corporeity that directs itself outward to delineate itself and make of itself a "presentation"' (p. 72). The material body becomes a part of the communicability itself.

Communication is particularly important in relation to trauma, because of its role in articulating the 'unseen story', as well as its role in connecting this experience to the self, as a tool of healing. If the source of the injury is unseen, then communication becomes integral to understanding both source and mode of injury in order to enable repair. Merleau-Ponty's human experience is integrated. Recent findings in trauma show how 'impenetrating' the body and psyche are (Brown Golden 2009, p. 73). When we discover that trauma is an inseparably psychological and physical event, with psychological and physical outworking, then the phenomenology of corporeity becomes central to understanding the *living* of trauma. For Merleau-Ponty, it is corporeity that 'mediates all structures', suggesting then that communication itself is rooted in the body (p. 73). The body responds and adapts to the experience of an event, which is then communicated outward. Brown Golden suggests that the role of speech is to show 'itself as signification of and intention toward expressing bodily desire to demarcate and signify self and other' (p. 81). This, I have argued, is also an important aspect of understanding how trauma can be lived through the conscious experience at the same time as it is lived in the body. For McDonald, trauma requires this unified bodied reading. Trauma is simultaneously always taking on psychological and neurobiological elements by influencing 'one's body, thought, as well as one's actions' (2019, p. 84), which reflects Carel's point about the dynamic unity of living an illness.

Merleau-Ponty is able to connect these different expressions through the preconscious experience of desire. Brown Golden refers to this desire as a directedness, which becomes the origin from which we get language and speech, even when this desire is absent in our expressed language and speech (2009, p. 83). This 'presupposed drive for spoken expression' is located in the body. This source is 'unreflected, nonverbal and unmeaningful' (Merleau-Ponty 1962, p. 183). Brown Golden suggests that this embodied pre-reflective desire is particularly significant to the 'meaning-ascription' in traumatic memory. The linguistic memory of the event is impaired, she concludes, because the unusual experiences and images of the event are at a 'dysjunction in human experience between integrated memory and dis-integrated memory', which clinicians also refer to as 'dissociative memory' (2009, pp. 81–82). The way in which memory is encoded is important to narrative recall of the trauma and how the event is incorporated into the rest of the life narrative.

But that is really the tip of the iceberg, if we are going to look at trauma phenomenologically. McDonald furthers this exploration of trauma by pointing out the coexistence of consciousness and the body (p. 527). While Brown Golden shows us the connection between understanding the pre-reflective origins of our experiences and how we read trauma narratives, McDonald challenges tendencies of reducing trauma to purely neurobiological explanations. For McDonald, any reduction of traumatic phenomena to a 'generic perspective of a scientific explanation' can risk a very 'detrimental oversimplification' (p. 560). This oversimplification is not just important to doing thoughtful philosophy. It also impacts the treatment of the traumatised person. For her, separating the body from the mind, as if they are two separate entities can mean missing what an experience of illness and treatment means individually, and how it connects to the wider meaning of being as a body in the world. This philosophical rumination has clinical import. For Merleau-Ponty, the role of philosophy is to re-learn how we 'look at the world' (1962, p. xx). In this re-learning, phenomenology performs the role of re-situating our discussions on consciousness 'back into existence' (p. vii). McDonald and Brown Golden show that this interconnected experience of consciousness can help us to avoid reducing trauma to simplistic explanations.

Merleau-Ponty's phenomenology offers tools for us to bring together somatic and psychoanalytic theories. For instance, in his attempts to reconcile the Cartesian dualism, Merleau-Ponty offers insights into how the body and the mind can both co-live and co-express traumatic experience. This is the prismic interaction of experiences that we have been referring to. In Part I of this book, we looked at how both psychoanalysis and body-based approaches to trauma offer alternate readings of the experience. Whereas the emphasis in psychoanalysis is the role of integrating unconscious experience and narrative identity, for bodied approaches, the emphasis falls on how the physiological structures of the body respond to the event and store the memory through bodily adaptation.

But what do these abstract conversations look like when applied to a specific situation such as human trafficking? In my work with human trafficking, I often came across complex trauma cases that ranged from physical abuse to child neglect and sexual assault. Understanding what it means for a person to live these traumas, according to Merleau-Ponty, requires figuring how the various planes of existence merge to form this person's bodied experience in the world. The person's experience cannot just be treated as a list of symptoms or objects of analysis; rather, it involves returning to the person, or 'things themselves', by 'reawakening the basic experience' of what it means for this person to be in the world. I have often wondered how this might change our engagement with others, particularly those I work with. I thought it might be helpful to imagine what an interpretation like this might look like: picture yourself in a police station. You come across a child who has been trafficked for pickpocketing. He is about 14 years old now and has been separated from his family for 4 years. The leader of the gang of pickpocketers is physically and verbally abusive, and the boy has been assaulted multiple times. The police have raided his accommodations and he is collected for examination. As he is examined, he exhibits dissociative traits whereby it is difficult to understand his story. He also seems tense; his eyes are wide, and his shoulders are pulled tight up to his ears. His breathing is irregular.

If we see this boy in front of us in this physiologically aroused state, there is a palpable sense that he is agitated. If we are reading his experience purely somatically, we can see that he exhibits some of the four components of traumatic reaction, which include hyperarousal, constriction, dissociation and freezing, or immobility, that is attached to experiences of helplessness (Levine 1997, p. 132). Levine tells us that these symptoms emerge as the body summons its defensive energy to mobilise itself for action. Understanding the trauma, then, requires exploring where these defensive energies have emerged from, and why they were not appropriately discharged and released back into the flow of bodily energy. Even though it is at a non-verbal level, the body is communicating. It signals that something has happened to the person, which has not yet been fully 'discharged or integrated' (p. 132). In the instance of the boy, the dissociative state might indicate that the body is trying to shield itself from a traumatic experience of, say, adult abuse. Here, faced with a life-threatening situation, a person might disconnect from their felt experience of the body.

Levine suggests that dissociation 'seems to be a favoured means of enabling a person to endure experiences that are at the moment beyond endurance', when hyperarousal in the body is disconnected from the undergone experience. The dissociative symptoms emerge out of a basic experience of disconnection. For instance, there could be a break between 'the consciousness and the body' (1997, p. 140). In order to integrate the person's felt sense, they require increasing their awareness of the dissociation in order to re-experience sense in the lived body (pp. 138–139). Communication is used by the practitioner to reconnect the self to its bodied state. What is interesting here is that the bodied state is the phenomenon that holds together this experience of trauma. For Levine, and other somatic psychologists, understanding the trauma of this boy requires figuring out how a split between consciousness and bodied experience is read through the symptoms of undischarged bodily energy. Consciousness in this interpretation is predominantly connected to the muscular interaction with the brain.

Levine's approach reads consciousness through the experience of the body's physiology. In this interpretation of trauma, dissociation involves a 'breakdown in the continuity of a person's felt sense' (1997, p. 137). However, Freud's psychoanalytic theory reads dissociation differently. For Freud, dissociative experience, as evidenced in the boy, reveals a structural drama of identity. To understand the experience of dissociation requires returning to the development of the ego itself. If the ego emerges through its relations of attachment to primary caregivers, through object-cathexis (Freud 1923/1975), then understanding the current symptoms in the boy requires understanding the relationship of psychic energy between the self and objects or persons, outside of the self. It is this base layer of ego development that is affected in what Freud termed 'neuroses', through which early traumatic symptoms were classified (Meganck 2017, p. 790).

As a result of this reading of ego development, repression becomes the primary way that Freud reads traumatised experience. This differs from his predecessor Janet, who localises this separation of 'phenomenological awareness and voluntary control' in *desegregation*, or dissociation (van der Kolk and van der Hart 1990, p. 1531). Whatever the case, both psychoanalytic thinkers show that 'nonconscious mental processes' are psychologically revealed in the experience of the person (Kihlstrom and Hoyt 1990, p. 181). If we read Freud's interpretation of the boy's experience, then, we have to look at how his current state of bodied existence is communicated narratively to uncover the unconscious mental processes of the ego development. But Merleau-Ponty develops Freud in a fresh way by showing how he draws out the relationships that were previously relegated to consciousness only. Merleau-Ponty writes that

> the significance of psychoanalysis is less to make psychology biological than to discover a dialectical process in functions thought of as 'purely bodily', and to reintegrate [experience] into the human being.
>
> *1962, p. 158*

For Merleau-Ponty, it is the way in which psychoanalysis expands these notions 'into the whole of existence' that make particular accounts of experience become ambiguous (p. 159).

Thus, Merleau-Ponty attempts to connect and clarify how different accounts connect in our conscious experience of various phenomena. He writes that 'life is particularised into separate currents' (1962, p. 160) that cannot all be understood through one expanded notion of ego development. Rather than a particular ego theory, 'living' (*leben*) must be the first process through which 'to live' (*erleben*) becomes a possibility, meaning that 'we must eat and breathe before perceiving and awakening to relational living' (p. 160). This 'return to existence', a belonging to the world of colour and lights through the experience of the senses, comes 'before arriving at the life of human relations' (ibid.). If we go to our example above, then the experience of the boy is lived in the body, but it is primarily phenomenologically read as consciousness interacting with the body. In order to understand this situation, we need to explore the communicated desire that the boy speaks or withholds from speaking because of this primary engagement of the body with its world.

McDonald reminds us that, for Merleau-Ponty, experience is not a matter of analysing the parts of either the body or consciousness, but interlinking, or rather, fusing these experiences into a whole. This means that 'phenomenology reveals that what is injured in trauma is not simply the mind or the body but the *entire worldview of the individual*' (2019, loc. 229–230). Though trauma's imprint can be read through the body and consciousness, it is really because something prior to these situations has been impacted. Trauma involves 'the intractable loss of one's blueprint of the world' (McDonald 2019, loc. 239). This ripples through each perspective of existence, showing us that Levine's reading of the somatic experience and Freud's understanding of ego development must be read 'from the inside', in order to capture a fuller picture of what this living of trauma means for an individual. Experiencing the trauma of being trafficked is, as Carel has previously showed us in her interpretation of illness, a colouring of a whole world. Merleau-Ponty is able to show us how trauma is not only a matter of reading neuroscience or psychology well but also understanding the interaction between politics and wider social relationships, the 'experience of the world' (McDonald 2019, loc. 494) in which this bodied being exists.

Conclusion

In this chapter, we have taken a specific lens to look at a particular kind of experience. Phenomenology has shown us how we can examine trauma as something that is lived. This lived experience requires understanding the interconnection of things, and, particularly in this instance, the interconnections that make up our experiences. The subject cannot just be reduced to a simple set of symptoms or a mythic representation.

Using Lévinas' phenomenology to understand how the self exists as a relational self, the questions of responsible relation emerge. How can a person experience an exit when she is overwhelmed by trauma? Ricœur uses the imagination to understand suffering as a place of blame and lament, which will become particularly important in examining the complex relation between the victim and the perpetrator, and subsequent intersubjective relations that implicate the health of communities. Merleau-Ponty's philosophy of the body as a site of meaning and exchange places a value on uncovering the complexity of embodied experience in a way that brings meaning and ethical illumination to relations. This section of the book has provided the tools for us to engage with the subsequent complex discussions of ethics, politics and relationship that will enable us to develop a philosophical interrogation on health, through exploring bodies situated in relation, exploring concepts of value, responsibility and experiences of self that emerge in trauma discourse. Now that we have been introduced to trauma as an experience of living in the world, we are ready to tackle the subsequent issues that emerge in this individually lived experience.

PART III

Living Trauma in Relationship

7

SILENCE AND COMMUNICABILITY

Speaking Truths

Phenomenology shows us that trauma is *lived* in the subjective experience of the human being. This experience cannot be reduced to either diagnosis or a specific reading of trauma; rather, it requires understanding how all the different aspects of experience merge with one another and are affected through this particular kind of suffering. Drawing on Ricœur, Lévinas and Merleau-Ponty, each philosopher reveals that experience incorporates consciousness into a bodied experience of life. This experience not only entails reaching beyond psychology to take hold of language of values, ethics, beliefs and our wider place in our wide world, but it also entails the basic assumption that our experience incorporates another. Here, I want to explore the phenomenological interrelationality of trauma; that is, how people *live* trauma through their relationships to other people and their sense of place. The self, as Jill Stauffer puts it, 'is a self *who resides in a shared world*' (2015, p. 127). For somatic theory, experience is rooted in a 'primary corporeal intersubjectivity' (2009, p. 27). But if the traumatised self is living in a shared world, then the relational parts that make up this shared world are important to understand what it means to *live* trauma.

This connection between the self, other humans and the non-human spaces that we inhabit is the traumatic context. Trauma interrupts our experience of being in the world as a particular relational self. While most people go through life feeling relatively secure in their relation to the world, experiences of abuse or violence that are inflicted on us by another person can leave this basic trust in the world and human relationships in fragments. What if it happens again, the person could easily justify wondering (O'Connell 'Gambling with the Psyche', pp. 295, 310, ct. in Stauffer 2015, p. 30). In this chapter, we are looking for this relational connection to the shared world. More specifically, we want to know how relationship connects to our experience of trauma. This book uses the phenomenological term of the other, which is useful in that it denotes a being that is 'outside' of oneself.

DOI: 10.4324/9780367800017-10

The *other* can be understood as a broad term to denote a being that is 'outside' of you, that is not you. This part of the book is about the other, and how the relation to the other can shape the experience of *living* trauma. This is where the story widens beyond the self. It requires looking at how we communicate or try to connect with this other. This part of the book is also about the body's orientation of home and homelessness, the ethics of political expressions of trauma and our relationship to the land. This shows how our subjectivity comprises these relationships. Here, we look at the social relation that constitutes the subjectivity: the relation to the human other, the relation to place. Uncovering the significance of these four categories reveals how trauma is a *prismic* experience, as McDonald points out in Chapter 6. It also helps us to hold the complexity of trauma without needing to reduce it too quickly to something that it is not.

Part II of this book looked at how trauma is understood as lived out through a particular person's experience of relating to the world around her. This person, Lévinas, Ricœur and Merleau-Ponty assert, is a relational being, an interconnected subject. In Part II, Lévinas and Merleau-Ponty show that this subject has to have some way of communicating to the world outside of her if it is to connect to it in a phenomenologically meaningful way. Lévinas introduces the concept of revelation, which he further develops through distinguishing between the *saying* and the *said*. Merleau-Ponty writes that it is the body that expresses the desire of the subject. This is interesting when we are speaking about trauma, because of the central role of communication in this experience. This chapter will primarily focus on using Lévinas and Merleau-Ponty to launch our discussion on the complex experience of communication, and its integral role in trauma experience.

Silence and the Limit of Language in Lévinas

van der Kolk writes: 'Therapists have an undying faith in the capacity of talk to resolve trauma...Unfortunately it's not so simple: Traumatic events are almost impossible to put into words' (2014, p. 231). For van der Kolk, the body has the capacity to store memory in a way that is not available to the communicative faculties of the body. It is stored in a way beyond the brain's usual language pathways, at a limbic level. van der Kolk motions to this potential incommunicability of experience with a quote from *Macbeth,* where Shakespeare writes: 'Give sorrow words; the grief that does not speak knits up the o'er wrought heart and bids it break' (Macbeth, Shakespeare). The challenge of putting something into words, of communicating experience, cannot be understood in a straightforward manner when it comes to suffering. It is as if the ordinary act of extending and receiving of language fails us. This is important when considering our relationship to other people, because a very basic function of language and memory recall will be different here.

Stauffer writes that this fragility of communication is twofold. It requires both the person speaking to express their inner world in a way that the other can understand and the other person to actually listen. For her, thought of the fragility of communication means that it may be impossible for everything to be heard, what matters is 'whether people who listen will, while paying attention to what is said, also watch out for what is not being heard' (2015, p. 24). This exchange can fail at either point because it involves the 'risk and uncertainty' of relationship. Drawing on the philosophy of Lévinas, Stauffer distinguishes communication, which she cites as critical to understanding another person, from knowing facts about someone. This is particularly pertinent when we are discussing trauma, because when communication becomes reduced to a retelling of facts, it cannot get at the point of the exchange, which is to actually understand the person who might actually have a very different experience from our own.

Understanding communication in this Lévinasian way challenges approaching other people through symptoms and theories alone and indicates that the person needs to speak individually. It also requires us to respond. Stauffer suggests that Lévinas shows how 'communication is rooted as much in our precognitive response to others as it is in its instrumental use to convey stable meanings' (2015, p. 21), and it implicates us in an ethical relation to the other person. Listening, and responding well, becomes a matter not only of communication but also of justice. The communication of the other is not merely a deciphering of symbol and stable meanings, as it is recognising a prayer, a cry for help and 'aid addressed to another' (Lévinas 1998b, p. 23). This problematises any straightforward or reductive account of our common exchanges.

The previous section references 'normal', linguistic communication, as you, for instance, see when a patient speaks to her doctor about some condition that she has. But Lévinas is particularly interested in showing us is how this bears out in experiences of suffering, where the appeal of the other is often found in the failure of language. What the patient may want to say in this instance can only be expressed as a sigh or a groan. Catherine Bjørnholt Michaelsen reminds us that Lévinas wants to bring 'trauma away from its most frequent psychopathological, psychoanalytic, or neurological areas of interpretation' (2015, p. 44) into the wider experience of relationality. Lévinas does not want the relation to the other to be 'subsumed in a system'. The other cannot be reached through methodology, but rather through revelation (Heaton 1988, p. 5). This kind of communication happens when the face speaks through its embodied presence to us, but it transcends, or 'precedes all thought and learning' (Zimmerman 2015, p. 155).

The self needs this encounter with the other, where the other speaks for herself, in order for the self to respond. Somatically understood, the second-person presence of a traumatised person, if severe enough, can leave physiological and psychological traces on the subject (Rothschild and Reid 2006). While Lévinas rejects a materialistic and systematic account of the other, he maintains that the rupture of our ego is essential to being human. The other disrupts me, and my isolated 'dwelling in the world' as a way of '*maintaining [myself]*' *(se tenir)* (Mumford 2018, p. 3; Lévinas 1969, p. 37). This traumatism is the beginning of our relation to the world. However, he distinguishes this rupture from the trauma of suffering that the other experiences in pain, and that is 'useless' in and of itself (Lévinas 1988, p. 158). This dual account of trauma brings the experience out of analysing structures of the mind alone and also shows the primordial relation towards the other. Trauma is understood in the ego's displacement by the call of the other, and in the experience of the suffering other. One is useless; the other is the very core significance of human subjectivity.

This complex dual understanding of trauma is revealed in Lévinas' writings on communication. Here, the other that I am responsible for is someone that can never be fully represented (Bjørnholt Michaelsen 2015, p. 50). The other interrupts me, but without linearity, Bjørnholt Michaelsen suggests, much as Freud's definition of trauma is its assertion of violence after the event. As such, it calls into question both linearity of time and '*the sovereignty of consciousness*' (p. 51). This prior responsibility to one whom I cannot fully represent, the 'alteration without alienation' (Lévinas 2000, p. 187), translates itself into the experience of response, or a '*despite myself* that is more me than myself' (ibid.). This is the notion of substitution – myself-for-the-other – which can be experienced as traumatic to me but addresses the trauma of the other. Now what actually is the appeal of the other, particularly if it is expressed in such a way? It is the appeal 'not to be killed' (Bjørnholt Michaelsen 2015, p. 50). As such, the responsibility that constitutes the trauma of our own ego actually contains in it the plea for another's life. This plea, as the other calling out to me, becomes the experience of *saying.* Opening towards and affirming the other, Bjørnholt Michaelsen reminds us, 'constitutes the very significance of language in signifying like an open mouth "exposed like a bleeding wound" (1998b, p. 151) before language scatters into words' (2015, p. 51). *Saying* itself is more about the response of relationship than about the translation of the mind into symbol.

As call and response, this relationship of communication becomes a vessel for justice. In Lévinas' account, our subjectivity starts in our obligation to the other. A person's ability to communicate her suffering, and be responded to, is the site of justice. Through Lévinas' reading of communication, which requires response, we can therefore bring the communication of trauma beyond the realm of diagnosis and into the discourse of justice. Trauma does not just require a psychological narrative. It is often linked to the rupture in relationships between others and the experience of isolation that accompanies this. Auerhahn and Laub write that these relationships can only be renewed when the hierarchy of testimony between the victim and perpetrator is undone. This involves the survivor regaining her own agency, transforming her hate and anger and re-establishing 'a shared subjectivity that makes the empty, traumatic world feel three dimensional again' (2018, p. 39). In this transformation, the experience of a shared world requires both a speaking of trauma and a listening. Without this listening, the other is left abandoned and isolated, as an object that feels placed in an unreal world (p. 59). We will come back to this notion of place later on in this chapter, but it is important here to see how the actual relationship of communication asserts not only a therapeutic role but also the beginnings of an experience of justice.

An example of the role of communication in the re-presentation of trauma is found in the work of Berel Lang. In recounting the trauma of the Holocaust, experiences are deemed unspeakable. But the first-hand experience also carries with it a privilege of 'unquestionable authority'. Lang writes that communicating trauma will always be a problem because '[t]rauma is deepest and most traumatic when it is least explicit or overt' (2005, p. 71). This means that insofar as we are dealing with traumatic experience, the issue of interpretation will feature centrally in the relational experience. Lang recounts how often the concept of unspeakability features in representing the events of the Holocaust. He cites Elie Wiesel's challenge that the experience cannot be written about in any accessible way: 'If it's a novel, it's not about Auschwitz; if it's about Auschwitz, it's not a novel' (ct. in Lang ibid.). Lang suggests that these accounts carry with them a forbiddenness to share, or even more radical, an impossibility of doing so.

But for Lang, the incomprehensibility of an experience does not entail its indescribability, because we often describe what we do not understand. What it does carry is the 'limit to the intelligibility and/or representability of the Holocaust', which is maintained to be 'beyond our...capacity to describe and understand adequately or, perhaps at all' (2005, p. 74). For Lang, the issue of representing trauma becomes a matter of differentiating between what makes an experience speakable and what makes it unspeakable. Lang suggests that it is the moral incomprehensibility of an event rather than the epistemic incomprehensibility that makes it difficult to speak about. But there are people who have tried to make even these morally incomprehensible experiences comprehensible, by passing the traumatic experience through language.

Lang suggests that the trauma of the Holocaust reveals a challenge to language, to adequately represent experience; a difficulty of working at it 'cognitively, morally, aesthetically'. Still, for Lang, it remains that 'far from moving that subject beyond the possibility of analysis and representation; if anything, such study demonstrates the place of the Holocaust *in* history' (p. 77). The events are 'speakable, thinkable, comprehensible', but in the limited way akin to other complex events in history can be (p. 77). Thus as far as semantics is concerned, it is possible to represent the event through speech. What Lang highlights is how other experiences interact with the speaking. Semantically, I would argue that it is possible to represent this trauma. However, phenomenologically speaking, when we see the moral violation of evil, as well as the bodied experience of pain and the ruptured processes of memory, it makes this representation through communication incredibly difficult.

The Body Speaks

To unpack this further will require recognising the role that the body assumes in communication. Lévinas shows us that communication needs both a person who cries out and one who responds. But this communication does not have to be fully articulated semantically in order for it to invoke a response. For Lévinas, communication can take place as prayer, through a groan or a cry. This brings the function of trauma out of a transference of knowledge and into the experience of ethics. It involves the *saying*, which is a constant revelation of the other to the self, prior to a symbolic generalisation, without reducing it to a reading of mind structures (Heaton 1988).

Suffering is experienced as a specific 'content' of consciousness, but it is an 'unassumable' content (1988, p. 156). For Lévinas, 'suffering is at once what disturbs order and the disturbance itself' (ibid.), an experience that is denied and refused meaning whilst being experienced in its 'sensible quality'. Lévinas writes that

> Taken as an 'experienced' content, the denial and refusal of meaning which is imposed as a sensible quality is the *way* in which the unbearable is precisely not borne by consciousness, the way this not-being-borne is, paradoxically, itself a sensation or a given.
>
> *ibid.*

This suffering that is paradoxically refused meaning through consciousness alone, and yet is experienced in sensation, contains a 'quasi-contradictory structure' (ibid.). It is a 'hurt' that is undergone 'in-spite-of-consciousness', which means that suffering 'is no longer *the performance of an act of consciousness*, but, in its adversity, a submission' (p. 157). This submission is experienced in the body, as hurt, an undergoing of the pain of being beaten, for example, but it is not just a reduction of experience to our senses, nor is it a reduction of experience to our acts of consciousness. Understood in this way, trauma cannot be summarised through its 'psycho-physiological' or its 'psycho-physical' conditions. This is particularly true as we try to understand how trauma is communicated.

Lévinas wants to bring communication into the prior conversation about the relationship between the self and the other. For him, experience of the world emerges out of this ability to respond to the other's cry for help, instantiated in the command 'do not kill'. The communication that Lévinas speaks about, as a communication of the experience of suffering, requires recognising that trauma moves us beyond acts of consciousness and psychological language games. It brings us into the realm of *meta*-ethics. Lévinas shows how suffering links us to the other, in a way that means that we cannot reduce a person's experience of trauma to a straightforward symptomatology.

This embodied expression of the self goes beyond language, into the experience of the body. In *Useless Suffering,* Lévinas reminds us that 'suffering sensibility is a vulnerability' (1988, p. 157). But Merleau-Ponty wants us to understand just how the sensible experience of the body might implicate our communication of trauma. This is interesting when we consider what van der Kolk theorises, which is that 'Traumatic events are almost impossible to put into words' (2014, p. 231). He suggests that language plays a role in naming and experiencing control over what is happening to the traumatised body (p. 232). However, while translating experience into language may help us to unify our life narratives and connect us with others by voicing what is experienced in the unseen, van der Kolk warns of the limits of language (p. 235). He suggests that when a person is asked to recount their traumatic experience, she is confronted with the choice of presenting a logical, linear and coherent account of what was experienced, or let the body feel what it had previously experienced in the trauma (p. 237). van der Kolk shows that the physical sensations of trauma and the narrative recollection of trauma are located in different areas of the brain, which requires mediation of the medial prefrontal cortex. The body therefore acts as a bridge, where the person 'can get past the slipperiness of words by engaging the self-observing, body-based self system, which speaks through sensations, tone of voice, and body tensions' (p. 238). The body exists here as a bridge of communication.

Merleau-Ponty brings out the significant role of the body in communication. He invokes phenomenology rather than neuroscience and physiology, mediating the disjuncture between reductive accounts of experience. This is how McDonald identifies his philosophy as prismic. But it is a prismic philosophy that experiences itself as a body, bringing home the significance of van der Kolk's current research on the body as a bridge of trauma communication. Just as Merleau-Ponty does not want to reduce human experience to mental representations, he is also keen to avoid accounts of experience based on reflection 'about' a person. An experience cannot be distinguished from the complex *living of* it (McDonald 2019, p. 570). But the lived experience is an embodied one. This bodied account of consciousness in Merleau-Ponty comes across when he gives the example of the animal form, which he says, 'is not the manifestation of a finality, but rather of an existential value of manifestation, of presentation' (2003, p. 188). Brown Golden suggests that this kind of communication, a communication between animal bodies, is what constitutes how we show others who we are. This is 'a process of communication as self-signification' (2009, p. 75). We present ourselves to the other in this particular, bodied way.

The communication of trauma, even via our bodies, requires the transmission of memory. Trauma is what has been undergone; it is an experience *after the fact*, as we see in Lévinas' account of a-linearity. As we saw in Part I, trauma involves both the storing and retrieving of experience, both in the body and the brain, as well as in various other narrative and value structures. Trauma symptoms reveal an unusual encoding of experience that keeps trying to represent, or misrepresent, itself in the present. The old traumatic experience, formed as memory, continues to disrupt our regular experiences of 'memory-images' and daily events (Brown Golden 2009, p. 82). Traumatic images from a past experience continue to 'demand attention' even though, at the same time, they remain 'steadfastly beyond view' (ibid.). Golden is writing about images of memory and their effect on experience. What van der Kolk was speaking about earlier had to do with the sensed experience of memory in the body. Merleau-Ponty shows us that both are contained in how we communicate this experience as memory by indicating that traumatic experience 'displaces' regular experiences (ibid.). This means that even though we experience new content, and our lives continue with 'new perceptions', the content of experience changes but the 'structure' of experience remains dissociated and 'fixated' on the old experience (Merleau-Ponty 1962, p. 83; ibid.).

If the structure of our experience changes in trauma, then verbal rearrangements of experience will be a superficial work. This is where Merleau-Ponty can be so helpful for us because we have to look at what is prior to the spoken and the felt experience. It means looking at what Merleau-Ponty points to as the 'directedness (or desire)' that is the 'origin of language and speech' (1962, p. 83). Now good analysts know that the language is never just a representation of what is seen, just as thoughtful psychiatrists understand that what we read in brain scans reveals a complex interconnection of human experience. But it is important to clarify more about what this means and how these planes of experience might interconnect.

For Lévinas, 'communication begins in response' (Stauffer 2015, p. 127), as a desire for the other who is beyond me. For Merleau-Ponty, communication emerges out of the bodied experience of desire. Brown Golden suggests that speech, in this understanding, 'emerges of and as the bodily desire to create sense amid conditions wherein none is yet' (2009, p. 83). But the body itself plays a role in communicating this desire. Brown Golden writes that Merleau-Ponty's animal body is actually 'constitutively communication' (p. 72). This body communication with the outer world 'ranges from the primordial (an eye moving and perceiving movements as a kind of interrogation and response) to the complex (human speaking and engaging in higher order cognition)' (ibid.) In this way, communication is connected to the body that is connecting outward and directing the subject outward to 'delineate' and make 'itself a "presentation"' (ibid.). Merleau-Ponty is showing just how the framework of our experiences is altered in trauma, and subsequently how the orientation of desire, experienced as woundedness, is taken up in and through bodied communication. This is not just represented in language, as Lévinas also shows us, in assigning the *saying* to a face. Merleau-Ponty reveals that the body, in its movement, constitutes communication. But in trauma, it is a wound then that keeps expressing itself through the body.

This bodied communication can, for instance, be seen when a person has undergone trauma and finds themselves inadvertently reacting to supposedly 'normal' events around them. Experience is still being filtered through trauma. Mary Raphaely recalls Suzi, a woman who had been abducted, raped and tortured. Once freed and undergoing therapy, Raphaely noticed how Suzi continued to respond to common noises with the heightened awareness of her trauma. For instance, when her caseworker knocked on her London flat door, Suzy had felt ready to jump out of her window in her fourth-floor room. She had been convinced that the knock on the door was the noise of the rebels who were coming to abduct her. It was only when she recognised herself in the surroundings of her flat that she realised she was safe and did not need to jump (Raphaely 2010).

Conclusion

Suzi's body communicates her experience beyond her sayable narrative. Merleau-Ponty's phenomenology shows us how trauma can impact multiple planes of experience, and how this 'prereflective' wounding can translate into the sensed experience. According to Brown Golden, speech emerges out of this communication: 'understood to be an expression of origin', it is 'less a mode of representation than a mode of bodily adaptation' (2009, p. 84). In both Merleau-Ponty and

Lévinas, we see how phenomenology can unite the experience of language with the experience of the body. This avoids any dualistic notion of communication. It also reveals the overlapping and complex challenges caused by trauma, when the representation of the present is interrupted by the past and the other, disrupting notions of linear time, enclosed egos and fully knowing a person's experience from the outside in.

8

HOMELESSNESS AND AT-HOMENESS

The Body as a Site of Integration

Chapter 7 was mainly concerned with how trauma can be communicated. We saw how Lévinas and Merleau-Ponty might offer helpful ways of understanding the interconnections in our experience of the world, as revealed in trauma. We looked at how the body represents itself in communication, as well as how communication requires a relationship between ourselves and another person. As Stauffer shows us, communication not only requires that a person can express her experience, but also that there is someone who wants to listen. The experience of trauma, as a challenge to communication, reveals itself in language and its limits, as well as in the expression of the body, as a way of revealing our experience to another.

Here I want to examine trauma through conversations of home and homelessness. Lévinas suggests an existential rather than a merely functional reading of home. For him, the home represents dwelling, that is, its place of origin and the actual 'condition for human life' (Langenthal 2014, p. 89). The other visits us and enters into our enclosure. By us welcoming them in, we experience the other's presence as an 'epiphany', a 'visitation' from beyond our enclosure (1987, p. 69). In *Totality and Infinity,* this act of hospitality becomes the moment of ethical encounter (1969). The home is reflected in our welcoming of the other, which Lévinas then also explores through the bodied experience of two faces. So home here becomes transformed into an encounter of bodies. But in trauma, rather than experiencing this act of welcome into a place, a person is often expelled from their source of origin. This experience of place is interrupted, demolished or destabilised. Furthermore, trauma theorists tend to examine trauma not only through the physical structure of home and homelessness. They also explore trauma through analysing the body itself as the first site of origin and welcome.

This chapter will explore how trauma affects our experience of ourselves as integrated beings. This means, of course, exploring what we have just looked at in terms of how our bodies process and are affected by trauma, how trauma orients us

DOI: 10.4324/9780367800017-11

towards the other person and what the 'foreign' actually means in its differentiation from the 'home' of the same. But it is more about displacement; it is about a sense of coming back to ourselves, and experiencing ourselves as whole. It connects us to the relationships that this has previously incorporated for us, be it family or a lover, or work, community or a divine other. It also connects us to our experiences of 'place', what that physical experience actually means from us, in terms of a site that we are displaced from, and want to return to. In these ways, this conversation brings out the social experience of trauma as well as our own individual experience of subjectivity. It places us in a web of relationships that trauma affects and looks at how the affect of trauma can connect us to the experience of displacement and exile. First, I will look at the home as the self, then I will explore home as a physical space outside of the self. For this, we will draw on Ricœur's notion of lament, and Lévinasian affect, as well as weaving together aspects of Merleau-Ponty's corporeal relatedness in discourse with Internal Family Systems (IFS), and other contemporary conversations on displacement and home.

The Home and the Body

For Lévinas, the experience of hospitality connects to his phenomenology of suffering. So Lévinas introduces us to a philosophy of revelation, through bodies capable of suffering, and language that requires the other to speak it for herself. What we looked at in the last section is how a lived experience of trauma is a unique experience, and how it also connects us to issues of responsibility, and, eventually, justice. Lévinas uses the language of justice and theology when he states that 'otherness resists the murderer's violence' of destruction (Zimmerman 2015, p. 155). The other presents herself as transcendent, while also as a body capable of injury. In *Totality and Infinity*, Lévinas presents human existence as an experience of dwelling. The home, like the ego, exists as the precondition of ethical relationship. For-itself, it is open to the interruption of the other: 'The possibility for the home to open to the other is just as essential to the essence of the home as the closed doors and windows' (1969, p. 173). But, as Davidson shows us, Lévinas' emergence from home also reveals itself later in *Otherwise than Being* as both betrayal and fidelity (1998b, p. 7).

Merleau-Ponty does something similar in his phenomenology of perception. He tells us that 'The world is not what I think but what I live through' (1962, pp. xvi–xvii). This world is lived through the sensibility of the body, but it cannot be limited to simplistic readings of what this is. Somatic theory challenges any notion of the body as object; for Maitland, 'the sentient body is not a fancy object or abode in which we somehow take up residence…it is the condition for inhabiting' (2016, p. 139). This experience of the body, he suggests, means that the body is experienced in a 'living' of 'embodied intentionality', in which consciousness assumes this somatic event (2016, p. 113). This ties in to Merleau-Ponty's understanding of bodily perception. Exploring lived phenomena requires apprehending the 'whole perceptual content' (p. 8).

But in order to understand this whole, and how we live from this bodied experience requires that we move away from categorising objective behaviours. Merleau-Ponty advocates that we acknowledge that each event 'is already invested with meaning' (p. 10). Being in the world, in this pre-integrated state, or this 'pre-objective realm' (p. 12) that we live, requires looking at the body, not only as an instrument of transmission but as an integrated event. Exploring experience as an integrated event is particularly relevant when we consider how traumatised people experience their body. My suggestion is that the traumatised body can be read through the experience of home and homelessness as a way of integrating the various perspective of trauma as a rupture of self. This image of trauma, as a rupture of home, will then connect with the conversation on home and homelessness as geographical displacement that is presented later in this chapter.

In trauma, the body can express itself in various ways as it responds to what has happened to it. For instance, Elizabeth Howell brings attention to dissociation, as 'a kind of self-structure that may divide and preserve parts of the self' and suggests that disruptions of attachment can deplete internal soothing experiences (2020, p. 50). The self can 'other' itself. I become an unstable and unsafe place. This means that turning inwards is not necessarily experienced as a place of restoration and self-integration. Paula and Alejandro Reyes describe traumatic experience through the symptoms of psychosis. Psychosis, they suggest, is caused by the 'detachment of the thinking process from the corporeal/emotional matrix that animates it'. This makes the person feel detached from their internal sense of self, as well as their connection of continuity that they share with other human beings ('their homogenous or symmetrical being', ibid.). It is often repeated and extreme forms of human-caused trauma that would cause this extent of rupture in a self.

Lévinas has helped us to understand that suffering is a relationship between both the body and the other. In *Totality and Infinity*, Lévinas shows how our sensibility enables our ability to respond to the other. We know what it is to have needs: we know what it is to be hungry and cold, and so the suffering of the other involves us from that shared experience. I can connect with this other person because I too am a sensing and conscious body. But even though I know what it is to be in need, I do not fully understand the experience of the other. I still require the other to speak for herself, because her experience of suffering is her very own. Later in *Otherwise than Being,* Lévinas writes that what is shown in the said (*le dit*) betrays the infinite experience of the saying (*le dire*). What we experience as the translation of someone's experience betrays the experience itself: 'the said...betrays the saying. So it must be unsaid and then said again' (Davidson 2012, p. 7).[1] In this betrayal, the other needs to be brought into justice, as if being 'translated' into justice, to take a second interpretation of the word *traduire* ('traduire en justice', ibid.). Lévinas' hospitality also reveals a betrayal but there is simultaneously an experience of closure (ibid.); the saying is reduced to representation in the said but needs to be extended from this said to somehow do justice to the living face. This is important, because Lévinas is able to tie a social element of otherness in suffering and the language of its communication, while also showing how the body as a site of need becomes the situation of suffering and its communication.

It is this bodily experience of need and woundedness, and the way in which we communicate it to others, that has significance here. The body's ability to *respond to a need* has become an increasingly important part of trauma research: a person flees because he needs safety, she fights because she needs protection, they dissociate because they need reprieve. Babette Rothschild notes the role of the autonomic nervous system in its regulation of trauma induced hypo-arousal, and the body's perception of terror and fear that causes the fight/flight system to be activated (2017, p. 39). Levine and van der Kolk also refer to the body's autonomic response as a reaction to a need to flee or fight a situation that invokes fear (1997; 2014). For instance, Levine maps out how the four general symptoms of trauma (hyperarousal, constriction, dissociation and helplessness) emerge out of this fight or flight response. He suggests that these four experiences are the 'physiological changes that occur when we are overwhelmed [with need] while responding to a life-threatening event' (1997, p. 155). Just as both Lévinas and Merleau-Ponty point out to us, the body is itself taken up in the living of trauma, and the need of the body shares itself as response. Rothschild, Levine and van der Kolk are keen to show that the body itself becomes the teller of tales, the expresser of need and the site of trauma's integration with the self.

These perspectives suggest that the body undergoes some kind of transformation in a traumatic experience. Levine writes that people who have experienced trauma often express the trauma 'through physical symptoms or through a full-blown interaction with the external environment' (1997, p. 173). The need that has not been met, and the rupture that this wounding has caused imprints itself on the lived body. For instance, if the nervous system is activated in a debilitating way because it cannot keep the heightened arousal level, but at the same time cannot find a way of discharging it, a small event like a telephone ringing might cause a traumatised person to exhibit hypervigilance, if the body interprets it as a dangerous sign of a past event (1997, pp. 146–147). Levine suggests that this is the body's survival strategy for coping with the unmet need and the rupture that trauma causes.

This is similar to what Charles Scott means when he says that trauma can 'threaten the living fabric' of a person's experience. He calls the event a 'limbic hit', as the body experiences an unreflective impact from a threat. Scott suggests that the impact that hits us renders us speechless, because it is outside the experience of story: language only pushes it into the distance. What really happens, he writes, is that 'Traumatic events and limbic reaction, in their violence and senselessness, allow that distance, that incomprehensibility, that presence without reason…' (2009, p. 122). But trauma not only hits the body with an incomprehensible presence, it also causes loss: 'parts of bodies, whole bodies, happiness, loved people, locales, societies, innocence, hope, affection, a sense of self' (ibid.). Our experience of our self becomes disrupted in the experience of trauma.

Trauma is experienced in a diversity of outcomes (Harris et al. 2013). What is common is how it impacts a sense of self. For some, the self becomes like an other – a place of hostility, an environment that lacks predictability and safety. One theory that explores this experience of the self is *IFS Therapy.* In an interview with therapist Robert Falconer, he explores his own history of trauma. As a victim of ongoing childhood sexual abuse at the hands of his parents, he developed ways of coping with these ruptures through physical activity and hard labour. But at one point, in the midst of recovering from an injury, he explained how all of the traumatic memories flooded back to him. His body that he could usually control was at the mercy of the memory; he could not sleep, and when he did, his sleep was filled with nightmares (2020). The experience of his body as a home was one that was unsafe to occupy.

Falconer suggested that this experience of internal hostility needed to be engaged with gentleness. He said that rather than treating it as 'internal civil war', the experience required gentle awareness. His internal hostile world was not only occupied by nightmares, but also self-loathing, which he saw as a way of protecting the more vulnerable aspects of himself. In using concepts such as protection and exile to explore the self, he is using the language of IFS. Developed by Richard Schwartz, this model reads the experience of trauma through a tale of Self and exiles surrounded by its protectors.

While emerging from Schwartz' own background in Family Systems Therapy, that treats experience according to the interactive relationships around the individual in the family (the family system), IFS looks inward. As such, there are similarities between IFS and particular instances of psychoanalytic narrative theory, while also rooting it in the bodied representations of experience. IFS reads the inner experience as a drama between these psychic parts and the therapeutic role of negotiating with these parts. Engaging with the 'inner polarities' of the person (Schwartz and Sweezy 2020, p. 108), the therapist explores how a chasm between the Self and its parts fragments into a system of survival. But it also shows how the embodied psyche acts to protect the itself and develops a theory that avoids psychopathic language in a way that can account for particularly complex traumas.

In a healthy experience, the Self, as the seat of consciousness, communes with its parts, or its subpersonalities, in a way that brings connection, compassion and curiosity, clarity, confidence and courage. But in traumatic experiences, the Self cannot be present. Though it is still 'there', it is not available to the personality. The parts take on different roles in order to try to re-establish safety. The exiled part is the wounded part of the system that is 'sequestered out of consciousness', while protector parts develop roles based on primal fear responses. For the Self to restore relationship between itself and the parts, IFS suggests that another Self (therapist) needs to speak to each protector in order to re-establish relationship with the exile if the person's own Self is unavailable. The therapist enters into dialogue with the exile through accessing and speaking through her own Self. Differing from *Ego-State Therapy* (Watkins 1993), consciousness is not altered during the work. It is a systemic approach, because it reads the experience of the self through our inner conflicts and fears, extreme behaviours and burdensome beliefs (Schwartz 2020). Liberating the parts from their restrictions and finding the reason for behaviours becomes a way of welcoming the bodied Self home.

The protective parts of the self usually have common concerns. For instance, they are afraid and concerned about what will happen to their own fate. How the fear manifests shows whether the part is an exile, which is the experience that is 'hurt or banished and continues to feel unbearably lonely and worthless' (Schwartz 2020, p. 104). This is the often unconscious part that wants to be rescued, seen and heard, and in that can manifest a counterreaction from the part of the protector, who either seeks to inhibit feeling that are overwhelming (acting as a 'manager'), or reactively distract from negative feeling (acting as a 'firefighter'). But Schwartz writes that though the parts serve a protective purpose in responding to trauma (and, particularly long-term complex traumas), 'neither the managers nor firefighters can heal the injuries of exiles' (p. 102).

In IFS, healing is interpreted an experience of the Self re-relating to its parts. This requires both witnessing the exiled part and allowing the Self to be present to that witness. The protectors are also brought forward to be witnessed by the Self, but as the protectors are encountered early on, it is often the Self of the therapist that is required to speak to them. Schwartz writes that 'Every time an exile tells its story, lets go of its burdens, and the client is reunited with her natural self-righting abilities – her Self – inner space and time expand' (2020, p. 110). The exiles no longer need to cause pain to be recognised. The protectors no longer must counteract the exiles to restore homeostasis. Schwartz's theory brings out three important things: first, the experience of exile is likened to the experience of living trauma. Second, each traumatic experience is lived differently and contains its own 'temperament, desires and a distinct way of communicating' (2020, p. 13). Third, the Self here is not experienced as a broken self, or a self that is marred by its past. The Self contains its own wholeness. This inner self cannot be damaged or broken. Falconer likens it to the presence of the sun on a wild day (2020). Despite the experience of the storm clouds, the sun remains undamaged, and though unseen, it is still present.

Reading trauma through the experience of a Self as home communing with a part in exile brings out the interconnections that living trauma as bodied consciousness demands. Lévinas and Merleau-Ponty show us how the body can be a site of vulnerability and need, as part of the experience through which we live towards the other. Schwartz brings out a fresh understanding of how we might read the experiences of the body through the great narrative of exile and protection of the parts. But this has focused on how we might understand the self as a space of home and exile. What we want to now discuss is how trauma might create a situation of homelessness in our relation to other people and to our geographical context.

Home as a Physical Space

In this section, we will refer to home as a physical and social space. This space could, for instance, be where we grew up, or the community that nurtured us when we were young. A particular social network, such as a parental or sisterly bond, might facilitate our experience of the material conception or 'thing' we call home. For

Ricœur, our experience of who we are as a 'thinking thing', as Descartes teaches us, is constantly mediated by outward 'things', such as institutions and actions. According to Ricœur, philosophy helps us to reflect even deeper still, on who we are after we have recovered ourselves from these outer things. Ricœur is interested in recovering our experience of existing (Ricœur 1970). For modern philosophy, the primary concern was with how we can understand the human as a singular, thinking being (we see this earlier in Merleau-Ponty and Lévinas' response to the problems of modernity).

Ricœur shows this first truth that defines the modern subject:

> the positing of the self is a truth which posits itself; it can be neither verified nor deduced; it is at once the positing of a being and of an act; the positing of an existence and of an operation of thought: I am, I think; to exist, for me, is to think; I exist inasmuch as I think.
>
> *1970, p. 43*

But the external factors that create the experience of thinking constantly modify this thinking being. If we view home under this understanding of subjectivity, then it could be interesting to see how *home* as an institution alters our way of thinking. So, when the thought structures of home around us change (for instance, when we change house, or our brother leaves home), then the experience of home changes for us. Experiencing the world through thought is of central importance. However, as Lévinas, Merleau-Ponty and Ricœur all point out, the experience of subjectivity and the world around us requires that we reach beyond the solipsistic thinking ego.

For Ricœur, as for Merleau-Ponty and Lévinas, subjectivity is more than discovering that we are thinking beings. Ricœur is concerned with 'recovering in its concrete fullness the I at the heart of the *Cogito*' (Doran 1973, p. 446). If the full recovery of the self is what Ricœur aims to achieve, then the experience of the self has to go beyond the experience of the world through the cogito alone. But Ricœur also wants to recover the world beyond the suspicion of consciousness that Freud, Marx and Nietzsche demand, towards a 'second innocence', which receives the world with care. For this, he suggests that we need to read experience hermeneutically, through its multiple meanings and interpretations. He appeals to the language of poetry, dreams and religion as tools that reveal a world rooted beyond the expressed language. This is a world where myth and symbol serve a purpose, to gain access to different interpretations of experience by elevating 'the symbols to the rank of existential concepts' (Ricœur 1986, p. 5). Reading experience in this way means that we can explore the concept of home as a phenomenon of place in a hermeneutical manner. This conversation reaches beyond cognitive cause and effect relations and brings into consideration how home and the loss of home might be interwoven in an experience of lament and celebration.

This phenomenological experience of home incorporates others in social and physical space. Physical and social spaces are constantly affected in trauma. In some accounts of sexual assault, children associate trauma with their home. They were abused by their uncle in the bedroom, or they saw the murder of their mother in the kitchen. In other accounts, such as experiences of war and political violence, people flee their homes and are exiled as a refugee. Homes are forcefully handed over or destroyed, or homes are returned to in an altered state; homes are experienced as a safe sanctuary, or as a place of woundedness.

What I want to consider here is how the experience of home and homelessness as phenomena might be interpreted through Ricœur's phenomenology of symbol. For Ricœur, language is constitutive of the self. He writes that 'Man then, seems to be no more than language' (1986, p. 256). Language is central in understanding both who we are, and how we understand the world around us. Understanding the *living of* something requires grappling with language. But language itself is not something that you just pick up and translate easily. Language can contain multiple meanings. In Ricœurian phenomenology, language takes on a symbolic function that we have to interpret hermeneutically. Exploring the 'symbolic significance' of words becomes our phenomenological task (Itao 2010, p. 3). Symbol, for Ricœur, refers both to the 'direct, primary, literal meaning' of something as well as 'another meaning which is indirect, secondary, and figurative' (Ricœur 2007, p. 13). This secondary meaning, however, is only understood through its direct first meaning. The symbol contains both patent and the latent meanings (Itao 2010).

One way of interpreting homelessness is through a phenomenology of symbol. In this case, the primary meaning of home indicates a place of origin. The place of origin is important in many instances of trauma because it often becomes the place in which a person experiences a dislocation from origin. Lévinas' interpretation shows this home to be the place of contentment, the place to which we welcome the other in an experience of hospitality. But in trauma, this experience of contentment and belonging can become replaced with the experience of need and exile. The self is literally re-placed, leaving the containment of home. Home then becomes symbolic also of the dis-placement of self that occurs in the trauma. This dis-placement, like the experience of the body in trauma, transforms the experience of home to such an extent that even if one returns home, the home is now unfamiliar. In this experience of symbol, homelessness can be interpreted literally through traumatic displacement. Homelessness can also be interpreted symbolically through the displaced experience of the traumatised body.

An example of this literal interpretation of homelessness is offered in Stauffer's exploration of trauma. Two examples that she gives reveal how being taken from one's place of origin affect our subjectivity. The first documents a report by the South African Truth and Reconciliation Council. Eric Stover writes that 'The few participants who experienced cathartic feelings immediately or soon after testifying…found that the glow quickly faded once they returned home to their shattered villages and towns' (p. 107, ct. in Stauffer 2015, p. 81). The second example recalls the description of a Holocaust Testimony. When liberated from the concentration camp, survivor Hannah F. recalls experiencing 'That I am alone in the whole world' (ct. in Stauffer 2015, p. 103). Despite the freedom to return to her place of origin, the events of her dis-placement forced her into a continued experience of homelessness. Stauffer writes that Hannah 'had nowhere to go, no loved ones left living to reunite with, she could not return to her home in Poland, and so she was simply "lost without words"' (ibid.). Both accounts show how physical and traumatic displacements continue, even as the person is released from their 'place' of trauma (Hannah is released from her captors). In the first instance, the traumatic displacement continues despite a return home. The home returned to is a collection of broken buildings. In the second instance, the original home cannot be returned to because the relationships that made it home are gone. Hannah experiences homelessness; she is now alone in the world.

This literal reading of dis-placement, or homelessness, shows how trauma can be caused by a violent removal from our place of origin. It also shows how this place of origin is transformed in the experience of trauma, be it through the physical destruction of place or the destruction of relationships that contextualised the experience of home. Something about the experience of this place, as an experience of contentment and belonging, has changed. Stauffer's nuanced account of this displacement ties it to the other relationships that surround it.[2] But what is happening here is more than an experience of removal from, and reconstruction of origin. Homelessness takes on a symbolic function. It expresses the state of living through the experience of ruptured relationship.

This is where it is helpful to return to Ricœur. He wants to connect suffering symbolically to the phenomenon of evil. But evil here is much like a Lévinasian reading; it is an embodied experience of suffering. Evil, for Ricœur, is an experience of physical pain and facelessness. Connecting the lived suffering of trauma to the symbol of evil problematises the experience of trauma, and the ambiguity of culpability, which we saw in the last part of the book and will look at later on as well. But the symbol of evil as the presence of a bodied suffering also brings a second reading and a double meaning to the notion of homelessness. Ricœur wants to reclaim the ambiguity of evil as symbol, suggesting that evil enigmatically encompasses diverse phenomena of 'sin, suffering and death' (1995, p. 250).

But most of Ricœur's work is used to address the human experience of discordance. For Ricœur, we are constantly making sense of our narrative that is being reconfigured through the act of relating to the world. This is where symbol can act as a type of 'anchor' as we plot our lives in the midst of is discordance, displacement and rupture. This 'configuration' of experience gives it a certain narrative 'readability'. However, the language extends beyond itself, as experience itself, meaning that 'language, while saying something about something, is about being' (Helenius 2012, p. 150). Situating homelessness in the phenomenology of subjectivity, then, becomes a matter of plotting the refigured experience as a verb-image of experience (p. 151). For this, we need to look at how this literal and symbolic experience of homelessness can hold together, as both a dis-placement from place of origin, and a lived dis-placement of relationship. For this, we will look to political theory, and a phenomenological account of justice and responsibility.

Conclusion

This chapter examined how trauma might be explored phenomenologically through the experience of home. We first read trauma as a displacement of subjectivity and explored how Lévinas and Merleau-Ponty might engage with contemporary theories such as IFS that map trauma through 'exile' and 'defender' parts. I suggested that this experience of subjectivity, as one of home and homelessness, could help us to understand how we live trauma. Then, I brought in another reading of home, as an external space, or place of origin. I suggested that this reading of home might benefit from Ricœur's hermeneutic of symbol, where home and homelessness contained a double meaning. This double meaning, I suggested, brings our discussion of trauma into further relations of subject and place, as well as the experience of lament, as a way of *living* the ongoing experience of the traumatic. Many of these points will be picked up as our exploration of trauma continues.

Notes

1 In Lévinas' interpretation of communication, what is revealed as said by the other does not fully represent the saying: '*Dans le langage comme dit, tout se traduit devant nous – fut-ce au prix d'une trahison*' (1998b, p. 6).
2 She links it to Lévinas' role of revelation: the loss of trauma requires both one who listens and one who speaks. We looked at that in the previous section.

9

THE INTERSUBJECTIVITY OF TRAUMA

Politics, Rights and Decolonisation

The preceding chapters show us that a *prismic* experience of trauma requires weaving together many different threads of experience. The dilemma of moral guilt and the interaction between the victim and the perpetrator are not just ethical questions. They are also existential questions. Lévinas shows is how this suffering person is implicated in a web of relationships that actually affect the very core experience of 'who we are'. In Chapters 7 and 8, we have explored different readings of trauma. Chapter 7 examined how communication is implicated in trauma, how we reveal ourselves to the other and how communication moves beyond language. We also reflected on how communication requires both a communicator and a listener for the experience of testimony. Chapter 8 analysed the effect of trauma on our experience of home. This involved recognising both internal and external experiences of origin and belonging, and the impact of trauma on each relation.

The Rights of Trauma

This chapter asks us to understand a further part of the traumatic experience, namely, how trauma holds ethical and political content. For this, we will draw on political philosophers to explore what a political reading of trauma might mean. These conversations will be developed through Lévinas' phenomenology of relation, suggesting that reading trauma phenomenologically enables us to bring together all of these different parts of the experience. This will specifically be explored through reference to the experience of children and the development of the Children's Charter of Human Rights (CHRC). The rupture of war, displacement of conflict and the disintegration of home are all often causes of trauma. This chapter will assess how these situations require understanding trauma alongside ethics and with wider political conversations in mind, in order to bring further clarity to the ambiguity of this experience.

DOI: 10.4324/9780367800017-12

The last few chapters have looked at the relationship between the self and the other. But this interrelationship is often mediated through institutional relationships. For instance, in Lévinas we see subjectivity emerge as responsibility for the other, albeit at a level of metaethics. This relationship of justice requires a normative outworking. The relationship of response looks like concrete actions done by specific individuals in order for it to actually address the need of the stranger that Lévinas writes about. For Lévinas, politics is the mediated experience between the subject and the other. It is an invocation of a third (*le tiers*) that 'interrupts the face to face of a welcome of the person, interrupts the proximity or approach of the neighbour' (1998b, p. 150). In this way, the responsibility is mediated and *le tiers* confers justice in the social life (see Herzog 2020). Responsibility needs to look like something in order for it to aid the suffering other. But this mediating third is not without its representative problems. As with Ricœur's hermeneutics of text, Lévinas expounds a type of midrash by which responsibility is extricated and interpreted (1994, p. x). This is where rights politics emerges as an intermediary through which relationship is secured and responsibilities towards the vulnerable other are upheld or violated.

This chapter explores the interconnection between the political discourse of human rights and the subjective living of trauma in the experience of children. An example of this is found in working out the implications of the CHRC, which was developed to protect children from experiences of suffering that could lead to trauma. This chapter will look at the implications of the CHRC on children suffering from trauma. It will then examine criticisms of the theoretical language employed to deliver this content through the political writings of Joseph Raz and Michael Ignatieff. Referencing critiques by Paul Farmer and Lévinas, the argument put forward here is that that in order for the content of rights to address the content of specific situational sufferings, the rights discourse needs to implicate both recipient and theorist in a revelatory way. This means that, once again, the experience of trauma has to be interpreted subjectively. It requires witnessing to the other who reveals her suffering to us. The specific context for this will be experience of trafficked children. I will suggest that human rights can benefit from a hermeneutic of revelation in which rights language is exchanged as a dialogue in which the child reveals herself to the observer, and political theory enters into the real, lived experience.

The Development of the CHRC

In 1946, the Universal Declaration of Human Rights created statutes that sought to recognise the dignity of all human beings, regardless of background or status. These universal principles were outlined as strategies to regulate the governance of an international community of equal rational people. However, as critics and proponents of human rights have long recognised, there is a difference between outlining a rationally conceived right and implementing that right in a meaningful way that affects real change in the lives of its recipients. Children are particularly targeted when the protective structures of the home, school and the community break down.

All around the world, children are vulnerable to the implications of living in situations of extreme poverty, civil unrest and violence. Often at the mercy of the actions and choices of the adults that surround them, a child's life can be particularly exposed to the traumas of conflict and community breakdown. More specifically, with little experience of the legal systems governing wider conversations about responsibility and rights, and often dependent on the care of the adults closest to them for survival, they can be susceptible to being exploited for human trafficking. For instance, the United Nations Children's Fund (UNICEF) notes that in all 53 African countries children between the ages of 12 and 16 are the most vulnerable demographic to be 'recruited as soldiers and sold into prostitution and forced labour' (Fleck 2004, p. 1036). These experiences are riddled with instances of complex traumatisation, ranging from sexual assault, psychological abuse, disattachment and physical trauma, in more fatal forms of trafficking that can lead to death, pertaining to witchcraft 'mutti killings of children' and organ harvesting (ibid.). In these situations, the child's lived trauma directly connects to the wider social relationships with which she is engaged.

Human rights, formalised in the language of the Universal Declaration of Human Rights in 1946, have emerged over centuries of philosophical and social discourse. In this time, the child was beginning to be seen politically, moving from 'an object of protection to an emerging citizen', to a person with rights that requires protection (Ben-Arieh and Tarshish 2017, p. 69). In order for the child to be a citizen, she must be protected, but pre-existing this, she must have an existential value in and for herself. In order for her to be safeguarded against labour exploitation, her value is located outside of simply her ability to do; in order for her education to be important, it is presumed that the child possesses reason. Thus, rights could not just be about protection, but also had to be rooted in 'enhancing their well-being' (Kahn 2010, ct. in Ben-Arieh and Tarshish 2017, p. 71). Further human rights theory supports this existential concept through the notion of intrinsic dignity, through appealing to existence grounded in humanity, a relation to the divine other and an appeal to an experience of consciousness.

Though there is a conceptual backing for a child's experience of human rights, application of these universals to particular situations has 'proved to be slow going' (Stearns 2017, p. 15). Exactly how we protect the wellbeing of a child through adherence to a system of values proves challenging. Farmer reveals this in his work on global power imbalances and the effects on poorer communities: rights are a great idea theoretically, but they need to have concrete content to be useful (2005). And, while Jonathan Todres notes that 'it is widely accepted that human rights are interrelated and interdependent' (2017, p. 21), the rights of children are particularly difficult to monitor. John Tobin, for instance, looks at how the rights of children are deeply interconnected with the lives of their parents (2017). He also notes that strong opposition comes from those who fear that children's rights will replace the protection and governance of the family for externally enforced legislative norms, which misrepresents the normative purpose of rights and creates suspicion around the use of the language (2017, pp. 55–56).

The rights of the child were formalised in early part of the twentieth century (Stearns 2017). The *Declaration of the Rights of the Child* was developed in 1923 by Eglantyne Jebb, who also headed relief efforts and the organisation of 'Save the Children' movement after the First World War (Stearns 2017, p. 13). Stearns writes that this initial document outlined criteria, including that:

> Children must be provided with conditions for normal development, both physically and spiritually. Sick children must be nursed, the hungry fed, the delinquent reclaimed, the homeless sheltered, the backward helped. Children should have first claim on relief in times of distress. Children must learn how to earn a livelihood but must be protected against every form of exploitation.
>
> *p. 13*

Stearns notes that while the original language was altered, much of the structure of these rights was maintained in the 1924 endorsement by the General Assembly of the League of Nations. From guidelines to a further formalised structure and additional principles added on, the General Assembly of the United Nations (1959) sought legal protection for children as a 'commitment to social security', and the 'commitment to a "happy" childhood' (p. 14). Like the development of the United Nations Declaration of Human Rights (UNDHR), these rights for children reflected an emerging existential phenomenology of what it means to *live* as a child, one in dialogue with religious practices (particularly, the Judeo-Christian protection of the child), the development of societal structures such as changing working conditions, and new political theories of John Locke on the importance of education and Jean-Jacques Rousseau's conceptualisation of the innate goodness of the child, that could be developed through education (Stearns 2017, p. 6).[1]

According to CHRC, the context of child trafficking, where children are bought and sold with the 'specific purpose of exploitation' (p. 3) violates human rights in numerous ways, including the demand for labour rights and protection of children, the right to liberty and the right not to be subjected to torture, as well as the 'right of children to special protection' (p. 4). On repeated occasions, the United Nations General Assembly and Human Rights Council have denounced human trafficking as a violation of human rights (UN 2014, p. 5). Morgan reminds us that Lévinas requires that we address the individual experience of the human face. As a result, each case of human rights encompasses multiple 'one-on-one relationships', and as each agent is the distinct recipient of 'concern, care, assistance, and attention', there will be special ways in which the features of each need is met, including how and to what degree it is met (2016, p. 111). As with general human rights, the rights of the child assume a particular context. Rights are also premised on a specific existential phenomenology about what it is to live as a child.

The context of child trafficking is a situation of trauma in which the responsible relationship that Lévinas outlines has been abused. In this context, the child's vulnerability makes them particularly at risk for traumatisation. The deep failure of rights to uphold this relationship of responsibility is a failure that is felt at the very basic level of the traumatised child who is lost in the unhearing and unseeing ego world around her. Working with children after they have been traumatised reveals that their bodies have incorporated the violence against them in complex ways. In the violation of physical boundaries, and relations of trust, the child can struggle to experience a 'sense of protection, feelings of safety and sense of self as a unit' (Drosdick 2020, p. 121). In other experiences, the children displayed outbursts of anger, depression and withdrawal (p. 123).

In the experience of violations of trust, connectedness and safety, this often plays out at the level of the family context. For Tobin, 'this institution still remains the fundamental unit of society and the optimal place in which all children should be raised and provided with care' (2016, p. 55). But the relationship between the family and the state is dialectical; as guardians of children engage with a network of protection, it clarifies the responsible outworking of a relationship that can protect a child from undue suffering. Through the perspective of children's rights, we can see the responsibility of the Lévinasian self-applied through the parent's obligation to care for their child. However, we can also see where the cracks begin to emerge. Because children do experience trauma and as human trafficking often shows us, it can be in the breakdown of our closest relationships that the experience of suffering most profoundly emerges.

The Challenge of Universalising Particular Rights

The Convention on the Rights of the Child (CRC) provides a formal language structure with institutional enforcement, aimed to protect and develop the well-being of each child. But, as Lévinas reminds us, in his philosophy of singularity, the challenge of ethics is about how we respond to the individual face, rather than adherence to generalised rules. Translated into rights discourse, this means that the challenge is for the universal applicability of rights to generate real change in communities. Highlighting this disparity between theory and practice, Ursula Kilkelly suggests that provisions are often too broad or inadequately precise, and that the 'protections are frequently weak and thinly veiled and caveats and gaps in the rights protected are too numerous' (2016, p. 85). This can often result in internal inconsistencies between individual children, and between other rights holders, which threatens how useful the rights can be (Kilkelly 2016). As we see in the example before of child trafficking, the basic relationships of trust are the ones that are compromised, and often because of complicated and interconnected narratives of violated rights, desperation, hunger and exploitation.

What Kilkelly notes is that the language of rights can often veil, in broad terms, the details of a practical needs-based reality. As Lévinas reminds us, it is the groan of the other that makes us hostage to her suffering, which cannot be blanketed by any kind of totalising knowledge 'about' something or someone. Each face has to reveal itself and be answered for. The conversation of rights is a political one; it is about what institutions owe individuals based on the dignifying fact that they are human beings. Lévinas is also concerned with this unique dignity of the human face, but he has a mixed relationship with a straightforward reading of the political. For Lévinas, 'the question of the political is first the question of the other's rights and freedoms' (Tahmasebi-Birgani 2014, p. 15). Lévinas advocates for a 'victim-centred' reading, Tahmasebi-Birgani suggests, because of his prioritisation of a subject's responsibility for the other. To some, Lévinas seems to be favouring a form of paternalism. Reading responsibility paternalistically, as a renunciation of autonomy could be seen as re-victimising the other. However, I would argue alongside Tahmasebi-Birgani that what Lévinas is doing not so much passive paternalism, as it is giving a 'voice and agency back to the victim' (2014, p. 15). It is the traumatised person alone who reveals her suffering to the person bearing witness.

A misreading of Lévinasian responsibility, therefore, is problematic if it reaffirms the inequalities of politics (Tahmasebi-Birgani 2014). So precision is needed in reading this experience, as is the grappling with Lévinas' own resistance to be normative. A Lévinasian reading of liberalism is complex because it both affirms and criticises its main aims. For instance, Lévinas critiques liberal Western philosophy in its 'effort to build a totality in which the individual is but an instance' (2014, p. 16). The individual is always to be treated as singular and unique. Tahmasebi-Birgani suggests that, for Lévinas, the subject is 'post-autonomous and post-individualist' and exists as a person who 'resists recuperation by totality and universal history' (2014, p. 17). Interruption and disturbance of experience by the other occur at every point. That means that for Lévinas' ethicopolitical subjectivity is instantaneous with the radical interruption of totalised history…' (ibid.). This is a call for a relationship of justice that takes the abstract relationship and works out what it looks for in 'a concrete, immediate, and face-to-face encounter with the other whose suffering calls me, and no other, to respond and to act' (ibid.). For Lévinas, this call of the other that makes me responsible for her is a demand for justice.

But Lévinas does seem to advocate for a non-reciprocal responsibility, so the idea that responsibility is paternalistic could have some value here, particularly if we are addressing the responsibilities that adults, or at least adult-states, have towards children. For Tahmasebi-Birgani as well as my own reading of Lévinas, this is a problematic assessment of what he is doing. The other cannot be reduced to the experience of the victim, because in doing this, one creates another sort of totality, which Lévinas resists from the very beginning. I agree with her that 'Lévinas' reading of the political "opens Lévinas" ethics to a radical political endeavor that is different from any political project thus far, be it liberal, Marxist, or conservative' (ibid.). Understanding rights becomes a conversation about revelation, and how our experience might be ruptured by the presence of the other.

Lévinas sees his ethical relation as concerned with an inner relationality. In contrasting a rights theory that is read as a series of external guidelines, Lévinas classifies his ethical relation as an inward orientation towards the other. Our institutions, then, become grounded in the interpersonal relationship of responsibility (Michael Morgan 2016, p. 111). The political serves the ethical; it organises our response towards the other. If we are examining the political theories of rights, then, rather than weighing conflicting needs and assessing our freedoms, the guidance of the state could serve to re-order the subjective experience of helping and responding to the other (Morgan 2016, p. 102). It is perhaps more accurate to say that Lévinas incorporates the rights discourse into his conversation. It is this inner orientation towards the other, grounding the state in charity, or love, 'rather than mistrust and conflict', in which rights can be read as 'an expression of infinite responsibility' (Morgan 2016, p. 104). Morgan writes that the measurement of political decency, then, becomes 'how a society and a state deal with refugees or aliens, on the one hand, and minorities, on the other' (p. 111). As such, the institutionalisation of politics, experienced through rights discourse, is really always about the revelatory meeting between individuals. If we read human rights discourse through Lévinas as a way of ordering our responsibility towards each human face, then rights can be a way of addressing the indescribable harms suffered by the unseen experiences of children in situations of human trafficking. This requires understanding the discourse of human rights, as it applies to children specifically, because, as we saw above, the child's experience is uniquely lived.

Some speculate that Lévinas promotes a passive responsibility for the other, because this responsibility is prior to other experience. But this kind of passivity, which is an assumed responsibility for the other, differs from an 'inertia' of inaction. This differs from Farmer's critique, which is that human rights is too theoretically passive to meet the real needs of people (Stephens 2005). For Farmer, bearing witness to suffering and addressing the needs of vulnerable individuals require understanding that 'the social determinants of health outcomes are also, often, the social determinants of the distribution of assaults on human dignity' (2005, p. 19). He advocates for a critical social justice approach that more significantly draws on liberation theology and requires a bottom-up restructuring of just relationship. It is this formal, theoretical language of human rights that Farmer critiques. However, he is sympathetic to the aims that it wishes to achieve. Political philosopher Michael Ignatieff also highlights this tension between theory and practical effectiveness in his recent global study on the effectiveness of human rights (1984). Ignatieff suggests that human rights need to take on a normative face, through the language of common virtues. This normative face is something that has practical significance; it can still contain the same content of human rights, but rather than the formal language, it assumes a social context of lived relatedness. It also assumes that the person has something to give. The concept of gift and hospitality become philosophically relevant by giving language to the ethical relationships between people.

Political philosopher Joseph Raz draws out the philosophical importance of this disjunction between universal and particular in his political philosophy. He suggests that there is an underlying normative tension in the application of universal theory to particular situations. While he writes that 'It is a good time for human rights' (2007, p. 1), he does not suggest that this is a result of a more ethical contemporary international context, or that we are living in peace with one another. Rather, he suggests that this is because the discourse on human rights has never been more internationally widespread as it is currently.

Raz suggests that current theory is divided into the two problematic categories of definition, from traditional universal humanism (Griffin) and political normativism (Rawls). He suggests that his theory, built on his concept of value as socially dependent, synthesises both while also addressing rights as social constructs. But Raz is unable to reconcile universalism with reductionism and is further unable to distinguish clearly between the conceptual differences of rights and value. As a result, though Raz provides a helpful analysis of current analytic problems in human rights theory, he is unable to come up with a conceptual analysis that will address these problems normatively. My concern is that in the midst of this current normative discussion on human rights, the phenomenological question of human rights often gets pushed aside in favour of short-term normative solutions. This is where I would argue that Lévinas' critique of totality enables us to identify and problematise a 'passive' notion of human rights (and, in this context, children's rights). What Lévinas also allows us to do is to keep some of the content of rights theory, by suggesting that rights can be the content of the political encounter that happens face to face with the other. We advocate on their behalf, for education, safety and food, for instance.

Trauma and Human Trafficking

In the preceding sections, we have observed the important development of children's rights as a result of new interpretations about children's experience, their capabilities and the responsibility to protect their wellbeing. Children are particularly vulnerable, due to their dependence on others. It seems, therefore, that rights would be an important method for securing their protection and flourishing. However, as we have seen subsequently, human rights theory has been criticised for its inability to cross from theoretical language to normative impact. I have suggested that Ignatieff, Farmer and Lévinas localise this challenge in the generalisation of rights theory and require reorienting us from abstract theory to the face-to-face human relation. Both Ignatieff and Lévinas speak about this as gift and hospitality, of a giving to the other.

Childhood trauma is particularly complex, because it disrupts the individual as they are first learning to map out what to expect of the world around them. van der Kolk notes that in some cases of childhood trauma, the past event continues to play out in the present as it shapes the expectation of each relationship formed after the event (2014). He writes that attachment research shows how when 'our earliest caregivers don't feed us, dress us, and comfort us when we are upset; they shape the way our rapidly growing brain perceives reality' (2014, p. 129). These interactions are what tell us the difference between safety and danger. What he considers necessary, then, when addressing childhood trauma, is to help the person to 'reconstruct their inner map of the world' (2014, p. 128). This is particularly important in experiences of human trafficking, where attachment is not only compromised, but distortions of safety and danger, abuse and neglect turn into experiences of an unsafe and unresponsive world.

But van der Kolk suggests that experience does not have to leave us in this traumatised embodied memory state. How we map experience, he writes, may be modified by a new experience of relationship: 'A deep love relationship…truly can transform us' (2014, p. 129). This is not a glib romantic plaster over a wound. van der Kolk suggests that a change in the emotional brain can alter our experience of the world. Lévinas suggests something similar in his phenomenological relation of responsibility. He shows how we can become the exit for the other's suffering, myself-for-the-other. In this, we can allow the other an exit from her situation of inescapability. It is in the relationship between the other and myself that the political receives its ethical significance. The political becomes a mediator of a unique relationship.

This is where human rights have their full expression. Here, the child's need is recognised as a duty, and the trauma of isolation caused by abuse or rejection expresses an ethical demand, where Lévinas' interpretation of 'Thou shall not kill' becomes 'Thou shalt cause thy neighbour to live' (Lévinas 1999, pp. 21–30; ct. in Morgan 2016, p. 114). In applying rights discourse to a child's trauma experienced through human trafficking, rights can emerge as a way of phenomenological reconstituting a child's relationship with the world, or, more urgently, never letting it happen in the first place.

Trauma in Relation: Decolonisation of the Body and Land

Part III of this book explores how trauma is affected by our relationships with other people. Whether it is through the language of rights and responsibilities or concepts such as homelessness, trauma can find representation in different ways because of how it implicates the human experience. This chapter will look at how trauma can develop a complex relationship between victim and perpetrator. The experience of the victim is not new to this book, but this chapter assesses how a victim and a perpetrator interact in traumatic experience. The chapter will then apply this phenomenological study to conversations about land practice.

This means expanding the self-other relationship to include the non-human sentient other, and, particularly in the case of Merleau-Ponty, extend beyond sentience to include relationships to the land itself. Reading human interaction with the land as a relation to a different kind of other, we will look at how instances of colonisation might be read as an experience of our own bodied world and interaction with the world around us. This section will reference contemporary discourses on decolonisation, using the tools of existential phenomenology to interpret the living experience of trauma. In his phenomenology of experience, Merleau-Ponty interprets a bodied living of our worlds. The lived experience is as bodied. Earlier one trauma was read as a suffering lived out in the 'home' of the body. As Richard Kearney will help us to understand, Ricœur goes one step further. He enables us to connect the lived body with the life of consciousness (the thought life). This phenomenology does not reduce itself to either body or thought, but weaves both together. Kearney refers to this aspect of Ricœur's subjectivity as a hermeneutic of flesh.

Now, if thought connects to the body, then any ethical discourse will require a bodied expression: values actually *touch* me. Ethical discourse becomes 'a mediation of flesh' (Kearney 2016, p. 219). When applied to the discourse on trauma and decolonisation, this reading by Merleau-Ponty and Ricœur requires a hermeneutic reading of history that is bodied. Thought cannot be separate from the body; a theory of colonisation loses its 'truth' when analysed outside of the lived 'flesh'. However, Ricœur reminds us that the flesh that we want to understand, this thinking and materially bodied being, is a being amongst others. I am myself for others or 'a body with others' (1994, p. 226). Ricœur's hermeneutic of otherness can help us to understand trauma in the context of colonisation. I will suggest that colonisation, as a philosophical exploration of the trauma of 'sameness',[2] benefits from Ricœur's work on the otherness. Ricœur, facilitated through Merleau-Ponty, allows thought and ethical discourse to be brought into the lived body of a particular being, as we try to understand how colonisation separates the other from its particularity and its bodied existence.

The Role of the Body: Reading Colonisation through Merleau-Ponty

Roughly, I am suggesting that colonisation, as read in this blunt manner, offers an experience of trauma through its inability to hermeneutically engage with the lived experience of the individual. If we read colonisation as, for example Bosi brings it to us, then colonisation is lived as a system of 'power relations' with a 'thick trace of domination'. I recognise that this is a reductive definition of colonisation. However, it also contains the key phenomena that delineate it as a specific kind of traumatic experience.

Contemporary reports on the traumatic effects of intergenerational colonisation reveal staggering numbers of Post Traumatic Stress Disorder (PTSD) cases, abuse, addiction and other mental health disorders. Part of what Rosalyn Diprose defines as the act of racism that shapes the social and political structures of colonisation is the unreflective shaping of what constitutes a 'natural attitude' of meaning (2017, p. 54). Bosi writes that colonisation involves an 'overdetermination' of the other, that demands the other, though the coloniser might not recognise it himself. The coloniser does not see himself 'as a mere conquerer', but rather 'he will try to take to the descendants the image of the discoverer and the villager, titles to which, as a pioneer, he would deserve' (Bosi 1995 p. 12).

Employing hermeneutics to this conversation can help restore the ethical relationship that is a bodied experience and reveals to ourselves how our subjectivity actually engages with the other as implicated in the trauma. Colonisation reveals the construction of a 'precarious identity' that justifies a claim to power over another group of people, that creates a problematic construction of self for the coloniser and self for the colonised: the 'excluded', the 'nonbeing without a proper world' (Diprose 2017, p. 54). This contrasts Lévinas' interpretation of the stranger and the orphan to whom a response is commanded. The experience of vulnerability situates both people similarly, but the phenomenological understanding of relationship to that particular body is different. This is why I would suggest that, using phenomenology, we can bring the theoretical discourse of colonisation into the situation of individual, bodied consciousness.

In this way Luna Dolezal and Danielle Petherbridge suggest that phenomenology can offer 'interrogating modes of embodied interaction' (2017, p. 2). Embodied interaction means that we cannot just fixate on mending our own individual narrative. Embodied narratives place us alongside other people and require that we give an account for the vulnerability of being human – as Lévinas puts it, the vulnerability of knowing hunger and pain. Dolezal and Petherbridge ask: 'what ethical obligations, if any, does the fact of our embodied relationality imply for us?' (2017, pp. 1–2). We can start to see more clearly how our perceptions of the world are embodied perceptions. Rather than being abstractly defined concepts, the trauma of colonisation can be explored as my relation to the other, situated in a world that connects consciousness and materiality, one that is 'materially situated'.

Situating rationality materially brings its own problems of accounting for difference and sameness (Davis 2018). These are two of the central problems that I think we can find when we phenomenologically analyse colonisation. This can, for instance, be experienced when assessing the trauma of racism. As evidenced in America, racism can be interpreted as a problem of othering. The other is interpreted in a way that excludes her from the world of the coloniser. But this relationship is precarious, because the 'colonised' and the 'coloniser' are incomplete phenomenological experiences that result from unsound phenomenological interpretations of subjectivity, if we are to take the phenomenology that Lévinas, Merleau-Ponty and Ricœur offer. Theologian Kelly Brown Douglas notes that the historic interpretation of lived human experience that slaveholders and colonisers embodied clashed with the black slave's experience of her subjectivity.

This tenuous relationship between slave and slave owner did not account for what the black faith tradition experienced as a human experience defined according to a relationship to the divine. Brown Douglas reveals these contrasting experiences: 'To listen to a faith that was born during the ordeal of slavery is to hear a people's testimony that God is not one with those who consider them chattel' (2015, p. 149). The slave owner's experience is developed in contrast to the slave, whose subjectivity is defined by a relation to the infinite other. This divine relation is an aspect of black faith tradition's core experience: '...there is a profound difference between God and those who would make chattel of black folk. God was not with the slaveholders' (ibid.). Contrasting the slave owner's relation to the slave as an object of possession, for instance, the black person's human experience is rooted in the freedom found through a relation to the divine. This relation to God is set against the destruction of the black body, confirming a 'belief in God who fosters life, even in the midst of death' (ibid.). It is freedom found in an infinite relation, to echo aspects of Lévinasian revelation. This divine relation becomes the primary relation of bodied consciousness that stands in opposition to the experience of being a 'nonbeing without a proper world' (ibid.).

But as Lévinas has shown us in previous chapters, the phenomenological relation of responsibility is invoked because of humanity's vulnerability. There is suffering in the experience of powerlessness and slavery, even when the human experience remains open to the divine relationship. The history of the First Nations people in Canada also shows the trauma that has been inflicted on a group of people based on misinterpreted phenomenologies of being. The historical trauma that included assimilating communities into residential schools, separating children from families often created legacies of discrimination, substance dependence, displacement from land, language and cultural practices. Reflecting on this traumatised relationship to the world experienced by whole communities of First Nations people, Gros Ventre spiritual leader Marvin responds to the claims that First Nations people can display 'chemical dependency' that is a bodied result of post-traumatic stress. He agrees with this observation but is concerned about the implications of only addressing the symptoms. 'Are there programs for treating Native Americans for [PTSD]? They just started. Because somebody said all Native Americans are [suffering from] post-traumatic stress. I agree' (ct. in Gone 2013, p. 684).

In the example above, the First Nations experience intergenerational trauma through the rupture in relations to land, language and each other. Systemic abuse, along with poverty and separation from family, over generations, provides a complex phenomenon that can be experienced as traumatic in numerous ways. Dolezal and Petherbridge show us that for us to interrogate and transform the experience of trauma, we must understand its subjective experience. We must seek to understand '…what it is to perceive or be perceived in terms of race, gender, sexuality' (2017, p. 1), that is, the everyday experiences of what it is to *live* as a person traumatised through colonisation. While this touches ethics, and policy reformation, this has to dialogue with the bodied experience. It is concerned with the 'intersubjective relations' that reveal what the 'cost of the absence of this relationality in conditions of isolation or imprisonment' (p. 2), separation and anxiety are experienced because of our interconnected experiences of human relationships.

Understanding the intergenerational trauma of colonisation has ethical and legal consequences to specific communities. This means understand how the 'embodied interaction' (2017, p. 2) is traumatised in these experiences. Dolezal and Petherbridge suggest that we really cannot do our ethical work without understanding the phenomenology of social encounter. I would suggest that in order to understanding this phenomenology of social encounter that is problematised in the trauma of colonisation, we need to see how the First Nations narrative reads as a bodied experience. Merleau-Ponty shows how the body relates to other bodies and experiences the world through receptiveness (Diprose 2017, p. 25).

The trauma that First Nations populations have experienced can emerge out of a range of relational experiences. Part of understanding an experience means *re-perceiving* how the experience interacts with a person's whole relational context.

Dolezal and Petherbridge suggest that this phenomenological approach can help to account for how 'embodied habits and forms of perception' can become a part of specific social contexts, whilst also showing how different habits and practices can be actively 'taken up and reiterated' into the lived body (2017, p. 2). Understanding the interaction between our relationship to ourselves and our communities means not only exploring the obvious, that we exist alongside others, but what that means. This 'fabric of lived experience' intertwines our bodies with ourselves, but also with others. As the First nations example above highlights, it also connects the bodied experience to wider experiences of relation to land, native language and ritual. These particular elements are important here because we want to understand how a person's experience of trauma might connect to these things that are 'outside' of the self, but somehow connected to the self.

We have explored how the body is implicated in trauma earlier in the chapter. This exploration is important with respect to the insights of how a body might experience trauma, through physical abuse and isolation, which are often experienced in this complex historical trauma. However, re-perceiving the trauma of colonisation requires bringing in other threads, because the ruptured relations are not just experienced as psychic or physical wounds. The trauma incorporates separation from places of origin and separation from experiences of language and ritual. In this way, some of the homelessness discourse, as well as the experience of unspeakability might help us to understand this form of trauma. But it does not consider the relationship to land which the black slave's experience as well as the First Nations experience require. Of course, both are completely different in so many subtle ways, as we have already seen. What I want to suggest is not that the trauma is the same, but rather that understanding what it means to live trauma that is a result of colonisation means needing to give an account for a peoples' relationship to their land. My suggestion is that both the rupture of language and the rupture of land-based practice can be explored through Merleau-Ponty and Ricœur's interpretation of bodied consciousness.

Kearney helps us to interpret how Ricœur can weave together language and embodied consciousness. He suggests that the interaction between the body and its interpretation of the world, 'carnal hermeneutics', is an idea that dates back to Aristotle. In *De Anima*, Aristotle shows that the 'flesh (*sarx*) is not an organ but a medium (*metaxu*)' (2015, p. 41). This means that touch is 'the most philosophical sense' because it is an experience of interpretation. As we experience the world through touch, we are making 'sensible differences' between textures and temperatures, thereby 'experiencing the world in terms of values and qualities, projects and possibilities' (p. 41). This bilateral process of touching and being touched constitutes the philosophical experience of the world; the interconnected way of being in the world is an ambiguous and 'co-implicated' experience (p. 42). Merleau-Ponty's phenomenology of the body does something similar. It requires both 'a *receptiveness* to circulating meanings embodied in others' as well as 'an *outward-orientation*', which reveals how our own 'history is not so much imposed upon the world but influences how one responds to and impacts on others'

(Diprose 2017, p. 25). This intertwined experience, active and passive, reveals the body as sensed and sentient; between my body and the world, 'there is reciprocal insertion and intertwining of one in the other' (Merleau-Ponty 1969, pp. 137–138, ct. in Diprose 2017, p. 25). These experiences are connected in the body's perception of the world.

The traumatic experience of colonisation is experienced in the repercussions of force a people away from their place of origin. This requires accounting for the connection between bodied consciousness and land. Merleau-Ponty's two-fold experience connects how we understand our experience as connected to our belonging in the world. This does not just come from having 'shared values' or 'social meanings'. If we only try to patchwork the traumatic phenomenon by re-interpreting experiences through the 'good old days' of ritualistic practice and symbols of meaning, we may miss on the whole interconnected experience of the body. Shared value and meaning are important, but they are not the full experience of belonging. As Ricœur writes, once a narrative is ruptured, there is no way of returning back to the initial naiveté. But there is the possibility of a second innocence. And in Merleau-Ponty, is re-perception that situates me and makes sense of my experience of the world (Diprose 2017).

This means that belonging is embodied. We can diverge from the experience of 'inherited meaning' and expressions of value because the ambiguity of the body allows for a 'dwelling', or a belonging, that 'is open to an open future…' (Diprose 2017, p. 27). I think this is important because it means that we need to interrogate overly simplistic notions of colonial traumatisms. Traumatic experience is ambiguous; it cannot be just a matter of re-inserting token acts of ritual, or new spaces for gathering. In *Institution and Passivity*, Merleau-Ponty writes that the 'vortex of experience lived by a human body always involves "institution"' (2010, pp. 6–8), through endowing an experience of an event 'with durable dimensions, in relation to which a whole series of other experiences will make sense, will form a thinkable sequel or a history' (2010, pp. 6–8). Diprose suggests that what this means is that a body that institutes itself requires receptivity to 'outside' events and experiences and opens up an experience of the future that is 'a singular or unique divergence from the past' (2017, p. 27). The traumatism of colonisation is not that it opened the person to an outside experience, but rather that it damaged and disabled the self from a 'future-oriented open divergence of intercorporeal dwelling' (Merleau-Ponty 2010, p. 8).

Merleau-Ponty's 'future-oriented open divergence' is significant for two reasons: First, it problematises reductive accounts of colonisation that suggest any new relationship outside of the first relational context will create a traumatic experience. It challenges simplistic notions of returning to ritualistic practice and giving back token land as a way of healing the trauma. Second, it reveals how colonisation, as an experience of 'political violence' (Merleau-Ponty 2010, p. 8), is traumatic. In disabling the person from experiencing and initiating 'something new', through receptivity to the significance of these outside elements, and incorporating them into the history of interaction, it breaks of the dynamism and the uniqueness of the individual's experience, which constitutes Merleau-Ponty's definition of belonging.

A Hermeneutic of Colonisation in Ricœur

In his writings about belonging and dynamism, Merleau-Ponty is developing his early theory of perception as being touched and touching the world. Kearney suggests that Ricœur wants to take this experience of perception further by re-connecting the bodied sensation to thought. For Ricœur, 'to feel is still to think' (*sentir est encore penser*) (Ricœur 1966, p. 86). The body is already thinking. This means that concepts such as values, and ethics require mediation through the body itself. But this is a hermeneutic movement; the body thinks, 'affectivity and thought' are already connected (Kearney 2015, p. 48). Both inward and outward relations to the world are actually making sense of, or 'reading', the same body.

In trauma, we often see the question of whether it is the mind or the body interpreting the situation (see, for instance, Part I of this book). But as phenomenology teaches us, both experiences are reading the same flesh. The same person is being expressed through each plane. Because they are not separate but speaking together about one experience, they need to be interpreted together. This is the hermeneutic of subjectivity and otherness. The stranger also says 'I', but this 'I' is not me. In *Oneself as Another*, Ricœur shows that transferring sense 'shows how "she thinks" signifies "she says in her heart: I think"', while simultaneously also showing the inverse, namely that 'she thinks and feels in a way that I can never think or feel' (1994, p. 355). In order to respond to the other, I need to 'read' my transcendent thoughts through my immanent body. That means that 'reading' another person's experience also requires hermeneutics. It means interpreting the differences and the distance between myself and the other.

Interpreting experiences of trauma caused by colonisation requires hermeneutically understanding of the traumatised self and a traumatised community. For Ricœur, interpretation is not just rational. We cannot read the trauma merely as history, or as analysed narrative, or as abstraction from ritual. It means coming to terms with all of the layers of experience that form the self and the other exchange and interpreting these nuances. Trauma reading in this regard requires what Kearney sees in Ricœur, which is a 'carnal hermeneutics across distance, gaps, and differences' (2015, p. 53). It is not just a hermeneutic of writing, texts and words, that is, 'intellectual understanding', but rather 'also of tangible orientation' (ibid.). This will require us to see the rupture between the self and the other, through the bodied response, through the isolation of self from family, as well as through the distancing from text, and embodied ritualistic practices. Reducing it to one element, or seeing it too abstractly, will not allow us to fully perceive the trace of trauma in the person's life.

Healing in Otherness

Kearney calls Merleau-Ponty and Ricœur's phenomenology a 'carnal hermeneutic' which helps them to understand the ambiguous experience of the self in the world.

The experience of the subject connects to our perception of the world, and how the world affects us. Ricœur suggests that this is not only an experience of the body, but also, simultaneously, one of thought. Our subjectivity, we find once again, is not isolated. It exists with others. We become ourselves in this interaction with the other, though we are a separate self. It is this ability to be open and affected by the world that actually enables our experience of belongingness.

Bosi reminds us in the beginning of this chapter that trauma implicates our 'corporeality'. I have suggested that colonialism can be experienced as traumatic when it shuts us off to the openness of a future by reproducing a relational experience that is '…always the same, body and features' (Bosi 1995, p. 54). As colonisation informs corporeality, delineating the experience of a body in the world, it problematises Ricœur's experience of otherness, as well as Merleau-Ponty's phenomenology of perceptibility. Kaplan suggests that experiencing subjectivity as the 'same', and the understanding of subjectivity as a 'self-founding' and 'enduring essence' (2003, p. 154) underlies the problem found in totalising readings of experience.

The philosophical turn that I have suggested is exemplified in Ricœur and Merleau-Ponty challenges 'the metaphysics of a self-founding subject as an enduring essence that underlies modern social ontologies' (ibid.). Kaplan notes that there is a problem with the 'self-founding subjectivity' because it can create a model that understands collective subjectivity 'as the subject of political action that denies difference, particularity, and heterogeneity among its members' (2003, p. 154). The definition of belonging as sameness, rather than belonging as bodied opening to the future, affected by the other, is explored through the concept of 'carnal hermeneutics'. It connects reductive readings of trauma to other reductive readings of being and suggests that both trauma and lived experience requires a hermeneutic of embodiment.

Until now, we have located it quite abstractly. Merleau-Ponty's reading of the body reveals it as 'a mutual interweaving between perceiving and perceived' (Kearney 2015, p. 42). The body that is touched, the 'flesh', links the touching to the one being touched. The flesh, Kearney suggests, holds both perception and language ('the word'), which unifies 'the becoming-body of my senses and the becoming-world of my body' (p. 43), the very experience of belonging that is threatened in violence. What is interesting here is that the traumatised subject is read, not in terms of a rational construction of the world, but as the bodied consciousness, whose language is re-perceived through the body experience itself.

Existential phenomenology means that it is not just the situation of the flesh that is important in mediating experience, but also the world outside of the body. In Plotkin Amrami et al.'s account of the Israel-Palestine conflict, they are able to note the similar experiences in the conflicting and traumatised communities. Referencing the Al-Aqsa Intifada, they write sociologically about the bodied experiences of both communities:

> Israelis had to cope with Palestinian suicide bombings in cafes and shopping malls, Palestinian shootings of Israeli civilians traveling on highways, and

> missiles raining down on Israeli cities. Palestinians, for their part, were living under siege, facing house demolitions, lethal brutality, and targeted killings by Israeli soldiers.
>
> *2016, p. 1*

While the experiences of subjectivity in place were marked with multiple distinct contrasts, Plotkin Amrami et al. note that a 'ubiquitous violence' ran through the total phenomenon experienced by both populations, which was marked by the bodied affect – 'widespread fear and suffering' (p. 1). The phenomenological perception of experience, we see that the experience goes beyond a purely rational rendering of traumatisation.

For Merleau-Ponty, 'the body signifies meaning because it is meaning', and for each person it is a particular kind of lived meaning (Kearney 2015, p. 44). This interweaving of sensibility, however, also reveals a 'chiasm' between myself and the world that I perceive (p. 42). Flesh links us to these reversible perceptions of the world and, therefore, also enables us to coexist with others. This is how Merleau-Ponty can define healing as 'a reopening of self to others through the body, a turning from *thanatos* (the death drive of closure) to *eros* (the life drive of communion)' (p. 45). This contrasts with Freudian theory, but it also contrasts with accounts of trauma that leave us with a perpetual cycle of victimhood. Knowledge (*connaisance*) of the other, Kearney suggests, becomes connected to this, as 'it is a *co-naissance* (co-birth) with the other' (ibid.). Healing then juxtaposes itself on the closure of traumatism that is referenced in the previous section. The flesh and the existence of the person are interconnected, as a 'woven fabric' of 'intercommunication' (Merleau-Ponty 1962, p. 166). So, we actually experience ourselves as being in the world through this mutual act of perception.

A Politics of Responsibility

Interestingly, Ricœur wants to connect this bodied relation between the self and the world into conversation with other 'readings'. The reading of the body is juxtaposed on textual reading. In this way, very originally, Ricœur derives his definition of law 'in relation to conscience' (Kaplan 2003, p. 144). Ricœur found the contrast between the law 'as universal, constraining, and objective' with the 'conscience as circumstantial, variable, and subjective' to be problematic, and instead suggests that in wise judgment they always work together (ibid.).

If this is true, then it is significant not only as it ties the healing process exemplified in Merleau-Ponty and Ricœur, as a bodied opening towards the future, but also in revealing how this way of 'reading' existence might have implications for how we interpret the law in relation to our subjectivity. More will be developed in relation to this in Chapter 10, but here it is worth noting that the trauma discourse, as exemplified in the complex interrelation of trauma through colonisation, reveals implications not only of a rupture of body, but also a re-perception through interpretation of body, thought and text. I have briefly extended Merleau-Ponty and Ricœur's carnal hermeneutics to also account for our relation to land that the First Nations example demands. It is in moving from abstract subjectivity and essentialism that we can dive into the body-subject that opposes dualistic philosophies of being and advocates for a healing that takes place through the connection of body and language, intentionality and communication (Robert Sweeney 1996, p. 97).

Conclusion

In eco-philosopher Joanna Macy's writings, she claims that our lives are a journey. In moving through our individual journeys, she points the reader to 'Remember again the old cycles of partnership', and to draw on these partnerships between the people around us and the earth that we inhabit. She writes that 'we are never separated from the living body of the Earth, nor will we ever be' (2010, p. 112). This experience of relational permanence can be extended to our bodies and to the people around us. Regardless of what happens to us, we will always be our bodies, we will always have other people.

But trauma has forced us into an experience of rupture, loneliness and loss that seems to deconstruct these very experiences of relationship that Lévinas, Ricœur and Merleau-Ponty point towards as being human. Simone Weil commented that 'To be rooted is perhaps the single most important and least recognized need of the human soul' (1952, p. 41). She goes on to suggest that it is uprooted people who go on to uproot others. Previously, Gros Ventre spiritual leader Marvin writes of the historical traumas that have ruptured his peoples' experience of health and whole connection: '…somebody said all Native Americans[3] are [suffering from] post-traumatic stress. I agree' (ct. in Gone 2013, p. 684).

But he does not leave it there, because he wants to re-assert the primacy of connection, and the possibility of health as a way of being in the world, despite trauma. For Marvin, the services used to mitigate the effects of PTSD are mostly still 'Western cultural programs'. For him, they are slowly starting to 'develop our [traditional] ways and means, [those] used in our cultural/ spiritual ways. We're just starting. And they're working' (ibid.). Like so many others that have experienced trauma, Marvin is looking for ways to transform the relational rupture that he and his community have experienced.

In a similar manner, reflecting on the Israel-Palestine conflict, Plotkin Amrami et al. suggest that concepts of 'intervention' need us to nuance what we mean by human experience, so that we avoid dualistic accounts of healing that reduce transformation to self-improvement 'and implies that intervention *imitates* the natural action of the psyche' (2016, p. 5). This is not just a matter of restoring these relationships to what they were – trauma has changed the experience. But it can mean transforming the relationship to the body, to the other person and to the experience of place in a phenomenological experience of healing.

Notes

1 For more on this, see Rousseau's *Emile* and Locke's *Some Thoughts Concerning Education*, two text that are considered to be pillars for interpreting and structuring earlier enlightenment forms of children's education (Ben-Arieh and Tarshish 2017, p. 69).
2 I am aware of the reductive definition associated with reading colonisation in this way but will nevertheless employ it for the purposes of clarifying this particular embodied experience.
3 Where the individual is referencing their own people group, I employ the term that they use.

PART IV

Living Trauma as Health

10

INDIVIDUAL HEALING

The Subject and Her Relationships

The previous parts of this book have explored how trauma is experienced subjectively. That means that we really need to understand the unique experiences of the person, how our various life events are interpreted hermeneutically alongside our other experiences of meaning-making and value within our unique contexts of relationship. This has involved looking through historic readings of trauma, assessing how science has advanced the development of diagnostic criterion and evaluating how philosophy can help us understand how each person might live trauma uniquely. We also see that trauma is inherently relational. For instance, Stauffer reminds us of the importance of witnessing and a proper hearing of a person's trauma, suggesting that the presence of the other, in this particular way, is crucial for the human experience to be lived well. And if, as attachment theorists say, trauma is occasioned from early insecure attachment, relationship, and concrete, particular forms of relationship, seems to be important for human experience. But then, each person also experiences an event differently. Resiliency theory and the different manifestations of symptoms suggest that each person sharing the common experience of trauma will *live* their trauma differently.

Defining Harms

Trauma originates in the Greek word for wound. Early readings, Brunner suggests, draw on a literal interpretation of this, stating that trauma involves some kind of injury of the mind that is caused by an exceptionally frightening experience. But this reading does not account for the moral aspects that often go hand in hand with experiencing trauma. Brunner writes that the problem with reducing trauma to a mental disorder is that traumatised people are often not only just considered ill but also seen as victims of a moral wrong. The harm that has been done to them is not from a pathogen, but rather 'the intentional act of another human being', as,

DOI: 10.4324/9780367800017-14

for instance, seen in rape, torture and sexual assault (2007, p. 97). When symptoms are read as a mental disorder, they also need to play an ethical or, in some cases, a legal function. The diagnosis needs to account for how trauma creates a collapse of autonomy, or of 'conscious self-control', and understand the wider experience of social belonging and relationship.

Brunner writes that trauma involves 'a rupture' and makes us question basic experiences that we have taken for granted about 'bodily boundaries, interpersonal relations and the structure of social reality in general' (2007, pp. 98–99). This means that in order to understand trauma, we also need to understand how the trauma impacts the other relational aspects of living in the world. For Brunner, the psychiatric discourse needs to converse with these other experiences of rupture and the 'intrusive forces that have the power to violate the boundaries of the self and shatter core conceptions about one's place in the world' (2007, p. 99). This book uses the phenomenological method to do this work because it places the emphasis on the lived and individual experience of the person (Walsh et al. 2020, p. 210). This means that we need to look at relationships between the self and other humans, between our experience of ethical responsibility and the context of our lived world (land). Having done this to some extent in the previous chapters, the task now turns towards figuring out how rupture is addressed by experiences of healing. The final task will be ascertaining how this influences our understanding of health.

Part of the challenge of understanding healing is that the definition is hard to pin down. Often different cultures have different descriptions of what health means. One can have physical health and spiritual health, economic health and soil health. Sages through the ages have often pointed out that one area of health does not necessarily mean that the whole organism is healthy. Another problem with defining health is that official definitions of health are often contested. For instance, the World Health Organisation (WHO) developed the often-cited benchmark definition for health in 1948, as 'a state of complete physical, mental and social well-being and note merely the absence of disease of infirmity' (2005). However, more recently, in light of research on chronic disease, the definition of health as a 'state of complete well-being' has become more problematic. Machteld Huber et al. suggest that health definitions need to avoid medicalising society, through accounting for a more expansive understanding of a healthy human experience. The current WHO definition, they argue, leaves most people lacking in health. This suggests that the norm is actually being unwell. This means that the definition of health emphasises the 'ability to adapt and self-manage in the face of social, physical and emotional challenges' (Huber et al. 2011, p. 343). This definition includes adaptability, or what I will refer to as transformation, as a main component of health, as opposed to it only being about the non-presence of disease.

This adaptive definition is taken up and read phenomenologically by Ola Sigurdson. He suggests that actively experiencing and incorporating the 'passivity' of suffering can enable us to transform the cause of suffering, or pain, into something meaningful for us, which he coins 'existential health' (2019, p. 87). This is a hermeneutic task that requires understanding how suffering connects to the wider story of our lives, and the relationship between language and our wider interpretation of meaning (ibid.). This is important for us because of how we have read trauma. Previously, we have explored how phenomenology requires us to connect varying experiences of the world to develop a whole experience of subjectivity, and how someone lives trauma. As we see from Brunner's work, trauma is inherently multifaceted, to place it in Merleau-Ponty's terms. It also needs to be hermeneutically interpreted, as Ricœur helps us to see. It requires making sense of the rupture and loss as it is experienced by us, uniquely, so it would make sense that health, and healing, would require a similar hermeneutic. But what the contested definition of health also reveals to us is how we might need to keep our definition of health a bit ambiguous as well.

The Experience of a Ruptured Subject

van der Kolk reminds us that 'The essence of trauma is that it is overwhelming, unbelievable and unbearable' (2014, p. 195). This means that every experience of trauma means that we need to 'suspend' what we usually determine as normal, by realising that there is a dual reality at play: 'the reality of a relatively secure and predictable present that lives side by side with a ruinous, ever-present past' (ibid.). Levine writes that trauma is incorporated as part of our wider human experience, encompassing our complex responses to rage and fear (2010, p. xiii; p. 61).

Trauma requires confronting the ambiguity of health. For some, health may be the complete absence of traumatic symptoms. For others, health could mean a transformation of a particular experience of dying, a healing of a specific rupture or a restoration of a certain loss. I want to show how phenomenology can hold both interpretations of health. It allows us to understand health through a phenomenology of transformation, where transformation does not reassert the naiveté of past reality, as if nothing had happened. Health engages the multiple planes of experience by 're-plotting' conscious and embodied experience and the relationships to the world, as the person orients towards the future.

This leaves us with a second challenge in healing trauma. McDonald shows that since Breuer and Freud, trauma treatment has taught that healing the 'traumatic event' means that it must be spoken: 'Speak what feels unspeakable, and the event loses its power' (2019, Loc. 1984). The challenge is not only that this could be re-triggering, but it also presumes that the therapeutic interpretation of a broken narrative can represent the trauma. McDonald suggests that everything does not need to be told, and Levine and van der Kolk require the body to speak in its own way, often beyond words. This means that the 'gold standard' that is used for combat therapy is premised on a 150-year-old hypothesis (2019, Loc. 1992).

She asks why there are still such high statistics of veteran suicide if these previous techniques could successfully treat trauma. For her, the theories that we are using require revision. Forcing 'what feels unspeakable into speech' does not necessarily equate to healing the trauma and may, for some, reassert the overwhelming dislocation of the trauma (2019, Loc. 1992). This means that in our second reading of health, we have to consider the complex experience of how traumatic experience challenges and shatters the self, what occupying different perspectives on the same event actually might mean and how the other plays a critical role in trauma narrative.

The previous sections have explored how trauma is experienced subjectively. That means that we really need to understand the unique experiences of the person; how our various life events are interpreted hermeneutically alongside our other experiences of meaning-making and value within our unique contexts of relationship. This experience of trauma, as our own, also then translates into how we experience healing and health. This chapter explores the subjective experience of trauma in order to bridge how someone might heal from this experience. This will involve returning to the role of communication, of what is considered 'unsayable' and 'sayable', and how we experience language. We will examine body boundaries and unpack what being labelled a 'survivor' means. The book will finish by looking at the ambiguous interconnection between victim and perpetrator, as an example of how the language of law and ethics features in the process of healing.

Healing Oneself: The Possibility and Limits of Health

Phenomenology interprets the experiences of life through its relational context. In the cases of suffering that carry symptoms and diagnostic tools for measurements,[1] this means that it is important to keep relating this diagnosis to the wider meaning of a person's life. Phenomenology helps us to see the 'meaning of symptoms as belonging to persons', which avoids the problems of reductiveness that can result from 'treating symptoms as merely signs of underlying brain-dysfunctions' (Sveneaus 2018, p. 4). Diagnosing trauma can be very important, because it enables the person to see the treatment available for them, as well as how others have experienced similar suffering, and how society might be able to provide some help, in terms of services and benefits. There is a very practical side to the help that can be afforded here. But Sveneaus reminds us that this is only a part of the experience. Understanding ourselves through symptomatology, however detailed, only provides part of the picture of our experience. I would argue that this same depth and broadening of analysis is required for understanding how a person can heal from trauma. If suffering, as Sveneaus points out, '*disturbs* the meaning processes of being-in-the-world in which one is leading one's life and understanding one's personal identity' (p. 5), then healing will have to involve understanding how trauma impacts these core experiences of who we are, and how (or whether) they can be mended.

A multifaceted approach to trauma is required in order to understand how events truly affect us. John Roberts writes that trauma presents us with a kind of 'psychological and cultural architecture' that tries to make sense of how particular events can 'dislocate' our experience of who we are (2018, p. 2). Bringing us back into the early theories of trauma in Charcot (1889), Freud (1920/1961) and McDonald (2019), and following into contemporary discourses such as van der

Kolk's theory of bodied memory (2014), he reveals that this particular suffering, known as trauma, marks itself on 'not only the way we think and speak, but also how we are affected and constituted' (2018, p. 2). The early psychoanalytic theories of trauma located healing in the broken conscious and unconscious narrative. For instance, Freud and Breuer's documented discoveries in *Studies on Hysteria* showed that traumatic symptoms decreased in patients who were able to give words to (verbalise) their previous trauma. They suggested that verbalising the memories could actually abate the body's symptoms of trauma, and that the symptoms could also provide clues to unconscious details about the trauma that the mind did not remember (McDonald 2019).

To heal the patient further, Freud and Breuer realised that they needed to uncover these unconscious hidden and repressed parts of the traumatised self. This meant using more unconventional methods, such as hypnotism. What was discovered in verbalising the unconscious in this way was that the events that had previously been overwhelming were finally able to be uncovered and spoken and, in that, connected to the physical symptoms that would then be able to disappear (2019). This cathartic release of memory is language-based. It gives a voice to the overwhelming emotions that are experienced as a living past, perhaps as the result of a triggering sound or smell.

In this analytical reading, language becomes the mode of healing, as well as serving 'as a substitution for action' (Breuer and Freud 1895/2016, p. 43). But McDonald suggests that language can only act cathartically if it really does express the trauma, that is, if it is an 'adequate reaction', which is not always the case. It suggests that language can account for a bodied experience in a complete way. McDonald suggests that trauma can remain despite being verbalised. This is what Levine refers to in his theory of somatic psychology. The body itself is responding to the trauma. The lack of completeness, the ruptured memory that leaves a person feeling immobile rather than powerful, out of control rather than in control of what is happening to them, requires completing the interrupted experience, which Levine cites as the source of trauma. McDonald writes that the patients who did not experience the catharsis of language were found challenging to treat because parts of their traumatic past kept unconsciously re-enacting themselves (McDonald 2019, Loc. 2053).

Kardiner, however, doubts the healing properties of the cathartic moment. For Kardiner it just does not happen like this all the time. He suggests that the traumatised person should slowly be brought to an understanding about how she has developed 'maladaptive tendencies' as a result of the suffering that she has experienced. Then, 'every effort should be bent to re-educating the patient to the *actual realities* in which he lives rather than to the dangerous and inhospitable world in which he fancies himself' (Kardiner 2012, p. 227). This shows how trauma can touch and transform many different parts of our experiences.

Freud shows us how we can reconfigure trauma through identifying language to represent what the trauma is. But this cathartic healing of the ruptured narrative is not the only way that theorists have suggested that we can heal from trauma.

Roberts suggests that Lacan can helps us with understanding just how deep and wide this 'marking' of our story can be. For Lacan, trauma changes us because it actually takes something from us, in a way that alienates us from our own experience. But trauma also presents us with something else, 'an Other, being in return' for what trauma has taken (2018, p. 3). I find this account particularly helpful, because it shows how a person not only experiences dislocation, rupture or 'tearing' in the experience of what is normal. She actually loses something. Trauma is an experience of an exchange: something is taken and something else is received in its place. In that case, healing requires a transformed relationship to the world and to oneself.

When I read Yehuda Amichai's poem 'Savage Memories', I think that I can start to see what Lacan means. Amichai writes:

> I think of the bullets that did no kill me, / but killed my friends / ... We must now balance everything/ with heavy dreams, and set / savage memories / upon what was once today.
>
> *2018, p. 38*

For Amichai, the trauma of war involves loss (the loss of a friend's life). It also involves receiving something in exchange, as the self tries to make sense of this loss. Amichai's narrator receives 'savage memories' and 'heavy dreams', as the experiences that constitute the traumatised self. Roberts suggests that trauma's exchange is not just felt individually. He writes that: 'Modern subjectivity, as erased or altered in the void of trauma, mirrors historical and cultural trauma, where shared realities are both simultaneously eclipsed and born' (p. 3). In this Lacanian reading by Roberts, who we become, both as individuals and as societies, is how we make sense of what has been taken from us. Healing, in this reading, involves not only mending a narrative but also mourning the loss of something real, and making sense of the 'stuff' of experience that has been born (or received) as a result of trauma.

In his exploration of trauma, Jung helps us to see how a reductive understanding of consciousness can result in a very narrow understanding of healing. Jung suggests that we have often reduced our psyche to the experience of consciousness and unconsciousness. Freudian thought aims to bring the unconscious drivers to light, in order to reduce their effect on the present. The unconscious is just suppressed bits of conscious memory. But for Jung, the unconscious is its own experience with its own reality. It is not just a by-product of consciousness (Jung 1967). For instance, in trauma, a person might experience dissociation when she smells a particular odour. Now dissociation, for Jung, is a result of an 'unbearable affect'. But it is this affect, this experience of being affected and affecting the world around us, that makes us who we are: 'The essential basis of our personality is affectivity' (1960, par. 78). Thus, affectivity is intrinsic to our subjectivity (Lévinas reminds us of this, in a slightly different way).

Interpreting Jung, Kalshed shows how a mild dissociative affect reveals a coherent self. This self, or ego, still remains as a 'functional unity of the complex- "gluing together" of all elements of experience (sensation, feeling, idea, memories, images etc.)' (1999, p. 467). But in extreme and unsystemic experiences of overwhelming affect, Jung suggests that it can destroy the 'architecture' of the self. It is in these experiences that people can, for instance, refer to being possessed by demons and spirits. The work to make oneself into a whole person feels 'superordinate'. This is where Kalshed suggests that Jung brings in the archetypal healing experience, or a kind of 'self-care'[2] system for survival. Traumatic experiences are played out fantastically, in a way whereby the 'fantasy can be just as traumatic as actual traumatic events' (Jung 1912, par. 217). The fantastical 'fills in' the real, trying to create some kind of cohesion. As a result, trauma actually develops a whole new experience, is transformed or, as Lacan suggests, gives us something in return for what has been taken from us.

What has been 'given to us' in this traumatic exchange is a self that is trying to piece herself together and move forward as the bodied consciousness continues to be haunted by the past. As such, these instances show a kind of first-order attempt at 'healing'. The fantastical, the dream world or the symptoms, are all an attempt to bring our attention to our woundedness and make sense of the pieces. But this is not an experience that we want to stay in. What is received in this experience is a new phenomenon, but it is still in the ghostly shape of the things that have died, of the wounds that we are left with. Is this the only healing that trauma can allow? Sigurdson suggests that this reconstitution of the world, in the midst of undergoing suffering, is itself a kind of health. Insofar as suffering is a part of the experience of being vulnerable, which he defines as part of being human (echoing Lévinas), then '[i]t is through suffering as an active passivity that we can transform the experience of pain (or any cause of suffering) to a constructive relationship that could be called *existential health*' (2019, p. 87). This is taking Kalshed's Jungian self-care system one step further. Just as suffering constitutes a part of our subjectivity, how we engage with suffering (rather than how we avoid it altogether) can be the source of our healing and even our health.

So far, we have looked at how trauma breaks apart and steals from the self, leaving the self to reconstruct itself and make sense of the experiences received in lieu of its theft. We have tried to make sense of how trauma can be healed from this experience of self-rupture, of picking up the pieces and completing the incomplete actions of escape, retaliation and movement. But now, we have ventured into a slightly different conversation. This is a conversation about how we might read trauma as a phenomenologically transformative experience.

Kalshed's notion of self-care suggests that trauma responses develop as a way of piecing together the ego personality that has been shattered by experiences beyond its ability to adapt. But these behaviours resulting from this primordial 'self-care' system can further disable the person's agency. Flashbacks, dissociation and nightmares occasioned by some kind of trigger results in a delicately balanced and unpredictable agency. Sigurdson wants to go one step further, suggesting that suffering involves 'a passivity' that 'does not cancel our agency' (2019, p. 89). Like Lévinas, he suggests that suffering is contained in the experience of being a human – of being vulnerable, which means that agency itself must have some kind of capacity for transforming this, without being annihilated. For him, pain can cancel agency through its severity, or through its causing death or loss of consciousness. However, the experience of suffering cannot cancel agency, because it 'belongs to the agency of the person' (p. 89). For Sigurdson, being human means being the kind of agent that is able to suffer. This invokes memories of Lévinasian passivity that is experienced by the suffering other. But here, Sigurdson places the transformation as an internal rather than an external act, enabled by another person.

Sigurdson uses the theological example of Jesus to show how suffering might serve as an experience that is passively undergone without cancelling his agency. In the Gospels, Jesus is shown to endure and suffer extreme forms of trauma through torture, betrayal and social humiliation that ends with a public crucifixion (p. 88). Sigurdson suggests that this example engages the historic social imagination to show how a person undergoes suffering, while still being actively 'involved in human existence' (ibid.). Referencing the example of Christian martyrs in the Book of Acts, he shows how the broken body is not seen as defeat, but rather read through the symbol of victory. This reading redefines subjectivity, not as a suffering that is done to the self from the outside, but rather as lived out, via an inward meaning (p. 91).

Sigurdson surmises that the martyr's self-definition is experienced through engaging with the suffering, rather than through avoiding it. As such, the martyr is actually the testifier of suffering: 'The martyr is not only someone who suffers pain, but a witness (*martureo* in Greek means "to bear witness" or "testify") and someone who testifies precisely through his or her suffering' (p. 91). This suggests that suffering can result in transformation of the pain experienced. It is not so much that the pain itself disappears, but rather that the relation between myself and my suffering 'allows me to encounter and confront it' (ibid.).

At this point, Sigurdson shows how the WHO definition of health, referenced earlier, might help us with this leap. He suggests that the 'state of complete physical, mental and social well-being' brings us to consider how this transformation might be possible. This transformative witness to my own suffering, he writes, is a kind of health that encompasses all the different parts of what being 'healthy' entails. It is not an absence from disease or pain, but 'our own intentional reflexive relation to experiences of both health and illness' (p. 96). For Sigurdson, then, we can be simultaneously both unwell and healthy (ibid.). This is an experience of health, Sigurdson suggests, that bears witness to a wholeness that we have not yet achieved, and yet live our lives confronting.

The reason that Sigurdson is adamant about keeping this agency in the midst of the passive undergoing of suffering is that vulnerability is a fundamental characteristic of human relational experience. The relational aspect of subjectivity, which Lévinas, Merleau-Ponty and Ricœur have advocated for, leaves us with a problem if vulnerability compromises our agency in the world. They do not want to keep the experience of enclosure and isolation: each advocates for an openness to the future, and to the world. The openness of the face, to put it in Lévinas' language, is that which enables us to experience 'joy, happiness and pleasure' (p. 100). As such,

Sigurdson's notion of existential health suggests that suffering does not need to compromise our agency, if we take agency to be the very basic ability to relate to the world and our experience of it.

But this theory is incomplete at the moment. It is also vulnerability that enables us to connect with, and to relate to, the other that violates us. If we are to apply it to trauma, particularly in light of Stauffer, Auerhahn and Laub's comments on rushing too quickly through trauma, then we need to account for an experience of healing that holds the possibility of health with the experienced totality of fragmentation, loss and death. I would suggest that Lévinas might help us to do this phenomenological work. In the previous chapters, we have seen how Lévinas reads trauma in two ways. There is the traumatism of subjectivity, where I actually become an ethical subject through the rupture of my ego invoked by the face of an other. But then there is also the trauma that we wish to save the other from; the messianic call to respond to the suffering of the other who is overwhelmed and shut off because of her trauma.

This is a dual understanding of trauma: trauma can be experienced as both the birthplace of subjectivity and hope and the initial experience of objectification and isolation from others. I think that this dual understanding is crucial to a philosophy of trauma because it can easily be reduced to either or. For Lévinas, both are present. In his writing, however, it is always we who are response-able. This ties us into a conversation about justice and how ethics, or at least the meta-ethical relation that Lévinas envisages, contains both a possibility of hope, or an 'otherwise' that suffering, and an invocation of justice and responsibility.

Healing Oneself through Interruption and Presence

The previous section examined initial ideas about healing. This included understanding that healing involves figuring out what we mean by health, and how a whole human experience is defined. With vulnerability and relationality at the core of who we are, it is this experience of relationship between ourselves and the outer world that becomes the site of trauma and its healing. Anna Hueneke suggests that trauma offers a unique experience of wounded relationship. Often characterised by violence, trauma is internalised and kept as a kind of symbol that represents a particular rupture for many generations. Some psychodynamic theorists even suggest that trauma, preserved in this symbolic form, can continue for generations, unless people learn how to transform and integrate it in some way. She shows how this symbolic interpretation requires associations to bring it into the rest of the narrative, through the imagination, metaphor and imagery (2012). Similarly to Sigurdson, she speaks of the transformation of suffering in a way that it can connect to the whole.

But while we may wish for this wholeness, how sure are we that it can actually happen? For instance, early Holocaust writing often suggested that the atrocities committed to the Jewish people in the Second World War transmitted trauma as a kind of 'deep psychology from one generation to the next' (Auerhahn and Laub

1998, p. 21). But to say that the Holocaust presented such permanent and long-lasting scars gave rise to criticism from writers such as Roseman and Handleman (1993) as well as the children of Holocaust survivors personally (Peskin 1981). Critics suggested that if a second generation could continue to be affected by Hitler's actions, it would mean that he had experienced a type of continual victory, and critics wanted to show that this was not the case. I disagree with this, as I believe it to be an overly simplistic view of phenomenological experience and does not give an account for the complexity of survival. But Auerhahn and Laub (1998) also write how overcorrections that emphasise post-traumatic health and reintegration can often end up trying to say too much. For them, correcting the bias held in the past where Holocaust suffering is read psychopathologically can create a new problem, namely, 'an overcorrection' that refuses to acknowledge the role of the Holocaust as a critical event shaping intergenerational existential and relational experiences (1998, p. 21).

Auerhahn and Laub suggest that this correction has also made it challenging to integrate the accounts of the Holocaust with other accounts of Post Traumatic Stress Disorder (PTSD) that would follow, with the development of the diagnostic criteria. What I think that they are alluding to here is that each experience needs to be read not only subjectively, as we have discussed earlier, but also in light of human experience more generally. It shows that traumas need to be read hermeneutically through the lens of subjectivity, but that there is also an aspect of this that requires assessing how this experience sits in the context of other similar experiences, that is, how it is read more generally. In trying to evade either, the whole experience of health can be short-changed.

Auerhahn and Laub importantly point out just how careful we have to be in speaking about transformation of trauma. They show that the division between reading trauma through its negative effects (as found, for example, in Krystal 1968), reading trauma through post-traumatic growth (for example, Harel et al. 1988), and suggest that a real reading of Holocaust trauma requires rejecting these polarised readings. The Holocaust has left heterogeneous marks on a population. This psychic trauma produces an 'individualised quality' that shapes and informs each person's future experiences, views of the world, what is chosen and what is possible (1998, p. 22). They are interested in 'what kind of traumatic knowledge' different people can acquire, suggesting that trauma may have intergenerational implications as an 'organisational principle'. This organisational principle serves as a way of approaching and seeing the world and can be passed in this way from one generation to another.

As an internalised unconscious presence, the effects of trauma can go somewhat unnoticed. It is just how that family 'does things', or the neurotic tendency of a father and his daughters. Trauma evolves (Auerhahn and Laub 2018, p. 22) as the traumatic memories are hidden and uncovered, reintegrated and passed over, in a sea of relationships. We are going to come back to the intergenerational experience of trauma later in this chapter. But what Auerhahn and Laub also show us is how traumatic memories can benefit from both subjective reading and more generalised diagnostic accounts.

One of the most popular ways of treating trauma is through interpreting a person's symptoms. But using the PTSD diagnosis alone presents challenges, if we see it as a tool of healing because it does not account for any ethical relationship. For instance, Brunner writes that the moral grammar of trauma can often present a complex set of interconnected relationships. He shows that until the development of the PTSD diagnosis, there were 'strict boundaries between victims and perpetrators' (2007, p. 104). One person inflicted the trauma, and the other was traumatised. However, when the PTSD diagnosis was developed in response to Vietnam protests, the diagnosis revealed similar symptoms lived out in the one who had suffered and the one that had inflicted the suffering. For instance, the Vietnam veterans, as perpetrators of trauma, showed evidence of bearing the symptoms of trauma in their own bodies.

For Brunner, this revelation should have enabled people to see the interconnection of relationships in traumatic experiences, but instead, each group seemed to remain faithful to their own cause. This means that even though there is no reason in principle for 'acknowledging that committing severe, violent crimes may have detrimental psychological effects on the perpetrators should eclipse the suffering of the actual victim', it seems that, in practice, there is often a competitive element between the politics of the victim and the politics of trauma (p. 105). For example, the initial studies documented Vietnam veterans but failed to document the traumatic symptoms in the Vietnamese population.

One can only speculate as to why this continues to be the case with trauma studies, for instance, why Holocaust trauma seems to separate itself from understanding the contemporary trauma of Palestinians, or why the Palestinian trauma is invoked as a cause against Israel. Perhaps we limit ourselves to such an extent that one loyalty always comes at the expense of another. But what each account seems to testify to is not only the need for multicultural sensibilities but also for the challenge of connecting the victim and the perpetrator, when both exhibit symptoms of suffering. How do we heal these individuals, when one loyalty seems to come at an expense of the other? In Merleau-Ponty's *Phenomenology of Perception*, he writes of a need to see the interconnection in experience. For him, the knowledge that we have of the world ('even my scientific knowledge') comes from our specific points of view: 'some experience of the world without which the symbols of science would be meaningless' (1962, p. viii). In this, he calls for a reawakening to the 'basic experience of the world' (ibid.), which Lévinas and Ricœur reveal is relationship towards the other person.

Living Trauma as Health

Merleau-Ponty, reflecting on the trends of modern philosophy, suggests that we often try to look for themes about life through which we can reduce and understand its complexity. These reductions of the world, however, do not reveal the real essence of existence and the interconnectedness of experience. Living trauma is also more than a generalisable experience. Like the rest of human experience, we have seen that is not shut up 'within the realm of science' (1962, p. vii), or understood abstractly. This requires an account of healing that is open to complexity: morally, scientifically, philosophically, theologically and politically. This is where we situate this transformational relation to the world.

For Stauffer, this is particularly clear. The traumatised narrative cannot be just understood as a series of facts. Instead, it is about how these experiences connected to her relationships with her life, and how that continues to be painfully present after the fact. The violence continues to be lived in the present, as embodied traumatic memory, and also reveals how a person can try to 'lead a normal life' after trauma (Gobodo-Maikizelu, ct. Stauffer 2015, p. 70). Stauffer quotes Henry, who summarises living his trauma: '"It has been hard living and not existing. I am alive but my existence continues to be ignored" (Henry)' (Stauffer 2015, p. 132). It is, therefore, important to understand the interconnection of events, the relational aspects of the self, and the notion of justice in order to have any ability to heal the continued traumatic experience.

Stauffer admits that healing trauma or, perhaps more basically, bringing 'hope to justice' requires surmounting incredible obstacles. But it is necessary (2015, p. 87). The healed person needs to confront these obstacles herself: even with an excellent therapist, she will still be required to repair herself. This healing, as an invocation of hope, can actually feel like an interruption. In Levine's titration experience, he oscillates between the bodied pain of trauma and an experience of comforting presence, gently coaxing the unfinished trapped terror out into a context of safety. But this requires that there is a felt experience of safety, and it involves a person having to exit from a reality that she has experienced as her own for a considerable time. The exit out itself requires trust.

If the narrative has been that a person has felt unseen, and unheard, then the interruption of someone who sees, and the ability to hear 'something other than what she expected', can present a considerable challenge (Stauffer 2015, p. 100). The received traumatised world, reshaped with its particular coping strategies, has become a way of saving oneself from complete annihilation. But this traumatised experience can also be incredibly lonely. To reconnect the lonely self with the outer world, and to restore trust and connection with this world, considerable obstacles need to be surmounted. Stauffer shows how this might include learning to be heard by another. Levine shows us that it is also the body itself that requires healing.

One contemporary example of a healing practice that seeks to regulate the body and restore connection with the external world has been through meditation. Traumatised people who are diagnosed with PTSD commonly have higher heart rate and display distinct responses in facial electromyogram tests when exposed to reminders of trauma, suggesting 'enhanced physiological reactivity' when confronted with reminders of their trauma (Hickling, Blanchard, Buckley and Taylor 1999/Orr and Roth 2000, ct. in Halligan et al. 2006, p. 721). Trauma, as we have seen, also affects memory recall and shows triggered retrieval of specific memories when exposed to particular stimuli (Blanchard et al. 1996/Shalev et al. 1997). Halligan et al. conclude that trauma creates a paradoxical embodied puzzle of trauma memory: physiological responses can be impaired because of the disorganised or incomplete retrieval of memory, or the individual can dissociate the cognitive from the emotional part of experience, as a result of previously 'uncoupling' psychological processes from overwhelming physiological experiences of pain response (Foa 1995/1997, p. 722).[3]

Meditation, in a way, seeks to transform bodied experience by the practice of being fully present to it. In *The Body Keeps the Score*, van der Kolk spends an entire chapter outlining the interconnectivity between yoga and trauma care. He suggests that the combination of breathwork (*pranayama*), positions (*asanas*) and meditation enables individuals to learn to self-regulate, cultivate interception and develop self-awareness (2005/2014, pp. 263–276). Because traumatic experiences can rewire the amygdala of the brain, triggering automatic responses of fight, freezing or fleeing when experiencing a trigger, the individual needs to learn how to be both aware of this automatic response and then how to reintegrate it into the embodied conscious experience of the present.

In their ethnographic work on yoga practice and trauma experience, Neely Myers, Sarah Lewis and Mary Ann Dutton suggest that yoga practice enables individuals to deepen the connection between their bodies and minds. This, they suggest, means that those with traumatic stress can develop an increased ability to focus on the present when training in meditative-based practices (2015, p. 487). Here, Myers et al. highlight not only the regulatory benefits of yoga practice in terms of Autonomic Nervous System (ANS) breathing and circulatory rhythms but also the meditative aspect of yoga that enables the self to experience itself temporally located in the present. This 'somatic self-reflexivity', as coined by Pagis (2009), is the ability to focus on being in the 'lived present'. Such awareness is particularly significant for the traumatised person, who is often caught in the somatic experience of the past traumatic event. Furthermore, Myers et al. suggest that the silent practice allows for a non-verbal recognition and situation of self (2015).

Finally, Myers et al. hypothesise that yoga practice could enable individuals to develop new capacities for self-acceptance and compassion. This concept of 'post-traumatic growth', first outlined in the work of Tedeschi and Colhoun in 1996, suggests that the 'legacy of trauma includes positive and transformative experiences' (Myers et al. 2015, p. 495). While not experienced in all traumatised individuals, Lewis' study of Tibetan monks, who had experienced political violence, recognised that some individuals in the community had 'managed to use pain as an opportunity to connect with their own vulnerability and tenderness', which, Lewis suggests, enabled them to 'strengthen their connection to the humanity of others' (2013, ct. in Myers et al. 2015, p. 496). We will explore this interconnection to the other as an aspect of traumatic experience later in this chapter.

It is further theorised that the practice of meditation can allow individuals to be present in the midst of suffering. That is, it is suggested that the practice itself facilitates an experience of connection that 'may help people learn to be-in-a-pain-full-world' (Myers et al. 2015, p. 497). However, it is not only yoga practice that enables these alternate forms of being present-to and being present-with. Meditative experiences are also reflected in religious ritual and communal practice. van der Kolk underscores that treatment has to focus on 'association' in order to mediate the dissociative state found in PTSD. That means integrating the 'cut-off elements of trauma into the ongoing narrative of life' so that the brain can begin to distinguish between what happened then and what is happening in the safety of the present (2010, p. 181).

Engagement with dissociative states of trauma is highlighted in Harris et al.'s study on traumatised individuals. They suggest that prayer, as a part of religious experience, can act as a means of regulating and making sense of the dissociative traumatic experience, though they recognise the individualised and nuanced outcome of these readings. As if to highlight this, they say that 'the nature and potential effectiveness of coping based on religious functioning varies as widely as do responses to trauma itself' (2011, p. 18). Similar to the post-traumatic growth hypothesis by Myers et al. (2015), Harris et al. examined the capacity for religious experience to facilitate growth in trauma. Using a variety of questionnaires and checklists, they show how measures of post-traumatic growth symptoms display negative growth correlations through traumatic experience of alienation from God fear of guilt and religious separations. Positive growth correlations, on the other hand, could be seen through the ability for religious experience to provide religious comfort, acceptance and connection, divine assistance and calm (2011, p. 19).

According to Boase and Frechette, biblical texts themselves require a recognition of the 'multiple facets of trauma' within the texts, whilst also understanding how ritual and divine relation feature in a reading of texts that uncovers modes of survival and a means of coping (2016, ct. in Esterhuizen 2018, p. 524). Interestingly, it is this textual, mythical and ritualistic narrative structure of the Biblical prophetic tradition that had been linked to the survival capabilities of 'remnant' populations, in these faith traditions (Esterhuizen 2018). For instance, Brewer-Smyth and Koenig suggest that 'Faith-based communities may promote forgiveness rather than retaliation, opportunities for cathartic emotional release, and social support' (2014, p. 251). They suggest that these opportunities are linked 'to neurobiology, behaviour, and health outcomes', and can be sources of hope, forgiveness and meaning – though they can also be linked to guilt and neurotic thinking (2014, p. 251). These varying outcomes reveal the different ways of experiencing faith in suffering. They also show the challenges of quantifying experience in comparative ways.

Bryant-Davis and Wong also develop this comparison between trauma processing and religious practice, in outlining that interpersonal trauma can be met with positive religious coping that can aid to 'decrease psychological distress' (2013, p. 671). This is furthermore in line with the American Psychological Association's noted need for 'recognition of spiritual and religious faith traditions as important aspects of the provision of ethical treatment' (Bryant-Davis and Wong 2013, p. 675).

Religious textual engagement and ritualistic enactment embedded in overarching narratives of hope can, therefore, enable individuals to process trauma, whilst developing strategies of resilience amongst survivors.

I have worked with traumatised people as a Pilates instructor and director of a small anti-trafficking network. In this work, I have been interested to see how exercise can provide a way of reconnecting a person with her body. Now, as a philosopher, I have intuitive theories as to how and why this works. For instance, in working with women who have been sex trafficked, the fluid and grounding Pilates exercises provide a way for the person to centre herself in her own body. Through breathwork, the regulated and cued breathing techniques allow the body to oxygenate and regulate through the experience of inhaling and exhaling. Inhaling, the body fills with nourishing oxygen; on the exhale, the body releases the waste. Through centring the body on the mat, releasing the muscle to stretch and strengthen within the limits of the instructor's safe cueing, the client is offered a context to explore herself as a body, as an individualised consciousness that experiences the felt and lived limit of her body. But to really understand why these modalities offer convincing ways of understanding and healing trauma requires us to examine how philosophy can help us to connect these experiences with the interconnected relational transfiguration of trauma.

As Merleau-Ponty has shown us, the living body is very different from a body that is just there to be objectified and studied. In trauma, we can see how the human responses are ongoing, as if living two experiences that interrupt each other, present and past. Alexandra Magearu suggests that Merleau-Ponty's concept of flesh can help us to understand this interconnection, which I would argue is essential to understand the possibility of healing. Flesh acts as a kind of 'elemental medium' that enables the body and the world to interact with each other (2019, p. 57). In Magearu's summary of this, it means that the lived body and the world are constantly interacting. This is because the body's sentient and sensible processed are part of circular and continuous feedback in the body, 'which entails the co-constitutive makeup of the body', rather than being individual and autonomous body processes. Looking at what Halligan et al. have found about the disorganisation between physiological and psychological responses in traumatised individuals, the ability to reconnect the sensed body with the outer world, in a living present, becomes crucial for healing.

Other practices that combine meditation with physical movement, like yoga, also show evidence of effectively mediating trauma experience. For instance, one review suggests that practices, such as yoga, meditation, Tai Chi and Qigong, focus on the mind-body interconnection to decrease trauma symptoms. Mind-body practices have been shown to reduce 'trauma-related symptoms (especially intrusion and avoidance) and emotional dysregulation', along with yoga breath serving as an effective mediator of 'psychological distress following mass disasters' (Descilo et al. 2010, pp. 289–300). Further meta-analysis shows that yoga can serve as an adjunctive treatment for a wide variety of mental disorders, including PTSD (Reinhardt et al. 2018).

Mediated practices such as somatic experiencing show how mindfulness that connects thoughts to an awareness of the body can help a person to be aware of their body's reactivity and ability to self-regulate (Winblad et al. 2018). Rather than focusing on the conscious memories alone, somatic therapy increases a person's ability to connect interoceptive cues with muscular awareness (p. 77). The movement is from the brainstem, implicated in the automatic bodily responses to experiences of terror. van der Kolk (1984) shows that one of the main language centres in the brain can 'shut down during reactions to trauma triggers', which means that a lot of the trauma memory is stored in the core response network, as a kind of 'wordless terror' (Winblad et al. 2018, p. 77).[4] The somatic experiencing technique tries to indirectly and slowly access trauma memories through mediating interoceptive experiences, by identifying resource experiences and correcting shifts in nervous system states. When fully integrated, these adjustments can 'in turn lead to changes in felt experience of safety, power and competence' (pp. 77–78). The method is essentially dysregulating the central response network, in order to restore connectivity between the lived experience of the person and the world around them.

Somatic experiencing draw on specific aspects of meditation practice (Winblad et al. 2018). Meditation seeks to restore interconnection, with body and world, past and present, self and other, making it a particularly important tool for healing. Neely Myers et al. conducted ethnographic fieldwork and interviews to assess how meditation-based practices enabled traumatised individuals to reconnect their body with their mind. They suggested that meditation enabled 'heightened somatic awareness and a focus on the present moment that they find to be therapeutic' (Myers et al. 2015, p. 487). When my friend Amira spoke about her own trauma experience, she mentioned the benefit of prayer, which, for her, created a safe, dysregulative context for her body. The healing benefits could also mean that individuals can experience the present more fully, rather than being caught in the traumatic memory, as well as accepting rather than overriding the pain, and be present with others in silent trusting connection, without actively having to process any of the pain and mistrust. As an alternative or a complement to other therapies, the meditation techniques enabled individuals to understand their thoughts, rather than exile anything painful, enabling a more cohesive sense of self.

Perhaps somewhat counterintuitively, pain is used, in a way similar to what Sigurdson mentions, as a 'tool' that can help the individual to open towards the other, through the experience of compassion and individual became more able to experience present time, rather than the force of past memory, through the tool of silence (2019). Pagis suggests that despite this being an individualised activity, the increased capacity for interconnection occurs because of meditation's ability to develop 'somatic self-reflexivity' or somatic awareness (2009, p. 491). The self learns that she can be present to her experience, however painful it is, in the safety of a quiet, regulated space. Meditation, experienced in this way, can promote an experience of well-being, and an ability to experience and be present to the body that helps prevent dissociation (2009). As Sigurdson briefly mentions at the end of his summary of existential health, Myers et al. also suggest that survivors of trauma can live the deep and painful suffering of their past into 'a place of compassion and acceptance', which they refer to as 'Post-traumatic growth' (Tedeschi and Colhoun 1996, ct. in ibid.).

As we have explored before, the notion of post-traumatic growth can be somewhat simplistic. But what it does point to is how an experience of trauma can problematically reduce a person to a single identity, defined according to a past experience. When I spoke to my friend about what being a survivor meant to her, she said that it was something that she needed to identify about herself, she needed to come to terms with the fact that she had survived trauma and that it had impacted her in a long-lasting way. However, she was also adamant that she did not want to be defined according to this experience in a way that left her without ability to respond. For her, healing occurred not only through her own journey of her memory and her body but also through actively engaging with others to ensure that trauma did not happen to other people. In this case, it looked like advocating on behalf of her community and religious minorities in the Middle East, as well as advising leadership. Amira shows us that the complicated healing of the self, the transformation of the mind and the body, requires a further connection to relationships in the world outside of us as well.

The Transformation of Social Relationship

Transforming the social relationship is crucial to healing trauma because trauma will often damage relationships. For many, trauma emerges out of a relationship to someone a person loves and trusts. This means that restoring trust in relationships is an important part of the healing. In experiencing a violation of trust, the traumatised person can feel cut off from the known world. Herman writes that once someone has experienced the isolation of trauma, a person is aware of how fragile human connection can be. This means that she needs 'clear and explicit assurance that she will not be abandoned once again' (2015, p. 61). For Herman, this reconnection of relationship that transforms the fractured trust is paramount to the 'restitution of a sense of a meaningful world' (ibid.). This does not place the burden of responsibility to re-establish trust on the traumatised person. Herman suggests that it is the community around her that needs to bear witness to and enact different events that can show the traumatised person that she can trust. This section will explore how phenomenology can help us to interpret the transformational social relationship required for healing trauma.

Re-establishing a trust in the world is naïve if it asks the traumatised person to return to things as usual. The world is not 'as usual' – basic relational experiences have been disfigured beyond recognition. When a mother sells her daughter into sex trafficking or a neighbour orders the arrest of a foreign neighbour, it is not 'business as usual'. The relationship is wounded by a rupture of trust and responsibility. There might be a need to mourn what has died and bear witness to what has been lost. These experiences are important parts of any conversation of healing. I would suggest that this experiential witnessing that needs to occur prior to a discussion on transformation (or perhaps as a first movement of this transformation) can benefit from the language of lamentation in theology. But I would also suggest that philosophy itself can help us to understand how lamentation can be experienced as a phenomenological moment that facilitates this transfiguration. Healing, in this way, can be interpreted through the problem of theodicy.

Theodicy is a particular rational argument that suggests there is a divine reason behind our experiences of suffering. Suffering is understood as a particular experience of evil that happens for a reason. Suffering is a rational problem that just needs to be solved so that we can figure out the meaning in this experience. Lévinas is not particularly fond of this line of argument. In 'Useless Suffering', he writes that the very invocation of a divine purpose in suffering shows that we do not understand the experience at all. Trauma is not a rational problem that we need to figure out. It is an experience that assumes itself into every part of our relation to ourselves and the world around us. If we look at it as a rational problem, then healing becomes a matter of solving the problem. It is nice and neat and we can do it without much emotional investment. For Lévinas, and Ricœur follows this train of thought in his own way, suffering requires addressing the evil that threatens to destroy the other anonymously. This language of evil might not be how you are used to reading trauma, as you want to avoid moralising tropes etc. I get that; it is easy to misuse. But humour me for a bit as I try to show you why it might be phenomenologically significant.

Understanding health in the wake of trauma is a philosophical challenge because it means trying to understand what makes healthy and whole individuals and communities. We could say, for instance, that it is eating balanced meals, or having a stable income. These assumptions direct how we engage and safeguard those conditions for health. However, when we do not engage with them critically as we should, it can form a very narrow view of the conditions for a person and community's whole experience of health. We can guarantee that our family has access to good food and secure job opportunities, while neglecting their emotional or spiritual health. A phenomenological exploration of health tries to figure out where we are not seeing interconnections, and where we might have missed part of the whole.

The history of philosophy, in its exploration of experience and truth, echoes the search for human wholeness. Trauma asserts that we are vulnerable, but that vulnerability itself reasserts a primary experience, which is of a relationship to ourselves and the world around us. This is where the discourse on healing lends from philosophy and theology – it is an exploration of vulnerability and interconnection. In Emil Fackenheim's philosophical exploration of healing in the wake of the Holocaust, he reasserts the connection between being human, being vulnerable in our relationship to the world, and healing. He writes that the lived conditions of our experience shape the relationship that we have with the world. For instance, in Hitler's *Weltanschauung*, Hitler distinguishes between human beings 'who really were human, indeed, who had the vocation of becoming superhuman', from others, who were experienced as subhuman, 'so-called *Menchentiere* ("human animals")' (Fackenheim 1994, p. xxxvii). These people are further distinguished from the Jewish people, who 'looked like humans, but were in fact [treated as] vermin' (ibid.). What Fackenheim notes is actually, I think, a phenomenological problem: the inability to perceive the relational world, as Merleau-Ponty and Lévinas show us, results in a misperceived totalisation of human experience. This totality is not only erroneous as a phenomenological description but also has traumatising consequences when acted out.

We perceive our relationship to the world around us; we can also mis-perceive it. Fackenheim writes that a destructive experience contrasts the logical perception of normal worlds. The logical perception conditions the possibility of hope and growth as well as the experience of rupture and pain. Earlier I have suggested through the phenomenological work of Merleau-Ponty, Ricœur and Lévinas that this is revealed through an experience of relationship and vulnerability. Fackenheim's logic sustains this perception: 'The logic of normal worlds is, if not creation, at any rate preservation' (p. xxxvii), which holds the relational experience together. Contrasting this, '[t]he logic of the Auschwitz word...was destruction... and this is what held *it* together' (ibid.). Fackenheim notes that this 'anti-world' presented 'a two-fold aim, the murder of the victims and, so far as possible, and prior to their murder, the destruction of their humanity' (ibid.). It is this rupturing of human experience itself that Fackenheim seeks to address when he speaks of the mending of the world, in the Jewish concept of *Tikkun Olam*.

I am interested in understanding how the lived experience of trauma can help us to understand how it can be transformed. *Tikkun Olam* necessarily involves exploring the interconnection of our experiences with others and us. It assumes that who we are is connected to our relationships with other humans and the natural world that we inhabit. This means that these relationships are essential for the healing of the self, as well. In the last section, we have looked at what this might mean when we are speaking about the individual self. But as we have seen, our human experience extends far beyond ourselves. How can traumatised people 'reawaken' to the interconnection found in a safe and trustworthy world, when their experience constructs an entirely different reality? The tension involves accounting for how trauma can both lead to transformative experiences of the self and painful disconnection and a permanent sense of isolation and loss.[5]

Fackenheim presents a theological and philosophical view of the world. Hitler's mis-perception lends to a destructive dualism of good and evil. Lévinasian phenomenology puts it as a totalisation where the other is annihilated without a face. But the paradox is that humans cannot be annihilated in this way. For Lévinas, '[t]he infinity of the other, the limitless extent of possibilities that appears in the event of the face, is not destroyed by murder' (Zimmerman 2015, p. 155). Murder cannot destroy the otherness of the face – 'even if the murderer has annihilated the body' (ibid.). For Lévinas, the phenomenological experience of evil, *le mal*, is an evil that lived through our experience of the world. It is lived in the evil of physical pain, of torture. It is inflicted on bodies that breathe, hear and feel. But the transcendence of the face calls out against it. For Lévinas, the problem of evil defies all rational calculations of cause-and-effect, because it is lived in real bodies.

For Lévinas, suffering cannot be explained rationally because suffering is experienced through sentience rather than reason. The responsibility in which subjectivity originates means that contained in who we are is the invocation to defend the annihilation of the other, even the event of annihilation contains the paradox that the other cannot be annihilated. The Leibnizian account of evil suggests that evil is a problem of reason: if we can quantify suffering as a problem that requires a logical outcome, then we can show how it can be solved. But suffering is not quantifiable, as Lévinas shows us in his phenomenology of revelation earlier in this book.

For Schonfeld, when we try to understand suffering through reason alone, we end up completely missing the point because it is not possible to quantify suffering. The phenomenon is deformed if evil is detached from 'its subjective qualitative root', because theoretical attitudes towards 'evil means to avoid looking at the phenomenon itself, to avoid being in relation with suffering' (2017, p. 17). Schonfeld connects suffering to the wider experience of evil, which is what Lavinas also does. This includes exploring the individual experience as relational and sentient and as a body to wider conditions of justice. Suffering requires these other phenomenological moments as well. Suffering needs to be read subjectively, outside of objective theoretical interpretations. A person cannot be read as a theory. What works for one person might not work exactly the same for another. The phenomenological structures of existence are not just a simple rational puzzle that is to be worked through. They are experienced through the individual body, the value systems and experiences of living in this world. This means that when we are 'looking at evil through the lens of Reason' alone, we can miss what suffering is.

If we miss what suffering *is for that person*, then it is difficult to understand how that person can heal. If we just keep our philosophy of healing as a rational theory, then we miss the incredibly significant experience of the body. Schonfeld shows this through his exploration of lament, which I have previously suggested is an essential part of the phenomenological reconfiguration of healing trauma. Schonfeld suggests that the work of Freud can leave us dubious about the comfort of a phenomenology of healing. For Freud, the drives of *Eros* and *Thanatos* strive to take control of the ego. However, the conflict of life and death that Freud writes about presents an erroneous dualisation of experience. In presenting the egoic drama as a constant clash of forces, Freud suggests that life is lived without consolation. Consolation is itself the deception that the ego has to overcome. In fact, consolation can be tied to the erroneous presentation of the real; one that hides in false narratives to provide comfort and escape from the real experience. Comfort contrasts the real experience which is the suffering life (Schonfeld 2017, p. 13). However, I would argue that the experience of consolation is a very real and important phenomenological moment. What we are left with after a traumatic experience is not just making sense of an ongoing suffering life. If consolation is impossible, then trauma cannot be mourned in a manner that enables it to be transformed.

Consolation, as I understand it here, is not the same as forgetting, which Auerhahn and Laub warn us of. It is also not the same as an imaginary reconstruction of reality, which Ricœur vies away from in his writing on second innocence. Schonfeld suggests that it is precisely our problematic tendency to dismiss aspects of reality that puts us in this place of hopelessness. Freud criticises what he holds to be the source of false comfort. He suggests that we need to re-examine the myths that we tell to situate our experience of the world (we see this in Ricœur's reading of Freud). But to equate consolation with a mythical understanding of the world seems to be entertaining the very reductive dualism that Freud seeks to avoid, and condemns us to suffering as the ultimate experience of reality. Sigurdson has suggested that human experience emerges from vulnerability, the possibility of relationship, which can result in suffering. However, suffering is not, in itself, the totalising experience of a whole relationship to the world. Understanding ourselves through suffering alone suggests understanding a fragmented experience of reality, rather than the relational whole.

For Schonfeld, consolation does not mean giving a rational account for suffering. It does not mean figuring out why the suffering happened, or whose fault it was (though justice is important for our wider conversation). Rather, it is about permitting ourselves to be open to, and even caressed by and cared for, the other. This Lévinasian experience of a caress takes up the experience of the body, of touch, as a relational experience, even at the very point of its isolation and sense of shut-offness to the world. Consolation, therefore, is not predicated on 'saying the right words' or on 'explaining evil' but is instead concerned with reopening the self to the future, 'of hope' and 'the dimension of otherness' (2017, p. 27). This consolation is not something that substitutes a myth for an experience of reality or relegates the person to an eternal recurrence of suffering. Rather, it suggests that a future is possible. It suggests a connection that is significant enough to console, to take up the suffering present and 'experience it otherwise' (2017, p. 28) and can be experienced by a traumatised person. It suggests that relationship is still possible. This relationship sees the person for who she is, bearing witness to her suffering, and to her body that contains the pain, without needing to fully solve the problem.

One can see an example of the challenge to console in the mass experience of COVID-19 that has caused people to refer to it in terms of trauma. The consoling presence of the other person can be lacking in contexts where people are unable to touch and connect because of fear that they might transmit the virus to one another, this phenomenological bodied connection to others that is safe and stable is missing. This consolation is lived in real experiences and contrasts the fictitious mythical consolation that Freud warns of. Schonfeld suggests that Nietzsche helps us with this movement. As he seeks to dismantle the false dualism between the imagination and the real, the experience of consolation becomes something real, rather than something that is metaphysically imagined. The subject is not lost. It is the experience of this person, their thoughts and fears, their pain and their loneliness, that becomes the externalised in the world as lament. Lament, in this way, verbalises the unsayability of suffering, placing it exterior to the self. As the 'language of silence', lament enables consolation, not because the other bears witness to the 'right words', or fixes the 'problem'. The relational subjectivity continues.

This experience of consolation, which Lévinas refers to as the caress, brings the person out of complete isolation. The person is no longer 'condemned to itself', but rather, 'transported "elsewhere" by the movement of the caress. The other is freed from the vice-grip of "oneself", it finds "fresh air", a dimension and a future' (Lévinas 1988, p. 91). Looking at Fackenheim's philosophy, this reconfigures the reading of existence as destruction and reclaims an existence of creation, or at least, interrelationality. So, Schonfeld shows us consolation here 'is neither a distraction nor a compensation but the redemption, in pain, of the moment of pain itself. Alterity – the contact of the other – has this miraculous effect' (p. 27).

Lament as Connectivity: The Role of the Therapist

If restoring a sense of relationship to others around us is essential to addressing the experience of isolation that trauma brings, then we need to be able to develop relationships with other people that promote this sense of being witnessed by, and perceived, without the need to be fully understood or 'solved' like a puzzle. In Ilit Ferber's work on lament, she shows how lamentation uses this relational structure between the one who has suffered and those who live and bear witness to the suffering, as a phenomenon that 'stretches between the revealed and the silenced' (2017, p. xiii). Lament, she explains, is textual, but it is also performative and embodied (p. xv). Rather than presented as an accusation that demands an answer, lament suggests that living the non-answer can suffice (p. xiii).

Mediating suffering without providing answers is part of the phenomenological experience of relationship after trauma. This can occasion a nuanced reading of the clinician's role, because she becomes an important relational figure to the traumatised person, through providing pain relief and medical aid, etc. Though some clinicians might experience secondary trauma from hearing about events or seeing the wounds of the people they care for, they are not experiencing direct trauma themselves. This means that the clinician can become a partial bridge, a phenomenological encounter that can console and caress the suffering one. This role sounds almost messianic (perhaps Lévinas would say that it is). But the clinician also offers a very particularised relationship. They are not family; they have not experienced the violence or the loss themselves. According to McDonald, the clinician's role is to help the traumatised person to distinguish between reality and the traumatic memory. She acts like a midwife, rather than 'as an exorcist of emotion' (Loc. 2086). The relationship between the clinician and the traumatised person, if it is to hold space for lament, requires serving the other, prioritising the first-hand experience of the traumatised person and connecting this experience to the whole.

McDonald suggests this kind of practice requires seeing how symptoms are connected to the trauma and demystifying the fears that the traumatised person presents. The clinician can then show the traumatised person how the traumatic experience differs from the current experience of reality, helping the person to distinguish between the real present and the adaptations that the person has made to facilitate for their past trauma as the present experience (what I previously referred to as the 'received' experience of trauma). The clinician witnesses to the lament, the unseen and unsaid experience of suffering. However, the clinician also acts as an interpreter and discerner of realities. The received experience of trauma, and its symptoms, has created a defence against the traumatised event. Even though this could have been very helpful in overcoming the traumatic experience, as Kalsched's self-care theory suggests, they 'become maladaptive' when they start to 'accompany experiences in the world in which there was no actual danger' (Loc. 2110).[6] Discerning these asynchronous interpretations of experience requires discerning the narrative that the person presents, the coherence and the series of causations, as well as the way that a particular perspective orders and reorders details, recognising the difference between mythologising and dismissing differences from acknowledging that a person colours her narrative in a specific way (Loc. 2155).

Attending to the narrative of the traumatised person, as a means of bearing witness to, lamenting and re-perceiving the traumatised persons experience, requires discerning the complex relationship between the embodied experience. This means being attentive to how the clinician, who is supposed to facilitate a re-relation to the body and the world, can also cause a re-rupturing of relation. For instance, as we saw in earlier chapters, Kalsched writes that Jung intuitively knew dissociative patient in psychoanalysis 'is continuously at risk of being flooded with overwhelming unmodulated affect' (2013, p. 471). This means that 'treatment' is individualised, embodied and relational. Jung's reaction to Freudian analytic interpretation was based on a fear of leaving a person 'feeling retraumatised', and the therapeutic relationship setting off 'hallucination-like symptoms, flashbacks, sleep disturbances, nightmares or incursions of traumatic emotion', with 'comments by the analyst' that 'precipitate sudden splitting and regression' and act as a site of traumatic transference (ibid.). The vulnerable relationship challenges any paternalistic notions of messianism that the clinician might experience, while reaffirming just how important this role as 'other' and intermediary actually is.

Relationship is critical to healing trauma because the human experience is relational. It is also relationship itself that so often causes trauma and requires transformation. Because the clinicians become part of the phenomenological experience of healing, they can often experience the effects of the trauma that they are surrounded by. For instance, Winblad et al. note that individuals who treat trauma can be at a high risk of what is known as 'vicarious traumatisation' and burnout (2018, p. 70). They suggest that clinicians can, therefore, benefit from the same practices, such as somatic experiencing that regulates the autonomic nervous system, as the persons that they are treating. This traumatisation usually occurs in two ways. It can be an experience of secondary trauma stress (STS), through one stressful exposure, or vicarious trauma (VT), or an experience of continued accumulation of affect from another person's trauma (p. 73). In these instances, Winblad et al. suggest that clinicians can become more effective in treating trauma, and PTSD symptoms, when they have learned how to 'manage, reduce and mitigate impacts of stress-based injuries' (ibid.). The vulnerability of clinicians recognises that the relational attachment models, and the experiences of witnessing to and being received by others is just as important to the clinician as it is to the traumatised person. This shows that the healing and health of each person is somehow connected, without deprioritising the healing of the traumatised person.

Justice and the Rupture of Victim-Perpetrator Totalities

Stauffer understands this relational complexity. The ego is involved in an interconnected drama that is both hidden and seen, past and present. Trauma, she suggests, acts through the relational feedback loop, meaning that the traumatised body and narrative of one person feeds into the lives of the people around her, and vice versa, meaning that it is not just individuals but societies that need to recover (2015, p. 147). In order for a person to heal, or recover, from trauma, the self requires these other relationships. The self is not 'sovereign from the ground up' and needs the intersubjective experience to heal as well. She writes that '[s]elves can be destroyed because selves are also built, and built cooperatively, by human relationships of various kinds' (p. 113). It is the world itself that needs rebuilding, trust in the relational and institutional structures that make the everyday living predictable and secure.

In Stauffer's phenomenological portrayal of suffering, she recounts the story of a woman who lost her son to bloodied conflict. After the loss, the woman suffered from an estrangement from herself, because her experience of herself was tied up with the one who was now dead. Stauffer recounts that: 'She wanted to be "us", but the killing of her son reduced her to an "I". This is what she suffered from' (2015, p. 211). In this instance, we see that not only do we need others to heal from our trauma, but we also require acknowledging just how much our experience of the world is tied to our relationships. In this instance, the experience of suffering occurs because of a loss of a relationship, rather than the wounding of the woman's body directly. The woundedness and death of the other wounds the woman.

In other instances, however, it is another person who wounds the traumatised individual. This wounding relationship that distinguishes the victim from the perpetrator becomes a mark of many traumas. It problematises the idea that relationships are safe and asserts the importance of justice in the experience of healing. Stauffer highlights the complexity of trauma when she illustrates how perpetrators also can be victims. Stauffer writes that 'sometimes our assumptions about both hide our own responsibilities from us' (p. 206). Previously, I showed how diagnostic criterion that is used alone can be problematic in accounting for a holistic phenomenology of trauma. I suggested that we should use it as a tool to assess symptoms that enable someone to receive the healing that they need, without interpreting them through diagnosis alone. I think that a similar recognition of victimhood is required. We need the label to identify who has been wounded, and how she is to receive justice. But reading her experience through victimhood alone totalises the experience in another way.

The experience of the victim helps us to understand the need for justice when we speak about trauma. It can, for instance, also situate the legal parameters of an event that can then be used in court to, as Herman shows us in the beginning of the section, actively create a new experience of trust and protection for an individual. This can, for example, be seen in the Canadian Legal Human Rights Tribunal case on Intergenerational Trauma of Residential Schools. The victimised population are identified as the Aboriginal people whose forced attendance in residential schools caused them to suffer 'from various physical and mental health problems compared to Aboriginal adults who did not attend'. This included 'being exposed to the neglect and abuse and the poor treatment', and the verdict from these evidences of victimhood led to the Tribunal ordering the discriminatory practices to cease and be redressed. The victimiser, in this case, was ordered to '…make available to the victim of the discriminatory practice, on the first reasonable occasion, the rights, opportunities or privileges that are being or were denied the victim as a result of the practice' (Canadian Human Rights Tribunal 2016, par. 416 and 474). Part III of this book explained how rights could be used to protect persons from trauma. This example shows that the violation of a person's rights can cause trauma. The language of the victim can allow the arbiters of justice to define the conditions of the violation. Similarly to what Amira said earlier, acknowledging the victimisation is central to transforming the situation of trauma.

But Amira also tells me that the experience of the victim is only one part of the phenomenology of trauma, and the life experience of the individual. This is helpful phenomenologically. In Carell's phenomenology of illness, she writes about the experience of changes in the body that are not subject to our own will. The lungs do not function as they have, making it difficult to do everyday things like walking to the shops and playing sport with friends. She calls it a kind of 'betrayal of the body' that increasingly feels like an alienation from the body that we know as ours (2008, p. 20). I would suggest that a very similar thing happens in trauma. The body that we have come to know, the responses that we have come to understand as normal and the way of being that we are used to are replaced with others – physical and mental symptoms that interrupt our present and erode our confidence in predicting how our body will respond to any given situation. Only, unlike illness, this bodily 'betrayal' emerges as a way of making sense of, and safeguarding the self from moments of the past.

For Carell, this strange power that the body has over our experiences can be made sense of through phenomenology. Phenomenology shows just how our bodies actually filter and interpret our experiences of the world. Unlike the dualistic theories of thinkers like Descartes, who think that we are our minds, and the body is an add-on, Merleau-Ponty argues that there is no such thing as mental autonomy from the body (Carell 2008). This means that mental action 'is always embodied', which is very similar to what contemporary research is trying to tell us about trauma. Further to this, Lévinas and Ricœur show us that the experience that we call subjectivity is inherently relational. What we experience as 'real' is not just a bodied mental event. It is also a relational experience. This relationality is bodied (Lévinas uses terms like vulnerability, hospitality and caress to make sense of it). It would seem to translate, then, that what happens to us relationally affects this bodied self existentially. This is particularly true when we look at trauma. If, as Lévinas shows us, our experience of ourselves is through our relationship to others (being-for-another), then the breakdown of these relationships will rupture through the entirety of our phenomenological experience. When the relation of response is broken in the experience of violence, torture and persecution, it 'betrays', to use Carell's term, our sense of the normal order of things, as well as the normal way that our body acts in the world.

An example of the traumatised body's betrayal is found in the experience of torture. Francois Fleury and Shadman Mahmoud-Shwana recount working as psychotherapists with migrant populations in Switzerland who had suffered through events of conflict and political unrest. The migrants who experienced torture were alienated from their bodies, at the hands of others. The acts of torture were done to deliberately and systematically 'reduce the human body to "nobody"' (2010, p. 102). This suffering endured by the body not only reveals itself through a symptomatology, but through the rupturing of relationship to other humans: the body's 'intimate links fragmented in every minute detail' (ibid.). Jean Amery reveals this relational shattering of the Holocaust when he explains that 'the experience of persecution was, at the very bottom, that of an extreme loneliness' (1980, p. 70). The physical suffering shatters the relational structures that are constitutive of human experience.

It is this relational rupture and experience of immense loneliness that requires addressing if we are to seriously consider any kind of comprehensive trauma healing. This relational component situates us in the realm of justice, but a conversation of justice that is in keeping with the phenomenology of embodied relationship that we have already been exploring. Lévinas' dethronement of any theoretical Being (Moyn 2005, p. 210) confronts us with an uncontainability, or 'infinity', of each human being (p. 3) that persecution seeks to totalise and obliterate – to make faceless. Healing, in this case, requires perceiving the other's unique face.

But how do we do this when the objective of war and persecution is to demolish the humanness of the other? Auerhahn and Laub write that the shared humanity of the Jewish and the Gentile after the Second World War is haunted by the 'role of memory in this interpersonal theatre' (2018, p. 44). The totalising sense of victimisation, the trauma of memory, creates barriers between the self and the persecutor: 'empathic and imaginative failure', as well as an experience of 'humanity's complicity in genocide that undermines trust in relationship' (p. 39). The undermining of trust, as well as trauma's effect on the imagination, provides challenges for redefining the self beyond victimhood.

Transfiguring Trauma through Justice

What trauma healing shows us is that the relationship between the self and the other continually needs to be reconfigured and transformed. Justice requires confession of crimes by the persecutor themselves and an affirmation of the victim's own unique humanness. Auerhahn and Laub suggest that relationship can only really be renewed between the persecutor and the victim if the 'hierarchical victim-victimiser relation' is undone. They suggest that this happens through testimony, which enables a survivor to restore agency 'transform anger and hate and re-establish a shared subjectivity' in a way that makes the traumatised world 'feel three-dimensional again' (2018, pp. 42–43). This relational reworking is a nearly impossible task. It requires forgiveness that also seeks a justice for wrongs. If that is not possible, then the forgiveness somehow requires a relationship to the world that is secure, despite the experience that the world is not secure.

Lévinasian justice necessarily prioritises the other person. In this case our response is on behalf of the uniqueness of each victim. He writes: 'The equality of all is borne by my inequality, the surplus of my duties over my rights. The forgetting of self moves justice' (1998b, 1997, p. 159). This asymmetrical prioritisation challenges any justifications of persecution, because the act of killing the other actually breaks down our own humanity. The question 'Who am I?' is an ethical rather than an ontological or epistemological one. This means that who I am is actually the site of responsibility, relationship with the other person. Sarah Roberts-Cady writes that 'subjectivity is a kind of response to otherness' (2009, p. 241). The self is called out as a subject. Working out this responsibility, which is actually constitutive of who I am, is what Lévinas refers to as justice, which is where I suggest an important aspect of the experience is transformed.

This phenomenology of subjectivity is important for two reasons when we consider trauma. First, it shows that justice has to be a part of working out our response to the human condition of bodily vulnerability, albeit abstractly. Second, it gives a preliminary explanation as to why the perpetrator might also, in some instances, be the victim. This is particularly important if we want to really get into how people who inflict violence also experience violence that is done to them, which is not only a commonly known situation for child soldiers in Sudan but also, in perhaps a subtly different way, the suffering soldier experiencing moral injury.

In some way, Lévinas opens up the possibility of exploring the victim-perpetrator experience in a way that prioritises the care and healing of the victim, without reducing a person's subjectivity to this totalising experience. Because if I am the victim, I am also the one who is responsible. I am not responsible for my injury, as if in some morbid chain of events. However, I am implicated, as a human and a relational being. There is something hugely challenging in this – a reassertion of primordial agency, which Auerhahn and Laub suggest can only be restored through the persecutor's recognition of such. Lévinas challenges this: the agency of response, insofar as someone is human, can never be taken away. This breaks any totalising notions of victimhood as a permanent state, whilst demanding response towards the one who finds himself or herself the victim of suffering.

For van der Kolk, the traumatised self can become stuck in her experience of living. There is an experience of being 'stopped in their growth because they cannot integrate new experiences into their lives' (2014, p. 53). Being traumatised means continuing to organise one's life as if the trauma was still going on – unchanged and immutable – as if every new encounter or event is contaminated by the past (ibid.). Whilst this is the phenomenological experience of PTSD, however, Lévinas challenges this as a totalising definition of self. In *Totality and Infinity*, Lévinas writes that a real experience of human life requires grappling with the experience that what has been declared to be 'definitive' is not actually definitive. Only our relational experience is definitive, and it is constantly calling us further into the 'unlimited infinity of the future' (1969, p. 282). Lévinas does not mean this as a glib romanticism, but a profound phenomenological statement, not a 'complacency in some romanticism of the possibles', but rather 'of escaping the crushing responsibility of existence that veers into fate, of resuming the adventure of existence so as to be to the infinite' (ibid.). Only, Lévinas writes this of this 'adventure of existence' with acute awareness of trauma. For him, it infuses our existence as being vulnerable people in the world. Particularly for him, he experienced its reality through surviving and losing his family in the Holocaust. As such, he writes how trauma exposes and demands an answer for the basic experience of being human in the world.

In fully occupying this unique human call of being for the other, Lévinas shows that the whole phenomenological experience of the self requires a relationship that orients us towards the other. Without an experience of pardon, we ourselves experience the shut-offness of suffering, a continuous suffering that breaks our relational subjectivity. Understood in this way, Lévinas offers a notion of pardon that redeems the self from self-enclosure. Pardon, he writes 'permits the subject who had committed himself in a past instant to be as though…he had not committed himself' (1969, p. 283). This pardon has an activity that differentiates it from forgetting, 'which does not concern the reality of the event forgotten'; pardon actively acts on the past by somehow repeating the event in order to purify it (ibid.). This is not some kind of abstract rational purification process. It is connected to the lived flesh of the face.

That means that pardon is also different from forgetting – the scars on the flesh are still present. Lévinas suggests that 'forgetting nullifies the relations with the past' (1969, p. 283). This differs from pardon, which keeps the 'past pardoned in a purified present' (ibid.). This is a present pardon that contains 'a surplus of happiness', which Lévinas poetically refers to as 'the strange happiness of reconciliation…given in an everyday experience which no longer astonishes us' (ibid.). Pardon here, which I read as transformative forgiveness, does not forget. As Auerhahn and Laub emphasise, forgiveness cannot be equated to forgetting. As van der Kolk shows us, the body itself remembers and that memory is what is required to be caressed, explored and connected. But the phenomenology of human subjectivity itself is still intact, despite this rupture of relationship and rupture of body. Forgiveness places human experience in its truthful context, as primordially bodied and relational, as *not alone*, even when the experience of loneliness has been confirmed to be the traumatised person's lot, as an object rather than as a face.

This experience of pardon is also the pardon that demands justice. It demands a response to the suffering person. Auerhahn and Laub recall Nazi SS Unterscharführer Gröning whose experience of being forgiven by God seemed to nullify his experienced need to be forgiven by the relatives of those killed and traumatised in the Holocaust. This misperceived forgiveness places the human experience outside of embodiment, and also outside of true relationship. The forgiveness of the Other (God or a Higher Power) is connected to the experience of being human. For Lévinas, the presence and the response to the other happens before all abstract thought (Zimmerman 2015, p. 36), and the otherness of God is revealed in the 'proximity' of the otherness of the person (p. 37). The suffering bodies are relational bodies; the infinite pardon is one that asks, what will you do for the least of these? Thus Auerhahn and Laub address the crucial point on which all discourse of forgiveness must hold together: that forgiveness and justice are two expressions of the same infinite relationship: 'It never occurred to Gröning that God's love is not divorced from his justice and that Gröning must consider that his own, true obligation is to the victims who survived' (2018, pp. 57–58). Integrating forgiveness, as an unshackling from totalising enclosure, which Lévinas' ethical self requires, also requires lamenting the loss and actively breaking in to extend aid to the traumatised person.

If the relationship between the self and the other is not transformed, there are other ways that the relationship can be experienced. For instance, in Herman's work, a revenge fantasy can be a way of reversing the role between victim and perpetrator without freeing the victim from the trauma. Rather, it 'increase[s] the torment', by exacerbating the person's 'feelings of horror and degrading herself' (1992, p. 189). Still, mourning presents the survivor with the realisation that it is impossible to get even and to reclaim what has been taken from her. But what it also does is permits an exteriorisation of the unspeakable pain, which Herman suggests can give rise to a positive relational anger: 'righteous indignation' (ibid.). In this transformational experience, the victim experiences herself as an agent again: as one who can still relate to the world around her, and one towards whom justice is required.

It is here that Lévinas' phenomenology helps us to map how this kind of complex healing might initially be explored. This enables a 'hope arising from the abyss of despair…within this despair' (2014, pp. 100–101), as Chalier writes about the biblical character of Ruth, who, after suffering the death of her husband, experiences that 'Even after death, there is still a human capacity, defying death, generosity and loving kindness, as though evil could not overcome it' (ibid.). Chalier writes that it is a '[s]overeignty of that primordial goodness or mercy that evil cannot overcome' (2014, p. 100). As trauma reveals, the experience of the body, and the suffering of the body, can infuse all of our experience of being human. But it is also this experience of being human, this primary relational being alongside others, which permits an exit from this totalising experience.

Auerhahn and Laub emphasise that it is not forgiveness but rather active witnessing, testimony and acts of justice that enable healing (p. 62). But Lévinas shows us that both are bound together in the phenomenological experience of being human. A shallow interpretation of forgiveness that discredits the body's capacity to remember cannot heal trauma. But the body, as we have seen, also has the capacity to release the memory into the full present and future lived expression. Surely this can also be the case for memory and relationality. As Lévinas helps us to understand, however, this task is immense and infinite: the healing of the world, and the traumas of existing, require making sense of how the other human being, who we share humanity with, can violate our boundaries and destroy our trust in the world (Stauffer 2015, p. 109).

In the experiences of torture, where humans are reduced to objects on which 'instruments of a well-thought out and smooth-running system' act to break apart the relation of a person to the world and 'divest them, as individual persons of all relationships', requires somehow reaffirming the uniqueness of their humanity, their primordial 'belonging to the human species' (Kaies 2012, p. xv), after they experience themselves as no longer humans. Healing, in this interrelational context, requires the seemingly impossible response of forgiveness and justice.

The Ambiguity of Moral Injury

As we have seen in this section, issues of healing pertain directly to wider discourses on justice and forgiveness, if we are to phenomenologically account for embodied relationality. Trauma is inherently interdisciplinary, because it involves relational rupture and loss. This means that reparation and transfiguration need to be an interdisciplinary conversation as well.

Brunner notes that the psychiatric discourse has to be in conversation with the juridic and political relations in order to fully account for this full measure of reparation (2007, p. 100). But the challenge of this is that the juridic and political status that victims require is often difficult to find. That is, 'some power and status is needed to be recognised [by the state] as a victim' (ibid.), because the silencing and alienation of the victim must be overcome. We have explored how Lévinas helps to challenge totalising experiences of victimisation. But Lévinas also suggests that we have an infinite responsibility to the suffering face, which itself is often unseen. Brunner reminds us then that: 'There is thus a fate worse than that of being a trauma victim, namely that of not being recognised as such' (p. 101). He suggests that this silencing can come from a refusal to perceive another person who suffers or from the suffering person refusing to express herself. This, Brunner suggests, could be found in the populations of Jewish Holocaust survivors who, reaching Israel, found that they were unable to voice their trauma in a publicly acknowledged manner (ibid.). As a result of this, much work in activism and making visible the 'unseen' face is required in order that justice might take place, at a juridical and political level.

For Brunner, these crossovers and ambiguities often mean that we feel we need to choose between one and the other: either we are suspicious of a story, or we have compassion. Either we victimise the person, defining them by their traumatic past, or we expect them to be able to overcome their trauma quickly and experience frustration when a past event continues to have such a huge impact on the present. Of course, experience tells us that it is not that simple, and that the complexity of being a human in relationships means that not only do we need to identify unseen experiences and avoid totalising tropes, or black and white interpretations of healing as either instantaneous or all-consuming, but we also need to acknowledge that the victim herself can be an ambiguous experience. As we see, for instance, in the Israel-Palestine conflict, how can we propose a comprehensive experience of healing, if the Palestinian people are still suffering? If a community is exposed to widespread trauma, what tools do we use to facilitate its healing, without taking sides?

Brunner writes that medical advancements have historically been preceded by politics. This was seen in the instance of creating a diagnostic tool for trauma. The DSM-III PTSD diagnosis was directly related to the antiwar activism of Vietnam veterans and American people (2017, p. 104). This means that the work of healing, as such, requires continual conversation and re-perceiving of our experience and the experience of others. But it also requires accounting for the ambiguity of experience, as the Vietnam veteran diagnosis shows. For those working with soldiers suffering from PTSD, this presents a specific challenge. Diagnosed with the trauma of war, their trauma is complicated by being both victim of terror and the perpetrator of harm. The US Department of Veterans Affairs offers a comprehensive analysis of what is termed 'moral injury', that is, the trauma of violating one's own 'deeply held moral beliefs and expectations' (Norman and Maguen 2018, p. 1). The traumatic moment here comes from what phenomenologists propose is the interconnection of the lifeworld: our experience of our body, tied to our system of values, our relationships and sense of self (Carel 2008). Protevi suggests that socio-political relations carry a somatic aspect: he speaks of a 'bodies politic' lived through the 'reflex, neuronal, and hormonal activity in the preconscious affective response to events when connections with things and others are made or broken' (2009, p. 35). The political is taken up and lived through the collective of bodies and the effect that they carry as a result of events.

What happens in the case of moral injury opens up another dimension of trauma, which requires healing beyond a straightforward body account. Moral injury is defined as 'perpetrating, failing to prevent, bearing witness to, or learning about acts that transgress deeply held moral beliefs and expectations' (Litz et al. 2009, p. 695). Lévinas, in his account of relationality, shows just how this guilt can cause distress, because of violating the basic tenant of relationality: 'do not kill' (1969, p. 198). In these situations, the ethical situation that comprises Lévinas' situation of subjectivity is violated: the soldier is commanded to kill. But the blame is borne by the soldier alone, rather than the community or government who commanded the order. As such, the body politic that initiates the command to kill breaks apart into subjects who initiate the killing on behalf of the group. It is, however, the subject rather than the collective body politic who bears the consequences of trauma. In studies on war veterans, significant numbers of veterans who experience suicidal ideation reveal an overlapping backdrop for the experience of moral injury: 'feelings that one is a burden on the others or society, and an acquired capability to overcome the fear and pain associated with suicide' (Maguen and Litz 2012, p. 2). This disruption of subjectivity is often experienced through immense guilt, or as a spiritual wrong-doing, that can heighten one's experience of Post-Traumatic Stress. As Lévinas, Ricœur and Merleau-Ponty point out, the breach of the ethical carries not only consequences of somatic affect but also wider ruptures of subjective relation and relation to the other.

In these instances, how do we maintain the imperative to heal, or transform, without sacrificing the basic phenomenological experience of being human? Healing, I would argue, requires this deep work – perceiving the silenced and the unsaid, the loss and the replacement, one's own guilt and one's own vulnerability. Trauma seeks justice. It also acknowledges an irrevocable loss. Both experiences show us that human experience assumes prior givens: the world of phenomena is relational, which accounts for whose attachment matters, and we experience loss. We are not just cast, alone into existence, contemned to be free. The suffering that we experience in trauma tells us otherwise: Lévinas, Merleau-Ponty and Ricœur emphasise our relation to the world, which, Lévinas points out, is prior to any thought.

Conclusion

Healing, in this way, requires a restoration of the relational world, and a receiving back something that has been taken away, even when the object itself is gone forever. It requires not just restoration, for as Lacan shows us, trauma means that something has been taken and replaced. Rather it requires a transfiguration of the present. It requires not just that we re-member, for some members will be permanently lost, and some memories will be horrific without the capacity for sense-making. Healing cannot be a theodicy of reason. As Ståle Fink writes: 'The cure does not consist in working things out at a cognitive level but is to be found in novel ways of re-enacting the affective scenario in the co-presence of an other' (2019, p. 40). Healing therefore requires opening to the possibility of a future when the past has permeated the present with the finality of death.

Notes

1 See, for example, the Clinician-Administered PTSD Scale for DSM-5, the PTSD Symptom Scale interview (PSSI), Structured Clinical Interviews, the Treatment Outcome PTSD Scale (TOP-8), Davidson Trauma Scale (DTS) and Impact of Event Scale (IES-R), to name a few.

2 For more on feminist theological implications of trauma, see O'Donnell and Ross (2020).

3 The Post-traumatic Stress Diagnostic Scale (PDS, Foa 1995/1997) is a standardised self-report measure of PTSD diagnostic criteria. This includes 'trauma characteristics, symptom severity and duration and resultant degree of life interference' and is diagnostically agreeable with the DSM. Furthermore, symptoms such as 'elevated heart rate corresponds to activation, suggesting that only emotional access which is accompanied by physiological arousal may have therapeutic benefits' (p. 731).
4 The Subcortical systems (CRN) includes the subcortical, limbic system, motoric pathways, interoceptive cues and basic arousal systems (e.g. ANS, hypothalamic pituitary adrenal axis and reticular activation system). Dysregulation of these protective systems corresponds to developing symptoms of trauma.
5 Learning how to be present to pain, in the midst of suffering is something that meditation has been purported to facilitate, with studies conducted on Tibetan monks who were found to be 'resilient refugees living in exile', while using their pain to continue to connect to the humanity of other people (Lewis 2013).
6 For Kardiner: trauma as 'an injury to adaptive processes, rather than [how Freud and Breuer] understand it as the result of interrupted affects' (p. 2121).

11

RELATIONAL HEALING

The Refiguration of a Place

In the previous sections, we have located trauma as an experience that is healed in bodied consciousness and in the interrelational space. What we have not discussed, though we have touched on it in the previous chapters, is how trauma impacts and disrupts physical space. What I mean here is how often it is our sense of place, marked by a relationship to a particular piece of earth, and to the environment that we know and we attach value to, that is impacted in trauma. If this is the case, then a discussion about healing requires that we examine the phenomenological experience of relationship to place. In this section, I want to explore how trauma affects our relation to place. I will then suggest that any phenomenological account of healing, as a transfiguration of wholeness, requires engaging with our relation to our place in the physical world.

Trauma as a Relation to Place

van der Kolk acknowledges that how we heal trauma results from how we interpret the person's experience of suffering. This means that how therapies and medical practice approach healing is often based on what technology is available to the clinician at the time (2014). But while the technological tools that enable healing change, the relational aspect of trauma remains the same. He stresses that it is this sense of secure relationship, attachment to the world and others around us that enables us to be healthy. The ability to 'feel safe with other people', he stresses, 'is probably the single most important aspect of mental health; safe connections are fundamental to meaningful and satisfying lives' (p. 79). This contrasts the incredible sense of isolation that can result from trauma.

And this sense of isolation is not merely individualised. Often it can impact whole communities. For instance, in experiences of conflict, the collective trauma is a result of a communal suffering (Ezerhuizen 2018, p. 523). Communal suffering

DOI: 10.4324/9780367800017-15

experienced as collective trauma becomes experienced phenomenologically as 'a blow to the basic tissues of societal life that damages the bonds attaching people together and impairs the prevailing sense of communality' (ct. Erikson 1995). Research shows that where political upheaval and conflict have taken place, trauma can reach as high as 60% of the community, existing as a 'hidden epidemic in our era' (Felitti et al. 1998/Winblad et al. 2018, p. 86). Given these levels of trauma throughout a community, similar recent examples of which we might see in the widespread devastating effects of Covid-19, a concerted effort at examining the interrelational aspects of trauma is required in order to ensure that symptoms are addressed in order to avoid widespread compassion fatigue, chronic disease and mental health challenges (ibid.).

The Phenomenological Relation between Trauma and Environment

But community relationship is not just about our relationship to other human beings, which means that healing communities goes beyond just healing individuals. For communities to heal, we not only need to examine the historical experience of the community as a whole. We also need to perceive how the community, as a collective of individuals in a particular place and time, relates to its place in the world. Some go as far as to say that the history of human is itself founded on traumatic structures (Charles 2019, p. 3). For Charles, being 'the historical subject of trauma' connects the individual to a wide web that includes practices, meanings, discourses and ethical frameworks that exceed any one categorisation of trauma (p. 5). For him, 'the heart of the matter is latent within many domains of knowing the living' (ibid.). This also includes an experience of one's material context. Place, or the non-human relation to the world, takes on particular significance here because it is often the interaction with this place, occasioned perhaps by violence or by natural disaster, that creates the phenomenological conditions for trauma.

There are countless examples of this. For instance, recent Swedish studies on child migrant populations[1] indicate widespread symptoms of Post Traumatic Stress Disorder (PTSD), anxiety and depression as well as suicidal attempts, particularly high amongst refugee children who come without parents (Hollander 2020, pp. 3–4). Brieger suggests that trauma reveals itself as an 'intertwined and inseparable social biological history' (ct. in Walters et al. 2011, p. 182). Further research on decolonsation suggests that the global context of trauma, including social and historical events, also needs to account for the relation between land and suffering of minority and non-Western populations (Andermahr 2016).

A consideration of place is particularly important when we consider continuing trauma, referred diagnostically through continuing traumatic disorder (CSD), where trauma is occurring on a regular basis. Mahmud Sehwail documented this experience in his work as a consultant in the Bethlehem Mental Hospital and visits with Palestinian prisoners in Israeli jails. The experience of place is crucial here, because it is the place itself, and the ongoing violence experienced in the place, that facilitates the trauma. Sehwail notes that:

> [w]hen army incursions routinely take place, shooting is heard in the night and houses are demolished, or when checkpoints are closed…or when we cannot visit family members in other Palestinian towns and villages, these are repeated, continuing traumatic events.
>
> *2005, p. 55*

In this physical context, the work of healing was particularly hard because the violence continued, and the place itself continued to be a source of trauma. For Dr. Sehwail, the violation of rights that enables the violence is part of the same discourse of healing as the individual cases that he sees in the hospital and prison (p. 56).

This experience of collective trauma has led researchers to suggest that trauma can be acquired and transferred individually and collectively through genetic, behavioural and psychological factors (O'Neill 2019). For instance, in accounts of First Nations trauma in North America, O'Neill suggests that the violence disconnection individuals experience from their country, community, family and language, and the loss that results from this, has created an experience of pain and anguish that has caused a dramatic alteration in the 'physical, emotional, intellectual and psychological functioning and the DNA of First Nations people' (p. 55). Suggesting that trauma can alter the DNA of communities is nuanced and requires further long-term epigenetic study. However, what O'Neill emphasises here is that the experience of trauma requires not only accounting for relational rupture between people but also an individual and a community's relational rupture and loss of 'disconnection from country'.

This interpretation differs from Protevi, who suggests that a subject is not genetically inherited, but that 'we do develop a subject when it is called forth by cultural practices' (2009, p. 23). Somatic affect, rather than 'gene-centric natural selection', carries through the organism of a population (p. 22). The different 'types' of subject that are called out ('the distribution of cognitive and affective patterns, thresholds, and triggers in a given population') create the affective condition of the population (p. 23). Ayer et al. also draw on this as they examine the loss of land occasioned by Palestinian populations in the Israel-Palestine conflicts. They suggest that ongoing exposure to conflict can lead to widespread changes in community experience, 'changes in the way Israelis and Palestinians think, feel and act', which might not always translate as a PTSD diagnosis, but do contribute to public health impact (2015, p. 1). In this example, trauma is experienced as a group of individuals, as a community, in a particular place.

Further work on decolonisation theory points to the traumas of minority communities. Andermahr critiques a static definition of trauma theory. For her, our readings of trauma require this continued engaged self-critique, continuing to situate each experience of trauma in its globalised context, by considering the individual historical and social contexts that produce and receive trauma narratives. This means then being 'open and attentive to the diverse strategies of representation and resistance' of these specific contexts (2016, p. 503). Any such attempt clearly requires understanding how a population responds to the physical context of their community. Evidence of the need for a dynamic critique of what constitutes trauma is found in ecosocial theory. Ecosocial theory develops an epidemiological framework that integrates social inequalities with biological conceptualisations of health and context, in a holistic picture of human embodiment (Krieger 1999). Historical trauma is defined by the experience of an event inflicted on another person, which includes perpetration against their environment, with intent of annihilation or painful disruption of traditional ways of life and identity (Walters et al. 2011).

Of course, this means that if we consider conversations about the healing of a community and an individual, then we really need to examine how a relation to place might be important. This relationship is often crucial to the experience of particular forms of trauma. Knotsch and Lamouche write that breaking relationship with the land is the 'single most important factor in health problems among Aboriginal peoples' (2010, ct. in Robbins and Dewar 2011, p. 13). Similarly, Walters et al. point us to how our measures of health need to account for not only intergenerational factors but also how historical and social experiences can impact on overall wellbeing. This could, for instance, include experiences of forced relocation or, in the example of First Nations individuals, the experience of federally mandated boarding schools for young children, as seen in the previous case (2011).

An example of this includes land-based interventions amongst Cree populations in Canada. A qualitative study connected the First Nations community's sense of attachment to their land as an 'integral part' of individual and communal wellbeing and a source of trauma healing (Walsh et al. 2020, p. 207). Here, the transformation of relationship takes shape in a relationship to place. The land-based healing practice included developing emotional health and relational connection through a series of activities that participants conducted while in the wilderness. Wildcat et al. note that the reconnection to land is particularly important in healing the traumas occasioned by colonisation, which included the dispossession of place. They suggest that the reconnection to land is a fundamental part of healing the trauma of Indigenous people. This reconnection extends beyond the repossession of the dispossessed and includes reconnection to 'the social relations, knowledges and languages that arise from land' (2014, ct. in Walsh et al. 2020, p. 208).

In ecotherapeutic practice, however, it is not just resituating a person in relation to place. Rather, this work of situatedness requires looking at the deeper connections between our subjectivity and the natural world. David Kidner explores how our experience of our self connects with this wider experience of the natural world. The task of healing requires understanding our interconnection with the natural order (2001, ct. in Buzzell 2016). The phenomenological splitting of experience between the natural world and the human experience requires reintegration. For this, Buzzell suggests that somatic work could enable us to extend our experience of bodied consciousness to incorporate the wider natural experience.

Our awareness of breath becomes connected to the wider 'breath of the world', and the experience of our bodies is one that links rather than splits us off from the body of nature (pp. 76–77). In some instances, the somatic therapy can be experienced as a kind of 'rewilding' of the self, reconnecting the body to its wider interaction with the natural world and its movement. In other instances, nature can act as the positive resource that enables a creative connectivity to something stable outside of the self (Kelly 2016, p. 90). In any case, the aims of ecotherapy generally include reconnecting the fragmented pathological human condition or loss to a wider relationship with the natural living world.

I have presented some examples in which the connection to nature and place can become a source of healing for the relational self. But what we see in the initial examples is also how the destruction of place can be experienced as traumatic to an individual and a community. The examples I gave were experiences of colonisation and conflict. However, increasing research is being conducted into trauma resulting from the destruction of nature itself. As such, this experience of splitting off and the ensuing destruction of the natural world become phenomenologically incredibly significant and complex. Kidner suggests that we somehow suffer with the earth, as if recognise 'that the world we inhabit is a "world of wounds"' (2001, p. 37). The woundedness of place, experienced as ecological disintegration in the form of flooding, deforestation, global warming, desertification, can be secondarily experienced as trauma in a range of ways, from conflict to starvation, immigration to political upheaval. But it can also be directly experienced as eco-trauma, as the widespread human community experiences a threatening dislocation of their place in the world (Buzzell 2016).

A Transformed Phenomenology

Joe Hinds suggests that the relation to nature can enable profound experiences of interconnectedness that brings individuals out of loneliness and into the possibility of connecting with the outer world. He proposes that 'an embodied emotional immersion within a…natural environment' can initiate transformational moments of self-realisation and an experience of one's connection to the rest of the world (2016, p. 52). The potential of nature to serve as a relational tool is particularly important as it presents a possibility of addressing trauma 'without an explicit therapeutic intervention' and without the limits of nature (ibid.). However, it is also important to note the destructive and traumatic effects that nature can have. That our connection to nature is pre-reflectively always 'good' and transformative offers a somewhat naïve interpretation of the nature that is 'red in tooth and claw'.

If, however, explored as a living experience itself, as well as an intermediary living experience that reconnects us with others, we can critically attune to the transformative benefits of this relation. This can be seen in Raphaely's work with survivors of torture. She suggests that the fragmentation of the bodied experience requires a need for 'extreme psychic containment'. In her work, nature (referred to as 'Mother Nature') can become a protective shield that 'can transcend the trauma, allowing a deeply peaceful external space in which the internal transformation can begin' (2010, p. 23). In these accounts, it is as if nature personifies the archetypal healer and haven of refuge.

In Amira's account of trauma introduced at the beginning of the book, she referenced how she felt the pain of trauma lift in her body when she left the city for the countryside. The clenched body was given opportunity to release from processing the constant hum of noise and movement. In these instances, the natural world becomes a route into the unspeakable experience that the individual has been carrying alone. In these ways, nature can have 'transformational effects of nature on the human condition' (Hinds 2016, p. 45). However, while much has been written about the intuitive or measured therapeutic benefits of ecological relationship, this means examining how the relationship between the human and the natural world can be experienced phenomenologically. Merleau-Ponty, Lévinas and Ricœur each consider the body in its separation and relation to the outer world. As a result of this, I would suggest that phenomenology of transfiguration might help us to understand how the relation to the natural world might heal trauma, as well as what the limits might be to these insights.

It is not just ecopsychology that brings attention to the transformational relation between human beings and nature. Theology makes note of it too. For instance, in Buddhist texts, the suffering of one being was connected to the suffering of the wider world, which included the natural world. It is a relational transformation. In the Buddhist narrative entitled 'The Great Departure', a young Siddhartha decides to leave behind the excess of royal life in pursuit of finding an end to suffering. This required recognising the interconnection of suffering amongst all sentient life (Gyal and Flanagan 2017). In the Hebrew Torah, the laws of Moses continuously connect the wellbeing of the land with the pursuit of justice and care for the orphan and the widow (see Deut. 16:20 and Deut. 11).

Hebrew scriptures continuously connect the outworking of justice with wider land-based practices (see, for instance, Deut 15; Deut 21:10–14; Deut 25:1–3; Deut 22:6–7; Isa 2:7). Lacking access to food and shelter, experiences which directly impact health and communal wellbeing, showed human dependence on nature (Gushee 2010, p. 250), and the flourishing of the natural world was experienced as a human good. Similarly in early Christian scriptures, Paul writes about the phenomenological interconnection between the healing of human beings and the natural world. He writes

> The creation waits in eager expectation for the children of God to be revealed...in hope that the creation itself will be liberated from its bondage to decay and brought into the freedom and glory of the children of God. We know that the whole creation has been groaning as in the pains of childbirth right up to the present time.
>
> *Rom. 8:19–22, NIV*

Paul uses personification to exemplify a relational transfiguration that is taking place here. Most modern interpreters translate the word *creation* here to refer to the non-human other, including animals and environment (Douglas Moo 2010, p. 28).

But what kind of body are we talking about when we make these, at times, questionable leaps of agency and materiality between the human and non-human experience? Espen Dahl suggests that Paul's account of the body makes an important distinction: whilst phenomenology via Husserl differentiates between the first person suffering and lived body (*Leib*) and the material objective body (*Körper*) (2019), Dahl suggests that this broken body, which Romans refers to as being 'liberated from its bondage to decay', experiences 'a profound sense of receptive passivity' (ibid.), which challenges straightforward relational notions of completely active agency and subjectivity.

Dahl suggests that the body plays such a central role in philosophy because of its ability to overcome the cryptic relationship between consciousness and the rest of the external world. He writes that '[a]s consciousness is a way of being in the body, the world never appears foreign: for the body irreducibly belongs to both consciousness and world, as a third dimension' (2019, p. 14). Charles Brown and Ted Toadvine show that phenomenology can also play a significant role in connecting this conscious experience to the wider world. The method requires starting from experience, rather than thought. So, starting from an experience of dislocation from place, for instance, becomes a phenomenological point of departure, rather than our ideas of what that 'should' theoretically look like. It gives us a space to look at the 'interrelationship between organism and world in its metaphysical and axiological dimensions' (2003, p. xiv). This means really grappling with the given 'stuff' of experience, rather than abstraction about that experience (p. xi). It helps us to see how different planes of experience intersect to form what we deem 'healthy', what we understand by 'place' and broad terms like 'natural'.

Philosophers have often argued that phenomenologists such as Lévinas promote a deeply anthropocentric view of relationship, because of references to the body (face, caress etc.). However, more contemporary scholarship suggests that Lévinas could help us to develop a 'deep' ethical relationship between humanity and nature. For instance, it could be easy to see how Lévinas' concern for the vulnerable other would translate into a responsibility for any situation that causes suffering, which could include trauma induced by destruction of habitat. Christian Diehm goes even further to suggest that 'every body is the other', in a way that extends to other sentient beings, though this differs from Lévinas' own hesitations (p. xvii). However, even in maintaining the human unique face, Lévinas continues to vie against totalisation, suggesting that even the natural world should not be reduced to assimilation (Diehm 2006, p. 173). Diehm suggests witnessing the suffering of another 'moves' us to respond: '[c]onsequently, it is the suffering of the other that initiates the "ethical perspective of the interhuman"' (p. 175). Suffering here, however, does not just refer to pain, or to a conscious awareness of suffering, but rather to the 'cries that emanate from the flesh', even if not fully conscious (p. 176). This brings Diehm to suggest that it is the body's vulnerability, the material flesh exposed, that preconditions the capacity to suffer, suggesting that it is the presence of flesh, rather than full consciousness, that becomes the precondition for responsiveness (p. 177).

While Diehm recognises that Lévinas hesitates to stretch responsibility past the human face, I would suggest that Diehm's reading permits us to show just how implicated our relation to the world is in this experience. The prohibition 'thou shall not kill', which grounds our subjectivity, the very prohibition that is so often violated in experiences of trauma, implicates us. And it implicates us not only in seeing and responding to the suffering flesh of another person but also in connecting our response to the wider relations that caused it, which invariably lead us to considering the traumatised person's experience of natural place. Whether or not this discourse extends into non-human animals goes beyond the intention of this book. But what Lévinas does show us is how our experience of trauma, if we take it from that very basic place, means that we need to examine how our relationship to the natural world can become a condition for another person's suffering – and when that is the case, then it very much does matter to our subjectivity.

Merleau-Ponty's phenomenology of existence may also shed some insight into the connection between natural and human healing, in instances of trauma. His emphasis on how our bodied lives exist in the world, in 'dialogic relation *with* the world', as well as his propensity to use phenomenology as a way of reevaluating the 'normal' structures of existence, suggest that he might offer important insight (Fischer 2007, p. 185). In Merleau-Ponty's critique of Cartesian dualism, for instance, he develops the notion of flesh as a 'formative medium' that unifies subject and object, the sentient and the sensed (Fischer 2007, p. 185). In doing this, he wants to think differently about what human experience is, and about how consciousness, filtered through the materiality of the body, really interacts and dialogues with the rest of the material world.

This somewhat two-dimensional existence helps us to rethink what constitutes subjectivity, as well as the 'blurring (but not fusion) of ego-boundaries between self and world' (Fischer 2007, p. 187). Fisher suggests that Merleau-Ponty offers a way of reframing the conversation, rather than providing 'a set of ahistorical maxims' (p. 186). This can be helpful in our interpretation of trauma healing, because Merleau-Ponty is directing our imagination towards the interconnection between bodied lives and the material world, while at the same time problematising exactly 'what' that differentiation actually is. Magearu argues that phenomenology can help us to think through the interconnection of experiences and destabilisation of self that occurs in trauma, such as the existential displacement of torture and its internal and external wounds (2019). For her, phenomenology can reveal a synergy of experiences that contrast with the experiences of a body's objectification, as experienced in historical violence of colonisation and racism, as well as torture (ibid.). An example of this can be seen in Douglas Brown's previous example of the black body, read as 'cartel' for the slave-owner in contrast to the embodied freedom of the body in relation to the divine.

Magearu explores this synergy through Merleau-Ponty's study of the perceiving and conscious body. For Merleau-Ponty, the body is distinguishable from other objects because of its ability to perceive, relate and orient itself in relation to other objects. But it is not a dispatched consciousness – this perceiving body is 'simultaneously immanent and intentional', acting as the intersection experience through which perception occurs (Magearu 2019, p. 52). Still, there is a separation between the body and the object. This 'bodily space' differentiates itself from 'external space' through being a 'vantage point' of 'lived unity of the senses and motor functions of the body' (ibid.). This unified perceptive phenomenon, the body, holistically connects us to the world, whilst differentiating us, our intentionality towards this world and ability to rework, absorb and experience the world outside of ourselves.

Conclusion

This interaction between the world and the body, between the perceiving consciousness that adapts itself as consciousness and matter to the world around it, through its intentional interconnection, will of course be affected by that world. In this account, Merleau-Ponty develops a kind of somatic empathy with the outer world. In later works, he shows us that the world is experienced through a holistic organism of sorts, but this relationship is with a flesh that is both sensed and sensing. This reversibility (Magearu 2019) shows that lived embodied consciousness connects a complex circularity: of touching and being touch. Returning to somatic theory shows us that bodied consciousness responds to, and is healed through, the circular phenomenology of proper touch. Many ecotherapists also accept the somatic experience of healing touch. In their view, touch can be extended out to the non-human other as well. Nature and other forces in our field of perception can engage with us in sentient interaction with the world that 'interfolds' into our experience of our bodies.

Note

1 According to a recent WHO report, about half of the world's refugees are less than 18 years old (Bradby et al. 2015).

12

CONCLUSION

This book has been a journey through understanding how trauma is *lived*. It has also been a reflection on how this phenomenological understanding can help us and our communities to heal. Trauma is deeply personal and individualised. It also has the capacity to connect a diversity of people through a shared experience. At the beginning of this book, I shared the story of my friend's experience of trauma. Amira showed me two things. First, her unique experience of suffering is tied to her own story. Second, she also recognises a connection between her trauma and others who have experienced their own pain. Trauma, I have argued, needs to represent this multidirectional experience (Rothberg 2009) that includes an experience of the material body and consciousness, while also including our social relationships and the collective experience of being human that emerge out of responding to the places that we live in.

Gaining insight into how someone lives their trauma uniquely requires understanding and interpreting the connections that form their subjectivity. This is why I have used phenomenology – to explore how human experience comprises relational moments that are lived through a bodied consciousness. I wanted to use philosophers who had written on, or had some experience of trauma, as a way of connecting this seemingly 'abstract' thought game into the real experiences that Lévinas, Ricœur and Merleau-Ponty each worked through. But then I knew that, if keeping to these philosophers and their view of experience, I had to also consider how trauma could be lived as transformative – that is, how healing might be possible. This was a particularly uncomfortable point for me because I recognise, both in my own work and in the clinical and communal work of those around me, that this is a difficult, personal and highly individualised experience. The philosophers I chose recognised this as well, but they persisted in acknowledging that a transformative experience is possible.[1]

DOI: 10.4324/9780367800017-16

Metaphorical Transformation in Ricœur

Transformation can be a loaded word, which is why it is important to situate phenomenologically in the conversation of healing. It is easy to end up saying too much, and thereby reducing the discourse to a well-meant series of wishes. This is not the intent of this book. Rather, it suggests that there is a possibility of a hopeful conversation about healing through holding space for the lived experience of trauma itself. But it must be held wholly. To unpack this, I have looked at Ricœur in particular, through his narrative phenomenology. For Ricœur, the literal telling of story is always going to have its problems for a variety of reasons. The challenge is that language involves us in the discipline of meaning creation. In *The Rule of Metaphor*, he devotes a whole book to unpack the role of metaphor, as the language phenomenon through which the 'poetic image "becomes a new being"' (Ricœur 2003, p. 214).

The problem with any literal 'telling' of trauma is that it does not reveal the nuance of what remained unsaid in a survivor's story; what could not be said. Nor does it address the images through which language was making this 'new being'. According to Ricœur, this is where metaphor is required. For Ricœur, metaphor uses language through the capacity to address the gap between the unsayable past and the 'becoming of expression' (2003, p. 214). It is this definition of metaphorical refiguration and opening that brings us into conversation with Ricœur. Kearney, in his interpretation of Ricœur, writes how the French philosopher is able to reconfigure the past time through 'the metaphorical function of "seeing as"', which Ricœur extends to the 'broadly imaginative function of "providing oneself with a figure of"' (2015, p. 178). It is this imaginative provision of a figure that was not previously there to refigure the current configuration of the experienced reality that spoke to the situation I found myself in. I needed to find images that would connect to literal interpretations of events in such a way that the factual experience would be refigured, and the unspeakable could be meaningfully traversed.

Ricœur starts *Rule of Metaphor* by developing Aristotle's definition of metaphor. In the *Poetics*, 'Metaphor consists in giving the thing a name that belongs to something else' (1996, lines 145766–145769), that is, 'a name that belongs to something else' (145767), or an 'alien name' (1457–1631). But the naming is not random: it works within a network of relation-rules, in order to 'disturb' the entire network through inventing a new order (Ricœur 2003, pp. 21–22). Serving a mimetic function, Aristotle's definition of metaphor holds us close to the tensions inherent in human reality, while at the same time stretching our ordering of reality to 'what could happen', that is' the far-ranging flight of fable-making' (p. 39). Metaphor enables us to see what is not initially apparent: the power of poetry that reveals an 'expression of existence as alive' (p. 42). This 'existence as alive' is phenomenologically significant to both somatic and narrative understandings of health, as lived in trauma.

Ricœur develops the poetic definition of metaphor phenomenologically. The metaphor involves a shifting from literal to a figurative sense of experience (p. 188).

Henle suggests that metaphor works through the resemblance between terms. Metaphor enables the cognitive meaning of language to expand into the realm of effect (p. 194). This draws on Aristotle's' concept of *epiphora* – the unity of two ideas that are at a distance to each other that develops an insight akin to a new kind of 'seeing' (p. 195). The difference between the terms is maintained, as the 'same' offers a new vision (p. 196). As such, 'enigma lives on in the heart of metaphor': the 'same' is present, along with 'the different' (p. 196).

This 'grasping' of a new identity, in the midst of difference, provides a way for identity and difference to confront each other, rather than melt into the same (p. 199). This is the moment where healing is possible. But if it remains in language, then it is devoid of the somatic dimension that psychology and phenomenology require. Ricœur presents metaphor as a moment in which the linguistic can open up into another – literally spring-board us out of the logic of the same, into another experience of being. In trying to 'tell' a narrative that is both present and absent, that is simultaneously the facts presented and that which is not present, metaphor can enable a reading of traumatic phenomenon that continuously opens and rearranges the previous logic of a narrative's fact-telling. But Ricœur cautions us that we need to unpack the intricacies of 'equivalence', that is, how we account for the comparatively equivalent orders of logic. We can 'say too much'. This 'seeing anew' that metaphor presents requires both the tension of reference and then recognising the poetic function of the 'totality', which is 'irreducible to a simple' string of metaphors (Ricœur 2003, p. 219).

Auerhahn and Laub, in reference to Holocaust testimony, cautions that there is often a tendency to 'say too much' about trauma. This, they suggest, is particularly problematic in psychological readings of experience, in which an experience of suffering is treated psychopathologically, in a way that 'discourages understanding [a traumatic event] as a core existential and relational experience' (1998, p. 21). Ricœur picks up on this in his analysis of psycholinguistic definitions of metaphor. He does not want to reduce it to a psychological concept, a diagnosis that can be treated through language. But rather, he is presenting a sensible moment for language: one that sets an experience 'before the eyes' (p. 219) and invites the reader into exploring an experience that is 'more than' its initial logic structure.

This metaphorical conception, drawing on Aristotle, regards the interaction between the terms: rather than offering an exhausted substitution 'between one and another sign, between the literal and the figural sense', Ricœur's metaphor expands the interaction. For him, 'the metaphor is a break with the contextual expectations: the metaphor is conceived as an interaction with a context', an expansion of the linguistic meaning (Rasmussen 2019, p. 26). Whereas Hester's definition of metaphor easily fuses the meaning of sense and senses in order to create a hard 'verbal icon' (p. 206), Ricœur suggests that the suspension and rearrangement of metaphor enables an 'evocation', rather than a fusion of phenomenon. For Ricœur:

> We must reserve the possibility that metaphor is not limited to suspending rational reality but that in opening meaning up on the imaginative side, it

> also opens it toward a dimension of reality that does not coincide with what ordinary language envisions under the name of natural reality.
>
> *p. 211*

This new dimension of reality provides a way of 'seeing as', in which the sense and the image are held in tension with one another. The poetic language itself becomes a 'source of psychic activity' that results in the growing of a new sort of being. In this new language being, both fusion and tension remain apparent.

Ricœur's metaphor teaches us what we do not yet know (cannot know through mere fact). As a figure of speech, it presents something new in its conflict, and in the conflict generates a 'fusion of difference into [an "open"] identity' (p. 198). As if it is half thought, and half experience, metaphor evokes experience and act. It fuses sense and the imaginary in a way that propels understanding into action (pp. 213–214). Now language, through the poetic image, becomes a 'source of psychic activity' (p. 215) by creating activity through the language game itself.

This is where I think that metaphor has always held a crucial place for trauma narrative and serves as a spring board to conversations about healing. It avoids the psycholinguistic problem of equivalence, because the poetic rendering is not trying to 'treat' but only re-present the unsayability of trauma in order for it to emerge out of an experiential 'stuckness'. But it must resist the post-traumatic narrative tendency of saying too much, too soon. Bringing trauma experience into the language play of metaphor, through the cathartic arc of tragic poetry, evokes the sensible aspect of metaphor, sense and image held together, but does not collapse either into each other.

For instance, consider Amichai's poem, where he writes (in translation) of the trauma of war in *The Precision of Pain and the Blurriness of Joy*:

> "This one's a throbbing pain, that one's a wrenching pain, this one gnaws, that one burns, this is a sharp pain and that—a dull one. Right here. Precisely here, yes, yes." Joy blurs everything. I've heard people say after nights of love and feasting, "It was great, I was in seventh heaven." Even the spaceman who floated in outer space, tethered to a spaceship, could say only, "Great, wonderful, I have no words".
>
> *2000, p. 99*

Seiden Henry suggests that the metaphor of the doctor's office visit to permit an open understanding of pain's precision and the blurring of joy (2016, p. 164). That which is rendered unsayable through factual representation is given another chance at opening.

Ricœur's phenomenology of metaphor can enable a reconceptualisation of the interplay between language and experience that offers what Stauffer requires for trauma to be witnessed. She writes that: 'Once established and held in safety, the trauma narrative, like the human subject, may require for its freedom a present moment in which something new is possible' (Stauffer 2015, p. 175).

Ricœur's phenomenology goes further into presenting a new being through language. Through disturbing the whole network of being, it makes one see things. Metaphor offers new footholds for us: the metaphor becomes a part of this act of living.

Healing Beyond Metaphor

The challenge, however, when discussing this approach in application to the lived narratives of trauma survivors is the naiveté with which it can be dogmatically applied. Surely metaphor alone cannot evoke the ethical imperative that this unsayable trauma reveals! Kearney picks up on this fear when he writes that, in making phenomenon visible that were not, the 'figural "as if" might collapse into a literal belief, so that we would no longer merely see-as but make the mistake of believing we are seeing' (1995, p. 179). This 'hallucination of presence' requires maintaining the tension of 'belief *and* disbelief, engagement *and* estrangement' (ibid.). In order for the language to reverberate through existence in such a way that it becomes a 'source of psychic activity' (2015, p. 215), an understanding of what that trauma gap entails (its *unsayability*) is required.

In *The Rule of Metaphor*, Ricœur posits that 'to understand is to do something' (2003, p. 213). The phenomenological exposition has an ethical implication that entails action. However, bridging that transformation between understanding and movement often requires a phenomenological extension beyond the current description of existence as we see it. Ricoeur's phenomenology of metaphor might address the issues of unsayability in the trauma narrative, through the unique use of language as a refiguration of seeing. Metaphor, therefore, serves a phenomenological purpose that engages the 'depths of existence', in which 'a new being in language' becomes 'a "growth of being"' (p. 215). The gap of unsayability is filled through the fusion of new images. 'Yes words really do dream', Ricoeur writes (ibid.).

In this book, we looked at how trauma and healing could be understood through the tools of phenomenology that allow us to connect the various points of experience into a creative whole. The aim of this was to give space for the point that we are continuously confronted with in the literature and experience: just as there is no 'one' experience of trauma, so neither is there one way of healing it. Existential phenomenology opens up a way for conversations to be connected between somatic and psychoanalytic theory, as well as wider conceptualisations of political and social experiences of health.

These chapters explored how wider definitions of health are required if we are to hold space for the ambiguity of traumatic experience. Healing trauma involves a variety of experiences, because the traumas themselves are varied and have a range of causes and interpretations. Healing trauma also requires that we acknowledge our own experiential part. Lévinas' subject becomes herself in relation to the other, and the relation transcends our ability to comprehend it. A similar experience takes place in encountering the traumatised other. It requires allowing the other's experience to affect us as well. For Stauffer, this is the only way that testimony can work. If we keep testimony to the individual experience of telling a story in order to 'exorcise it' and 'move one from past harm', then we are not truly listening to the other. The work of healing requires something of us. This is why Stauffer writes that hearing that is meaningful 'has to be embedded in an openness where what is said might be heard event if it threatens to break the order of the known world for those who listen' (2015, p. 112). Just as the embodied consciousness in conversation with itself is required, a phenomenology of healing also needs the experience of relationship to the other and the world.

Healing needs to acknowledge interrelationship. Kearney suggests that interrelationality transforms exile to homecoming. In Lévinas, it is from the moment of home or the 'interiority within the self' that we can extend the opening of our 'home' to the 'radically alien' (Kearney 2009, p. 168). Ricœur's own experience of captivity made him aware that his relational subjectivity had to account for 'the dark traversal of the abyss' (p. 172). This re-connection between the bodied consciousness, to the other, and extended into a relation to place transforms each element of the suffering experience as a re-perceiving of its place in the whole relational experience.

Writing on the intergenerational trauma of the Holocaust, Rothberg states that we need to challenge all exclusivist and hierarchical attempts to make sense of trauma. It is not a matter of acknowledging one trauma at the expense of another. Trauma is experienced in particular contexts, but it is the ambiguously unified experience of suffering that exerts itself on the body and memory that unifies each of these disparate accounts. This is because 'collective memories of seemingly distinct histories – such as those of slavery, the Holocaust and colonisation- are not easily separable' (2008, p. 524). Of course, Brunner has shown us that practically this can be very hard. In order to hear the voice of suffering, we have to have acknowledged at some level that this person is a victim. Concurrently, our understanding of victimhood must be maintained within the wider dialogue of phenomenological experience.

Concluding Thoughts

Understanding the phenomenology of healing means that we need to account for the interconnection of trauma experiences. For instance, ascertaining that the body stores memory, that the activation of the stress response (the hypothalamic-pituitary-adrenal axis) over time can lead to detrimental epigenetic and neurobiological health effects and that traumatic experience is unlikely to disappear over time (Scheeringa and Zeanah 2001) is all important to constructing the phenomenological experience of individualised trauma. It is also important to account for the high rate of attrition in individual therapies and that attachment can relate to worsening effects of psychological trauma symptoms (Nugent et al. 2016; Gold and Jordan 2018) and exploring how memory constantly interconnects with experience and re-negotiates itself shows that relationship is central to both the experience and healing of trauma. It also reveals that this relationship is not just exclusive to human beings but with the wider world around us. To understand healing, we need to go beyond engaging with trauma as a straightforward Post Traumatic Stress Disorder (PTSD) symptomatology.

The imperative to live this healing journey of trauma is increasingly evident as we move into the paradoxical convergences of chaos and reform, progress and regression that characterises the twenty-first century. But, whilst demanding much of us and our abilities to listen, pause and re-figure fractured relationality structures and forms, this call to heal is an imperative of hope. It signals that health is, indeed, possible, if only re-imagined with our old and tired eyes and re-lived in our broken and bruised bodies, in our torn and used spaces.

Note

1 For example, as shown in Merleau-Ponty in the intercorporeal communications between people, Fink writes that, for Merleau-Ponty, '[t]he cure does not consist in working things out at a cognitive level, but is to be found in novel ways of re-enacting the affective scenario in the co-presence of an other (the analyst)' (2019, p. 40).

BIBLIOGRAPHY

Alford, C. F. (2012). 'Winnicott and Trauma'. *Psychoanalysis, Culture & Society*. 18(3), 259–276. doi: 10.1057/pcs.2012.28

Alford, F. (2013). 'Forgiveness as Transitional Experience: A Winnicottian Approach'. *International Journal of Applied Psychoanalytic Studies.* 10(4), doi: 10.1002/aps.1329

Améry, J. (1980). *At the Mind's Limits: Contemplations by a Survivor on Auschwitz and its Realities.* S. Rosenfeld & S. P. Rosenfeld (trans.) Bloomington, IN: Indiana University Press.

American Psychiatric Association. (1993/1980). *Diagnostic and Statistical Manual.* Washington, DC: APA Press.

Amichai, Y. (2000). *Selected Poems.* T. Hughes & D. Weissbort (eds.) London: Faber & Faber Ltd.

Andermahr, S. (2016). *Decolonialising Trauma Studies: Trauma and Postcolonialism.* Basel: MDPI.

Anderson, I. (2016). *Ethics and Suffering since the Holocaust: Making Ethics 'First Philosophy' in Levinas, Wiesel and Rubenstein.* New York, NY: Routledge.

APA (2013). *Diagnostic and Statistical Manual of Mental Disorders. Fifth Edition.* Washington, DC: American Psychiatric Association.

APA (1994). *DSM -IV: Diagnostic and Statistical Manual of Mental Disorders.* Washington, DC: American Psychiatric Association.

APA (1980). *Diagnostic and Statistical Manual of Mental Disorders. Third Edition.* Washington, DC: American Psychiatric Association.

Arboleda-Flórez, J. & Stuart, H. (2012). 'From Sin to Science: Fighting the Stigmatisation of Mental Illness'. *The Canadian Journal of Psychiatry.* 57(8), 457–463.

Aristotle (1996). *Poetics.* M. Heath (trans.) London: Penguin Classics.

Auerhahn, N. C. & Laub, D. (2018). 'Against Forgiving: The Encounter that Cannot Happen Between Holocaust Survivors and Perpetrators'. *The Psychoanalytic Quarterly.* 87(1). doi: 10.1080/00332828.2018.1430401

Auerhahn, N. C. & Laub, D. (1998). 'Intergenerational Memory of the Holocaust'. *International Handbook of Multigenerational Legacies of Trauma. The Plenum Series on Stress and Coping.* Y. Danieli (ed.) Boston, MA: Springer, 21–41.

Auerhahn, N. C. & Laub, D. (1993). 'Knowing and Not Knowing Massive Psychic Trauma: Forms of Traumatic Memory'. *The International Journal of Psychoanalysis.* 74(2), 287–302.

Ayer, L., Venkatesh, B., Stewart, R., Mandel, D., Stein, B. & Schoenbaum, M. (2015). 'Psychological Aspects of the Israeli-Palestinian Conflict: A Systematic Review.' *Trauma, Violence and Abuse.* 18(3), 322–338.

Badenoch, B. (2008). *Being a Brain-Wise Therapist: A Practical Guide to Interpersonal Neurobiology.* New York: W. W. Norton & Company.

Beardsworth, S. (2009). 'Overcoming the Confusion of Loss and Trauma: The Need of Thinking Historically'. *The Trauma Controversy.* K. Brown Golden & B. G. Bergo (eds.) Albany, NY: SUNY, 45–70.

Ben-Arieh, A. & Tarshish, N. (2017). 'Children's Rights and Well-Being'. *Handbook of Children's Rights.* M. D. Ruck, M. Peterson-Badali & M. Freeman (eds.), New York City: Routledge, Ch. 5.

Bjørnholt Michaelsen, C. (2015). 'Tracing a Traumatic Temporality: Levinas and Derrida on Trauma and Responsibility'. *Levinas Studies.* 10, 43–77. doi: 10.1353 /lev.2016.0003

Blanchard, E. B., Hickling, E. J., Buckley, T. C., Taylor, A. E., Vollmer, A. & Loos, W. R. (1996). 'Psychophysiology of Posttraumatic Stress Disorder Related to Motor Vehicle Accidents: Replication and Extension'. *Journal of Consulting and Clinical Psychology.* 64(4), 742–751. https://doi.org/10.1037/0022-006X.64.4.742

Blonigen, D. M., Hicks, B. M, Clarson, M. D., Patrick, C. J., Iacono, W. G. & MGue, M. (2013). 'Psychopathic Personality Traits and Environmental Contexts: Differential Correlates, Gender Differences, and Genetic Mediation.' *Personality Disorders: Theory, Research, and Treatment, 3*(3), 209–227. https://doi.org/10.1037/a0025084

Boase, E. & Frechette, C. G. (eds.) (2016). *Bible Through the Lens of Trauma.* Atlanta, GA: SBL.

Bonanno G. A. (2004). 'Loss, Trauma, and Human Resilience: Have We Underestimated the Human Capacity to Thrive After Extremely Adverse Events?' *American Psychologist.* (59), 20–28.

Bloom, H. (2009). *Bloom's Modern Critical Views: Margaret Atwood.* New York City: InfoBase Publishing.

Bosi, A. (1995). *Brazil and the Dialectic of Colonialization.* Champaign, IL: The University of Illinois.

Bowlby, J. (1969). *Attachment and Loss: Vol. 1. Attachment.* New York, NY: Basic Books.

Bracha, S. & Maser, J. D. (2008). 'Anxiety and Posttraumatic Stress Disorder in the Context of Human Brain Evolution: A Role for Theory in *DSM-V?*' *Clinical Psychology Science and Practice.* 15(1), 91–97.

Bradby, H., Humphris, R., Newall, D., et al. (2015). 'Public Health Aspects of Migrant Health: A Review of the Evidence on Health Status for Refugees and Asylum Seekers in the European Region'. *Health Evidence Synthesis Report.* 44. Copenhagen: World Health Organization (WHO).

Breuer, J. & Freud, S. (1895/2016). *Studies in Hysteria.* Palala Press.

Brewer-Smyth, K. & Koenig, H. G. (2014). 'Could Spirituality and Religion Promote Stress Resilience in Survivors of Childhood Trauma?'. *Issues in Mental Health Nursing.* 35(4), 251–256. https://doi.org/10.3109/01612840.2013.873101

Brewin, C. R., Andrews, B. & Valentine, J. D. (2000). 'Meta-analysis of Risk Factors for Posttraumatic Stress Disorder in Trauma-Exposed Adults'. *Journal of Consulting and Clinical Psychology.* 68(5), 748–766. doi: 10.1037//0022-006x.68.5.748. PMID: 11068961.

Brown, C. & Toadvine, T. (2003). *Eco-Phenomenology: Back to the Earth Itself.* Albany, NY: SUNY York Press.

Brown Douglas, K. (2015). *Stand Your Ground.* London: Orbis.

Brown Golden, K. (2009). 'Trauma and Speech as Bodily Adaptation in Merleau-Ponty'. *The Trauma Controversy.* B. Bergo and K. Brown Golden (eds). Albany, NY: SUNY, 71–98.

Brown Golden, K. & Bergo, B. G. (2009). *The Trauma Controversy: Philosophical and Interdisciplinary Dialogues.* Albany, NY: SUNY Press.

Brunner, J. (2007). 'Trauma and Justice: The Moral Grammar of Trauma Discourse from Wilhelmine Germany to Post-Apartheid South Africa'. *Trauma and Memory: Reading, Healing and Making Law.* A. Sarat, N. Davidovitch & M. Alberstein (eds.) Stanford: SUP, Ch. 6.

Bryant-Davis, T. & Wong, E. C. (2013). 'Faith to Move Mountains: Religious Coping, Spirituality, and Interpersonal Trauma Recovery'. *American Psychologist.* 68(8), 675–684. doi: 10.1037/a0034380

Bulut, S. (2019). 'Freud's Approach to Trauma'. *Psychology and Psychotherapy: Research Study.* 3(10), 1–2. doi: 10.31031/PPRS.2019.03.000554

Burke, L. A. & Neimeyer, R. A. (2012). 'Spirituality and Health: Meaning Making in Bereavement'. *The Textbook On Spirituality in Healthcare.* M. Cobb, C. Puchalski, & B. Rumbold, (Eds.) Oxford, UK: Oxford University Press, 127–133.

Buzzell, L. (2016). 'The Many Ecotherapies'. *Ecotherapy: Theory, Research & Practice.* M. Jordan & J. Hinds (eds.) New York, NY: Palgrave Macmillan, 70–82.

Canadian Human Rights Tribunal (2016). 'First Nations Child and Family Caring Society of Canada et al. v. Attorney General of Canada (for the Minister of Indian and Northern Affairs Canada) CHRT 2 (CanLII)'. Available at: http://canlii.ca/t/gn2vg [Accessed on 20 August 2020].

Capili, A. D. (2011). 'The Created Ego in Levinas' Totality and Infinity'. *Sophia.* 50, 677–692. doi: 10.1007/s11841-011-0263-3

Carbone, M. (2004). *The Thinking of the Sensible: Merleau-Ponty's A-Philosophy.* Evanston, IL: Northwestern University Press.

Carel, H. (2008). *Illness.* Stocksfield: Acumen Publishing Ltd.

Carel, H. & McNaughton, J. (2016). 'Breathing and Breathlessness in Clinic and Culture: Using Critical Medical Humanities to Bridge an Epistemic Gap'. *Edinburgh Companion to the Critical Medical Humanities.* A. Whitehead, A. Woods & S. Atkinson (eds.) Edinburgh: Edinburgh University Press, Ch. 16.

Carr, C. P., Martins, C. M., Stingel, A. M., Lemgruber, V. B. & Juruena, M. F. (2013). 'The Role of Early Life Stress in Adult Psychiatric Disorders: A Systematic Review According to Childhood Trauma Subtypes'. *Journal of Nervous and Mental Disease.* 201, 1007–1020. doi: 10.1097/NMD.0000000000000049

Carré, J., Hyde, L., Neumann, C., Viding, E. & Hariri, A. (2013). 'The Neural Signatures of Distinct Psychopathic Traits'. *Social Neuroscience*, 8(2), 122–135.

Cassel, E. (1991/2004). *The Nature of Suffering and the Goals of Medicine.* London and Oxford: Oxford University Press.

Cassidy, J. & Shaver, P. R. (eds.) (2008). *Handbook of Attachment: Theory, Research and Clinical Applications* (2nd ed.). New York City: The Guilford Press.

Cataldi, S. L. & Hamrick, W. S. (2007). *Merleau-Ponty and Environmental Philosophy.* Albany, NY: SUNY Press.

Chalier, C. (2014). 'Ruth: The Meaning of a Conversion'. *Levinas Faces Biblical Figures.* Y. Lin (ed.) Plymouth: Lexington Books, 97–108.

Charcot, J. M. (1889/1961). 'Clinical Lectures on Certain Diseases of the Nervous System. Lecture VII. On Six Cases of Hysteria in the Male Subject'. *Classics in Psychology.* T. Shipley T (ed.). New York: Philosophical Library, 370–416.

Charles, M. (2019). 'Trauma, Identity and Social Justice'. *Psychoanalysis, Culture and Society.* https://doi.org/10.1057/s41282-018-0114-z

Choi, K. R., Seng, J. S., Briggs, E. C., Munro-Kramer, M. L., Graham-Bermann, S. A. & Ford, J. D. (2017). 'The Dissociative Subtype of Posttraumatic Stress Disorder (PTSD)

Among Adolescents: Co-Occurring PTSD, Depersonalization/Derealization, and Other Dissociation Symptoms'. *Journal of the American Academy on Child and Adolescent Psychiatry.* 56(12), 1062–1072. doi: 10.1016/j.jaac.2017.09.425

Cloitre, M., Stolbach, B. C., Herman, J. L., van der Kolk, B., Pynoos, R., Wang, J. & Petkova, E. (2009). 'A Developmental Approach to Complex PTSD: Childhood and Adult Cumulative Trauma as Predictors of Symptom Complexity'. *Journal of Traumatic Stress.* 22(5), 399–408. doi: 10.1002/jts.20444

Cohen, L. (2018). *The Flame.* Edinburgh: Cannongate Books.

Dahl, E. (2019). 'Weakness and Passivity'. *Phenomenology of the Broken Body.* E. Dahl, C. Falke & T. E. Eriksen (eds.). London: Routledge, 13–28.

Davidson, S. (2012). 'Linguistic Hospitality: The Task of Translation in Ricœur and Levinas'. *Analecta Hermeneutica.* 4, 1–14.

Davis, C. (2018). 'Life Stories: Ricœur'. *Traces of War: Interpreting Ethics and Trauma in Twentieth-Century French Writing.* C. Forsdick (ed.) Liverpool University Press, 119–133. doi: 10.2307/j.ctt1ps33bb.10

Davis, C. (2017). *Traces of War.* Cambridge: Cambridge University Press.

Davis, E. (2017). *Post-Truth: Why We Have Reached Peak Bullshit and What We Can Do About It.* London: Little Brown.

Descilo, T., Vedamurtachar, A., Gerbarg, P. L., Nagaraja, D., Gangadhar, B. N., Damodaran, B., Adelson, B., Braslow, L. H., Marcus, S., Brown, R. P. (2010) 'Effects of a Yoga Breath Intervention Alone and in Combination with an Exposure Therapy for PTSD and Depression in Survivors of the 2004 South-East Asia Tsunami.' *ACTA Psychiatrica Scandinavica.* 121, 289–300.

Diehm, C. (2006). 'Ethics and Natural History'. *Environmental Philosophy.* 3(2), 34–43. Available at: www.jstor.org/stable/26167954 [Accessed on 5 August 2021].

Dierckxsens, G. (2017). 'Responsibility and the Physical Body: Paul Ricœur on Analytical Philosophy of Language, Cognitive Science, and the Task of Phenomenological Hermeneutics'. *Philosophy Today.* 61(3), 573–593.

DiMauro, J., Carter, S., Folk, J. B. & Kashdan, T. B. (2014). 'A Historical Review of Trauma-Related Diagnoses to Reconsider the Heterogeneity of PTSD'. *Journal of Anxiety Disorders.* 28(8), 774–786. doi: 10.1016/j.janxdis.2014.09.002

Diprose, R. (2017). 'The Body and Political Violence'. *Body/Self/Other: The Phenomenology of Social Encounters.* Albany, NY: SUNY, 5–14.

Dolezal, L. & Petherbridge, D. (eds.) (2017). *Body/Self/Other: The Phenomenology of Social Encounters.* Albany, NY: SUNY.

Doran, R. (1973). 'Paul Ricœur: Toward the Restoration of Meaning'. *Anglican Theological Review.* 55(4), 443–458.

Drake, C. C. (1967). 'Jung and His Critics'. *The Journal of American Folklore.* 80(318), 321–333. doi: 10.2307/537409

Drosdick, C. (2020). 'Art Theory Treatment for Survivors of Sex Trafficking, Boys'. *Art Therapy Treatment with Sex Trafficking Survivors: Facilitating Empowerment, Recovery, and Hope.* M. K. Kometiani (ed.) New York, NY: Taylor & Francis, 113–138.

Dunphy-Blomfield, J. (2007). 'Harmony in a Dislocated World'. *Merleau-Ponty and Environmental Philosophy.* S. L. Cataldi & W. S. Hamrick (eds.) Albany, NY: SUNY Press, 217–234.

Edwards, E. (2011). 'Trauma and Event in Merleau-Ponty's Reading of Mythical Time'. *Aporia.* 21(1), 37–47.

Ericson, M. & Kjellander, B. (2018). 'The Temporal Becoming Self – Towards a Ricœurian Conceptualization of Identity'. *Scandinavian Journal of Management.* 34(2), 205–214.

Erikson, E. H. (1995). *Childhood and Society*. London: Vintage.

Erikson, K. T., (1995). *A New Species of Trouble: The Human Experience of Modern Disasters*. New York: W. W. Norton & Company.

Esterhuizen, L. (2018). 'Decolonising Biblical Trauma Studies: The Metaphorical Name Shear-jashub in Isaiah 7:3ff Read through a Postcolonial South African Perspective'. *Old Testament Essays*. 31(3), 522–533. doi: 10.17159/2312-3621/2018/v31n3a7

Fackenheim, E. (1994). *To Mend the World*. Bloomington, IN: Indiana University Press.

Falconer, R. (17 Jul 2020). 'Sexual Abuse Trauma'. Available at: https://robertfalconer.us/category/trauma/ [Accessed on 2 November 2020].

Farina, B., Liotti, M. & Imperatori, C. (2019). 'The Role of Attachment Trauma and Disintegrative Pathogenic Processes in the Traumatic-Dissociative Dimension'. *Frontiers in Psychology*. 933. https://doi.org/10.3389/fpsyg.2019.00933

Farmer, P. (2005). *Pathologies of Power: Health, Human Rights, and the New War on the Poor*. Berkeley, CA: University of California Press.

Fazzio Simão, M. & Casimiro de Camargo Sampaio, J. (2018). 'Body and Decoloniality in Performing Poetic Composition'. *Revista Brasileira de Estudos da Presença, Porto Alegre*. 8(4), 665–690. Available at: http://seer.ufrgs.br/presenca

Fegert, J. M. & Stötzel, M. (2016). 'Child Protection: A Universal Concern and a Permanent Challenge in the Field of Child and Adolescent Mental Health.' Child and Adolescent Psychiatry and Mental Health, 10(1), 18.

Feinstein, A. (2006). *Journalists Under Fire: The Psychological Hazards of Covering War*. Baltimore, MDL: Johns Hopkins University Press.

Feinstein, A. (2003). *Journalists under Fire*. Baltimore, MD: The Johns Hopkins University Press.

Felitti, V. J., Anda, R. F., Nordenberg, D., Williamson, D. F., Spitz, A. M., Edwards, V. & Marks, J. S. (1998). 'Relationship of Childhood Abuse and Household Dysfunction to Many of the Leading Causes of Death in Adults: The Adverse Childhood Experiences (ACE) Study'. *American Journal of Preventive Medicine*, 14(4), 245–258.

Ferber, I. & Swebel, P. (eds.) (2017). *Lament in Jewish Thought*. Berlin: Walter de Gruyter.

Fink, S. (2019). 'Perceiving the Vulnerable Body: Merleau-Ponty's Contribution to Psychoanalysis'. *Phenomenology of the Broken Body*. New York, NY: Routledge, 29–48.

Fischer, S. (2007). 'Social Ecology and the Flesh: Merleau-Ponty, Irigaray, and Ecocommunitarian Politics'. *Merleau-Ponty and Environmental Philosophy*. S. L. Cataldi & W. S. Hamrick (eds.) Albany, NY: SUNY Press, 203–216.

Fleck, F. (2004). 'Children are Main Victims of Trafficking in Africa'. *British Medical Journal*. 328(7447), 1036. doi: 10.1136/bmj.328.7447.1036-b

Fletcher, J. (2013). *Freud and the Scene of Trauma*. New York, NY: Fordham University Press. doi: 10.2307/j.ctt13x015n

Fleury, F. & Mahmoud-Shwana, S. (2010). 'The Rupture of Links in the Context of Migration: Open-Mouthed and Sewn-Mouthed'. *Bearing Witness: Psychoanalytic Work with People Traumatised by Torture and State Violence*. A. Gutier & A. Sabatini Scalmati (eds.), London: Karnac. 91–114.

Flynn, D. (2019). 'The Clinical Paradigms of Melanie Klein and Donald Winnicott: Comparisons and Dialogues'. *The International Journal of Psychoanalysis*. doi: 10.1080/00207578.2019.1674655\

Foa, E. B. (1995/1997) *Posttraumatic Stress Diagnostic Scale Manual*. National Computer Systems Inc.

Freud, S. (1925). *Fragment of an Analysis of a Case of Hysteria*. C. P. A. & J. Strachey (trans.) 3, 13–146. 'The Standard Edition of the Complete Psychological Works of Sigmund Freud'. Available at Psycholanalytic Electronic Publishing [Online]: https://pep-web.org/search?facets=&preview=SE.007.0001A&q=se.007.0001a [Accessed on 3 November 2021].

Freud, S. (1923/1991). *On Metapsychology – The Theory of Psychoanalysis: Beyond the Pleasure Principle, Ego and the Id and Other Works.* A. Dickson (ed.) London: Gardners Books.

Freud, S. (1920/1961). *Beyond the Pleasure Principle.* J. Strachey (trans.) New York: W.W. Norton & Co.

Freud, S. (1893). *On the Psychical Mechanism of Hysterical Phenomena.* London: Hogarth Press.

Gaines, A. D. (1992). 'From DSM-I to III-R; Voices of Self, Mastery and the Other: A Cultural Constructivist Reading of U.S. Psychiatric Classification'. *Social Science & Medicine.* 35(1), 3–24.

General Assembly (2 November 1959). 'UN Declaration on the Rights of a Child'. Public Enquiries Unit. New York: United Nations.

Gilbert, R., Kemp, A., Thoburn, J., Sidebotham, P., Radford, L., Glaser, D. & Macmillan, H. L. (2009). 'Recognising and Responding to Child Maltreatment'. *Lancet.* 373(9658), 167–180.

Glas, G. (2003). 'Idem, Ipse, and Loss of the Self'. *PPP.* 10(4), 347–352.

Gold, R. & Jordan, E. (2018). 'Grief, Poetry and the Sweet Unexpected'. *Death Studies.* 42(1), 16–25. doi: 10.1080/07481187.2017.1370413

Gone, J. P. (2013). 'Redressing First Nations Trauma: Theorising Mechanisms for Indigenous Culture as Mental Health Treatment'. *Transcultural Psychiatry.* 50(5), 683–706.

Grant, W. W. (1898). 'Railway Spine and Litigation Symptoms'. *JAMA.* 30, 956–958. doi: 10.1001/jama.1898.72440690016002a

Green, J. G., McLaughlin, K. A., Berglund, P. A., Gruber, M. J., Sampson, N. A., Zaslavsky, A. M., et al. (2010). 'Childhood Adversities and Adult Psychiatric Disorders in the National Comorbidity Survey Replication I: Associations with First Onset of DSM-IV Disorders'. *Archives of General Psychiatry.* 67, 113–123. doi: 10.1001/archgenpsychiatry.2009.186

Gushee, D. (2010). 'Environmental Ethics: Bringing Creation Care Down to Earth'. *Keeping God's Earth.* Nottingham: IVP, 245–266.

Guy, M. (2009). 'Relativism, Revelation, Infinity: Emmanuel Levinas on the Rhetoric of Possibility in the Talmud'. *JAC.* 29(3), 661–687. Available at: www.jstor.org/stable/20866918 [Accessed on 13 August 2020].

Gyal, P. & Flanagan, O. (2017). 'The Role of Pain in Buddhism: The Concept of Suffering'. *The Routledge Handbook of Philosophy of Pain.* J. Corns (ed.) Abingdon, OX: Routledge, 288–296.

Halligan, S., Michael, T., Wilhelm, D. C., Clark, D. & Ehlers, A. (2006). 'Reduced Heart Rate Response to Trauma Reliving in Trauma Survivors with PTSD'. *Journal of Traumatic Stress.* 19(5), 721–734. https://doi.org/10.1002/jts.20167

Hannah, T. (2004). *Somatics: Reawakening the Mind's Control of Movement and Flexibility.* Boston: Da Capo Press.

Harlow, C. (1999). *Prior Abuses Reported by Inmates and Probationers.* (Publication No. NCJ 172879) Washington, DC: U.S. Department of Justice, Bureau of Justice Statistics.

Harel, Z., Kahana, B. & Kahana, E. (1988). 'Psychological Well-Being Among Holocaust Survivors and Immigrants in Israel'. *Journal of Traumatic Stress Studies,* 1(4), 413–428.

Harris, J. I., Currier, J. & Park, C. P. (2013). 'Trauma, Faith and Meaning-Making'. *Psychology of Trauma.* T. Van Leuwen and M. Brower (eds.), Hauppauge, NY: Nova Science Publishers.

Harris, J. I., Erbes, C. R., Engdahl, B. E., Thuras, P., Murray-Swank, N., Grace, D., Ogden, H., Olson, R. H. A., Winkowski, A. M., Bacon, R., Malec, C. Campion, K. & Le, T.V. (2011). 'The Effectiveness of a Trauma Focused Spiritually Integrated Intervention for Veterans Exposed to Trauma'. *Journal of Clinical Psychology.* 67(4), 425–438.

Heaton, J. (1988). 'The Other and Psychotherapy'. *The Provocation of Levinas: Rethinking the Other.* R. Bernasconi & D. Wood (eds.), London: Routledge, 14–24.

Helenius, T. (2012). '"As If" and the Surplus of Being in Ricœur's Poetics'. *Études Ricœuriennes / Ricœur Studies*. 3(2), 149–170. doi: 10.5195/errs.2012.113

Herman, J. (2015/1992). *Trauma and Recovery: The Aftermath of Violence*. New York: Basic Books.

Herman, J. (2013). 'Crime and Memory'. *The Trauma Controversy*. K. Brown Golden & B. Bergo (eds.) Albany, NY: State University of New York Press, 127–143.

Herzog, A. (2020). *Levinas' Politics: Justice, Mercy, Universality*. Philadelphia, PA: University of Pennsylvania Press.

Hickling, E. J., Blanchard, E. B., Buckley, T. C. & Taylor, A. E. (1999). 'Effects of Attribution of Responsibility for Motor Vehicle Accidents on Severity of PTSD Symptoms, Ways of Coping, and Recovery Over Six Months'. *Journal of Traumatic Stress*. 12, 345–353.

Hinds, J. (2016). 'Eudemonic Philosophy and Human(istic)-Nature Relationships'. *Ecotherapy: Theory, Research & Practice*. New York, NY: Palgrave MacMillan, 45–57.

Hollander, A. K. (2020). 'Hur migration påverkar den psykiska hälsan'. *Läkartidningen*. 117, 1–5.

Horowitz, G. M. (2009). 'A Late Adventure of the Feelings: Loss, Trauma, and the Limits of Psychoanalysis'. *The Trauma Controversy*. K. Brown Golden & B. Bergo (eds.) Albany, NY: SUNY, 23–44.

Howell, E. F. (2020). *Trauma and Dissociation Informed Psychotherapy: Relational Healing and The Therapeutic Connection*, New York, NY: Norton.

Huber, M., Knottnerus, J. A., Green, L., van der Horst, H., Jadad, A. R., Kromhout, D., Leonard, B., Lorig, K., Loureiro, M. I., van der Meer, J. W. M., Schnabel, P., Smith, R., van Weel, C. & Smid, H. (2011). 'How Should We Define Health?'. *British Medical Journal*. 343. https://doi.org/10.1136/bmj.d4163

Hueneke, A. (2012). 'From Politics to Poetry'. *Psychotherapy and Politics International*. 10(1), 55–68. https://doi.org/10.1002/ppi.1250

Husserl, E. (1999). *The Idea of Phenomenology*. L. Hardy (trans.) Dordecht: Kluwer Academic.

Husserl, E. (1931). *Ideas I*. W. R. Boyce Gibson (trans.) London: George Allen & Unwin Ltd.

Ignatieff, M. (1984). *The Needs of Strangers*. New York, NY: St. Martin's Press.

Itao, A. D. S. (2010). 'Paul Ricœur's Hermeneutics of Symbols: A Critical Dialectic of Suspicion and Faith'. *Kritike an Online Journal of Philosophy*. 4(2). doi: 10.25138/4.2.a.1

Janet, P. (1889/2018). *L'Automatisme Psychologique: Essai De Psychologie Expérimentale Sure Les Formes Inférieures De l'Activité Humaine'. Classic Reprint Series*. London: Fb&c Ltd.

Janet, P. (1976). *Psychological Healing: A Historical and Clinical Study*. 2 vols. E. & C. Paul (Trans.). (Original work published in 1919).

Jones, L. (2014). 'Each Scar is Different'. *Aeon*. 22 May. Available at: https://aeon.co/essays/the-more-we-label-every-trauma-with-ptsd-the-less-it-means

Jung, C. (1967). *Collected Works of C. G. Jung, Vol 7: Two Essays in Analytical Psychology*. New York: Pantheon.

Jung, C. (1960). *The Psychogenesis of Mental Disease*. Princeton, NJ: Princeton University Press.

Jung, C. G. (1960). 'Good and Evil in Analytical Psychology'. *Gut unit Böse in der Psychotherapie*. Stuttgart: Klett-Verlag. DOI: https://doi.org/10.1111/j.1465-5922.1960.00091.x

Jung, C. G. (1912/1956). *Symbols of Transformation: Volume II – an Analysis of the Prelude to a Case of Schizophrenia*. New York City: Harper Torchbooks.

Kaës, R. (2012). 'Foreward'. *Bearing Witness*. A. Gautier & A. Sabatini Scalmati (eds.) London: KARNAC, xiii–xvi.

Kahana, E., Kahana, B., Harel, Z. & Rosner, T. (1988). 'Coping with Extreme Trauma'. *The Plenum Series on Stress and Coping. Human Adaptation to Extreme Stress: From the Holocaust to Vietnam*. J. P. Wilson, Z. Harel & B. Kahana (eds.) New York: Plenum Press, 55–79.

Kahn, A. (2010). 'From "Child Saving" to "Child Development".' *Child Welfare to Child Well-Being. Children's Well-Being: Indicators and Research.* S. B. Kamerman et al. (eds.) Dordecht: Springer Netherlands, 3–7.

Kalsched, D. (2013). *Trauma and the Soul.* Hove, East Sussex: Routledge.

Kalsched, D. (1998). 'Archetypal Affects, Anxiety and Defence in Patients Who Have Suffered Early Trauma'. *The Post-Jungians Today: Key Papers in Contemporary Analytical Psychology.* A. Casement (ed.) London: Routledge, Chapter 5.

Kaplan, D. M. (2003). *Ricœur's Critical Theory.* Albany, NY: SUNY.

Kardiner, A. (2012). *The Traumatic Neuroses of War.* Eastford, CT: Martino Fine Books.

Karpman B. (1941). 'On the Need of Separating Psychopathy into Two Distinct Clinical Types: The Symptomatic and the Idiopathic.' *Journal of Criminal Psychopathology.* 3, 112–137.

Kearney, R. (2016). 'Between Flesh and Text: Ricœur's Carnal Hermeneutics'. *Eco-ethica.* 5, 219–231. doi: 10.5840/ecoethica2016516

Kearney, R. (2015). 'What is Carnal Hermeneutics?'. *New Literary History.* 46(1), 99–124. doi: 10.1353/nlh.2015.0009

Kearney, R. (2009). 'Returning to God after God: Levinas, Derrida, Ricœur'. *Research in Phenomenology.* 39, 167–183. doi: 10.1163/156916409X448157

Kearney, R. (2006). 'On the Hermeneutics of Evil'. Revue de Métaphysique et de Morale. 2, 197–215. Available at: www.jstor.org/stable/41825831 [Accessed on 1 October 2020].

Kearney, R. (1995). 'Narrative Imagination: Between Ethics and Poetics'. *Philosophy and Social Criticism.* 21(5–6), 173.

Kearney, R. (1994). *The Wake of Imagination.* London: Routledge.

Kelland, M. (2015). Personality Theory in a Cultural Context. OpenStax CNX. Available at: https://open.umn.edu/opentextbooks/textbooks/personality-theory-in-a-cultural-context

Kelly, D. (2016). 'Working with Nature in Palliative Care'. *Ecotherapy: Theory, Research & Practice.* London: Palgrave & MacMillan, 84–97.

Kenaan, H. & Ferber, I. (2011). *Philosophy's Moods: The Affective Grounds of Thinking.* Springer. doi: 10.1007/978-94-007-1503-5

Kessler, R. C., Sonnega, A., Bromet, E., Hughes, M. & Nelson, C. B. (1995). 'Posttraumatic Stress Disorder in the National Comorbidity Survey'. *Archives of General Psychiatry.* 52(12), 1048–1060. doi: 10.1001/archpsyc.1995.03950240066012. PMID: 7492257.

Kidner, D.W. (2001). *Nature and Psyche: Radical Environmentalism and the Politics of Subjectivity.* Albany, NY: SUNY.

Kihlstrom, J. & Hoyt, I. (1990). 'Repression, Dissociation and Hypnosis'. *Repression and Dissociation: Implications for Personality Theory, Psychopathology, and Health.* J. L. Singer (ed.) Chicago, IL: University of Chicago Press, 181–208.

Kilkelly, U. (2016). *The Child and the European Convention on Human Rights. Second Edition.* London: Routledge.

Klein, M. (1940). 'Mourning and its Relation to Manic-Depressive States.' *International Journal of Psychoanalysis.* XXI, 125–153.

Knotsch, C. & Lamouche, J. (2010). *Arctic Biodiversity and Inuit Health.* Ottawa: National Aboriginal Health Organization.

Krieger, N. (1999). 'Embodying Inequality: A Review of Concepts, Measures and Methods for Studying Health Consequences of Discrimination.' *International Journal of Health Services.* 29, 295–352.

Krystal, H. (1968). *Massive Psychic Trauma.* New York, NY: Int. Univ. Press.

Langenthal, A. (2014). 'Welcoming the Other'. *Levinas Faces Biblical Figures*. Y. Lin (ed.) Lanham, MD: Lexington Books, 35–59.

Lahousen, T., Unterrainer, H. F. & Kapfhammer, H. P. (2019). 'Psychobiology of Attachment and Trauma – Some General Remarks from a Clinical Perspective'. *Frontiers in Psychiatry*. 10, 914. doi: 10.3389/fpsyt.2019.00914

Lakoff, G. (1993). 'The Contemporary Theory of Metaphor'. Metaphor and Thought. *Second edition*. A. Ortony, (ed.) Cambridge and New York: Cambridge University Press, 202–251.

Lambek, M. (2013). 'Trauma's Wake and Its Subjects'. *The Trauma Controversy*. B. Bergo & K. Brown Golden (eds.) New York City: SUNY Press, 235–262.

Lambek, M. (2009). 'Terror's Wake: Trauma and Its Subjects'. *The Trauma Controversy*. B. Bergo & K. Brown Golden (eds.) Albany, NY: SUNY, 235–262.

Lang, B. (2005). *Post Holocaust Interpretation, Misinterpretation and the Claims of History*. Bloomington, IN: Indiana University Press.

Langer, L. (1991). *Holocaust Testimonies: The Ruins of Memory*. New Haven, CT: Yale University.

Lévinas, E. (2006). *Humanism of the Other*. N. Poller (trans.) Chicago, IL: University of Illinois Press.

Lévinas, E. (2003). *On Escape*. B. Bergo (trans.) Stanford: Stanford University Press.

Lévinas, E. (2001a). 'Interview with Salomon Malka (1984)'. *Is it Righteous to Be? Interviews with Emmanuel Levinas*. J. Robbins (ed.) Stanford: Stanford University Press, 93–104.

Lévinas, E. (2001b). 'Being-for-the-Other (1989)'. *Is it Righteous to Be? Interviews with Emmanuel Levinas*. J. Robbins (ed.) Stanford: Stanford University Press, 114–120.

Lévinas, E. (2001c). 'Interview with Myriam Anissimov (1985)'. *Is it Righteous to Be? Interviews with Emmanuel Levinas*. J. Robbins (ed.) Stanford: Stanford University Press, 84–93.

Lévinas, E. (2001d). 'Interview with François Poirié (1986)'. *Is it Righteous to Be? Interviews with Emmanuel Levinas*. J. Robbins (ed.) Stanford: Stanford University Press, 23–83.

Lévinas, E. (2000). *God, Death and Time*. B. Bergo (trans.) Stanford: Stanford University Press.

Lévinas, E. (1999). *Alterity and Transcendence*. M. B. Smith (trans.) New York City, NY: Columbia University Press.

Lévinas, E. (1998a). 'Existence and Ethics'. *Kierkegaard: A Critical Reader*. J. Rée & J. Chamberlain (eds.) Oxford: Blackwell Publishers, 26–38.

Lévinas, E. (1998b). *Otherwise than Being*. A. Lingis (trans.) Pittsburgh, PA: Duquesne University Press.

Lévinas, E. (1998c). *Of God Who Comes to Mind*. B. Bergo (trans.) Stanford: Stanford University Press.

Lévinas, E. (1997). *Difficult Freedom*. S. Hand (trans.) Baltimore, MD: Johns Hopkins University Press.

Lévinas, E. (1996). 'God and Philosophy'. *Emmanuel Levinas: Basic Philosophical Writings*. R. Bernasconi (ed.) Bloomington, IN: Indiana University Press.

Lévinas, E. (1995). *Alterité et Transcendence*. J. P. Enthoven (ed.) Paris: Fata Morgana.

Lévinas, E. (1994). *Beyond the Verse: Talmudic Readings and Lectures*. G. Mole (trans.) Bloomington, IN: Indiana University Press.

Lévinas, E. (1993). *Dieu, la Mort et le Temps*. J. P. Enthoven (ed.) Paris: Éditions Grasset & Fasquelle.

Lévinas, E. (1990a). *Difficult Freedom: Essays on Judaism*. S. Hand (ed.) Baltimore, MD: Johns Hopkins University Press.

Lévinas, E. (1990b). *Carnets de Captivité et Autres Inédits (Œuvres 1)*. R. Calin & C. Chalier (eds.) Paris: Grasset/IMEC.

Lévinas, E. (1988). 'Useless Suffering'. *Entre Nous*. R. Cohen (trans.). London: Bloomsbury, 156–167.

Lévinas, E. (1987). 'Meaning and Sense'. *Collected Philosophical Papers. Phaenomenologica (Collection Fondée par H.L. van Breda et Publiée sous le Patronage des Centres d'Archives-Husserl)*. 100. Dordrecht: Springer. doi: 10.1007/978-94-009-4364-3_6

Lévinas, E. (1983). *Le Temps et L'Autre*. Paris: Presses Universitaires de France.

Lévinas, E. (1982). *Entre Nous*. J. P. Enthoven (ed.) Paris: Éditions Grasset & Fasquelle.

Lévinas, E. (1982). *Éthique et Infini*. Paris: Librarie Artheme Fayard.

Lévinas, E. (1978). *Autrement Qu'être ou Au-Dela de L'essence*. P. J. Enthoven (ed.) Paris: Kluwer Academic.

Lévinas, E. (1969). *Totality and Infinity*. A. Lingis (trans.) Pittsburgh, PA: Duquesne University Press.

Levine, P. (2015). *Trauma and Memory. Brain and Body in a Search for the Living Past: A Practical Guide to Understanding and Working with Traumatic Memory* Berkeley, CA: North Atlantic Books.

Levine, P. (2010). *In an Unspoken Voice: How the Body Releases Trauma and Restores Goodness*. Berkeley, CA: North Atlantic Books.

Levine, P. (1997). *Waking the Tiger*. Berkeley, CA: North Atlantic Books.

Lewis, S. (2013). 'Trauma and the Making of Flexible Minds in the Tibetan Exile Community'. *Ethos*. 41(3), 313–336.

Lifton, R. (1980). 'The Concept of the Survivor'. *Survivors, Victims and Perpetrators: Essays on the Nazi Holocaust*. J. E. Dimsdale (ed.) New York, NY: Hemisphere, 113–126.

Liotti, G. (2009). 'Attachment and Dissociation' in *Dissociation and Dissociative Disorders: DSM-V and Beyond*. eds. P. Dell and J. A. O'Neil (New York: Routledge), 53–65.

Litz, B. T., Stein, N., Delaney, E., Lebowitz, L., Nash, W. P. & Silva, C. (2009). 'Moral Injury and Moral Repair in War Veterans: A Preliminary Model and Intervention Strategy'. *Clinical Psychology Review*. 29, 695–706. doi: 10.1016/j. cpr.2009.07.003

Lloyd-Jones, H. (1998). *Sophocles: Antigone. The Women of Trachis. Philoctetes. Oedipus at Colonus*. Loeb Classical Library 21. Cambridge, MA, and London: Harvard University Press.

Luhrmann, T. M. (2000) *Of Two Minds: The Growing Disorder in American Psychiatry*. New York, NY: Alfred A. Knopf.

Luke, H. (1995). *The Way of Woman*. New York: Doubleday.

Macy, J. (2010). *Pass it On: Five Stories that can Change the World*. Berkeley, CA: Parallax Press.

Magearu, A. (2019). 'Torture and Traumatic Dehiscence'. *Phenomenology of the Broken Body*. E. Dahl, C. Falke & T. E. Eriksen (eds.) London: Routledge, 49–65.

Maguen, S. & Litz, B. (2012). 'Moral Injury in Veterans of War'. *PTSD Research Quarterly*. 23(1), 1–6. Available at: https://icds.uoregon.edu/wp-content/uploads/2011/07/Maguen-LItz-2012-Moral-Injury-review.pdf [Accessed on 20 July 2021].

Maitland, J. (2016). *Embodied Being: The Philosophical Roots of Manual Therapy*. Berkeley, CA: North Atlantic Books.

Mate, G. (2010). 'Introduction'. *In an Unspoken Voice: How the Body Releases Trauma and Restores Goodness*. Berkeley: North Atlantic Books, xi–xiv.

Mazis, G. (2016). *Merleau-Ponty and the Face of the World: Silence, Ethics, Imagination, and Poetic Ontology*. Albany, NY: SUNY Press.

McDonald, M. C. (2019). *Merleau-Ponty and a Phenomenology of PTSD: Hidden Ghosts of Traumatic Memory*. Lanham, MD: Lexington Books.

Meganck, R. (2017). 'Beyond the Impasse – Reflections on Dissociative Identity Disorder from a Freudian–Lacanian Perspective'. *Frontiers in Psychology*. 8, 789. doi: 10.3389/fpsyg.2017.00789

Merleau-Ponty, M. (2016). 'Eye and Mind'. *The Primacy of Perception: And Other Essays on Phenomenological Psychology, the Philosophy of Art, History and Politics*. W. Cobb (trans.) Evanston, IL: Northwestern University Press, 159–190.

Merleau-Ponty, M. (2010). *Institution and Passivity*. L. Lawlor (trans.) Evanston, IL: Northwestern University Press.

Merleau-Ponty, M. (2003). *Nature: Course Notes from the College de France*. R. Vallier (trans.) Evanston, IL: Northwestern University Press.

Merleau-Ponty, M. (2002). *Phenomenology of Perception*. C. Smith, trans. London: Routledge.

Merleau-Ponty, M. (1990). *Humanism and Terror: Essay on the Communist Problem*. Boston, MA: Beacon Press.

Merleau-Ponty, M. (1969). *The Visible and Invisible*. A. Lingis (trans.) Evanston, IL: Northwestern University Press.

Merleau-Ponty, M. (1964). 'Eye and Mind'. *The Primacy of Perception: And Other Essays on Phenomenological Psychology, the Philosophy of Art, History and Politics*. Evanston, IL: Northwestern University Press, 159–190.

Merleau-Ponty, M. (1962). *Phenomenology of Perception*. C. Smith (trans.) London: Routledge & Kegan Paul Ltd.

Moo, D. (2010). 'Eschatology an Environmental Ethics'. *Keeping God's Earth*. N. J. Toly & D. I. Block (eds.) Nottingham: IVP, 23–46.

Morgan, M. L. (2016). *Lévinas's Ethical Politics*. Indianapolis, IN: Indiana University Press.

Morris, D. (1969). *Primate Ethology*. London: Weidenfeld & Nicolson.

Moyn, S. (2005). *Origins of the Other*. Ithaca, NY: Cornell University.

Mumford, J. (2018). 'The Experience of Obligation: The Enduring Promise of Levinas for Theological Ethics'. Studies in Christian Ethics. London: SAGE, 1–18.

Murphy, J. (2015). *Illness or Deviance? Drug Courts, Drug Treatment and the Ambiguity of Addiction*. Philadelphia: Temple University Press.

Myers, N., Lewis, S. & Dutton, M. A. (2015). 'Open Mind, Open Heart: An Anthropological Study of the Therapeutics of Meditation Practice in the US'. *Cult Med Psychiatry*. 39(3), 487–504. doi: 10.1007/s11013-014-9424-5.

Neher, A. (1996). 'Jung's Theory of Archetypes: A Critique'. *Journal of Humanistic Psychology*. 36(2), 61–91. https://doi.org/10.1177/00221678960362008

Nicholson-Weir, R. & Hill, D. (2008). 'Emmanuel Levinas and Jewish Thought: Translating Hebrew into Greek: Editors' Introduction'. *Shofar*. 26, 4.

Nomikos, N. (2017). 'Injuries in the Greek Epics of Homer'. *Chinese Journal of Traumatology*. 21(2). doi: 10.1016/j.cjtee.2017.09.005

Norman, S. & Maguen, S. (2018). *PTSD: National Center for PTSD*. US Department of Veterans Affairs. Available at: www.ptsd.va.gov/professional/treat/ cooccurring/moral_injury.asp [Accessed on 15 May 2020].

Nugent, N. R., Goldberg, A. & Uddin, M. (2016). 'Topical Review: The Emerging Field of Epigenetics: Informing Models of Pediatric Trauma and Physical Health'. *Journal of Pediatric Psychology*. 41, 55–64. doi: 10.1093/jpepsy/jsv018

O'Connor, N. (1988). 'The Person is Political: Discursive Practice of the Face-to-Face'. *The Provocation of Levinas: Rethinking the Other*. R. Bernasconi and D. Wood (eds.), London: Routledge, 57–69.

O'Donnell, K. & Cross, K. (2020). *Feminist Trauma Theologies: Body, Scripture and Church in Critical Perspective*. London: SCM Press.

Ogden, P., Minton, K. & Pain, C. (2006). *Trauma and the Body*. New York City, NY: W. W. Norton & Company, Inc.

O'Neill, B. (2019). 'Decolonising the Mind: Working with Transgenerational Trauma and First Nations People'. *Judicial Officers' Bulletin*. 31(6), 54–58.

Orr, S. P. & Roth, W. T. (2000). 'Psychophysiological Assessment: Clinical Applications for PTSD.' *Journal of Affective Disorders*. 61, 225–240. doi: 10.1016/S0165-0327(00)00340-2

Ozer, E. J., Best, S. R., Lipsey, T. L. & Weiss, D. S. (2003). 'Predictors of Posttraumatic Stress Disorder and Symptoms in Adults: A Meta-Analysis'. *Psychological Bulletin* 129, 52–73.

Palacios, Janelle F. & Portillo, Carmen J. (2009). 'Understanding Native Women's Health: Historical Legacies'. *Journal of Transcultural Nursing*, 20(1), 15–27.

Pagis, M. (2009). 'Embodied Self-Reflexivity'. *Social Psychological Quarterly.* 72, 265–283. doi: 10.1177/019027250907200308

Papero, D.V. (2017). 'Trauma and the Family: A Systems-Oriented Approach'. *Australian and New Zealand Journal of Family Therapy.* 38(4), 582–594. https://doi.org/10.1002/anzf.1269

Perelberg, R.J. (2015). 'On Excess, Trauma and Helplessness: Repetitions and Transformations'. *The International Journal of Psychoanalysis.* 96(6), 1453–1476. https://doi.org/10.1111/1745-8315.12438

Peskin, H. (1981). 'Observations on the First International Conference on Children of Holocaust Survivors'. Family Process. 20(4), 391–394. https://doi.org/10.1111/j.1545-5300.1981.00391.x

Plotkin Amrani, G. & Brunner, J. (2016). 'Constructing the Resilient Subject in Israeli Classrooms: Professional Interventions, Culture and Politics in a Protracted Conflict'. *Pedagogy, Culture & Society.* London: Routledge.

Porges, S. (2017). *The Polyvagal Theory.* New York, NY: W.W. Norton & Company, Inc.

Protevi, J. (2009). *Political Affect: Connecting the Social and the Somatic.* Minneapolis, MN: University of Minnesota Press.

Rambo, S. (2010). 'Trauma and Faith: Regarding the Narrative of the Hemorrhaging Woman'. *International Journal of Practical Theology.* 13(2), 233–257.

Raphaely, M. (2010). 'Routes to the Unspeakable: Working with Victims of Torture'. *Bearing Witness.* A. Gautier & A. Sabatini Scalmati (eds.) London: KARNAC, 13–26.

Rasmussen, K. S. (2019). 'Divergent Convergent: Ricoeur, Derrida and Metaphor.' *Concentric: Literary and Cultural Studies.* 45(1), 17–41.

Raz, J. (2007). *Human Rights without Foundations,* Oxford Legal Studies Research Paper No. 14/2007, Oxford: University of Oxford, Available at http://ssrn.com/abstract=999874 [Accessed on 10 April 2025].

Reinhardt, K. M., Noggle, J., Zaneer, A., Cheema, S. & Khalsa, S. B. (2018). 'Kripalu Yoga for Military Veterans with PTSD'. *Journal of Clinical Psychology.* 74(1), 93–108. doi: 10.1002/jclp.22483

Richter, S. (2014). 'Langage, son et voix dans les Carnets de captivité d'Emmanuel Lévinas'. *Trajectoires.* 1–17. Available at: https://journals.openedition.org/ trajectoires/1459 [Accessed on 4 April 2021].

Ricœur, P. (2012). *On Psychoanalysis. Writings and Lectures, Volume 1.* D. Pellauer (trans.) Cambridge: Polity Press.

Ricœur, P. (2007). *The Conflict of Interpretations: Essays in Hermeneutics.* Evanston, IL: Northwestern University Press.

Ricœur, P. (2007). *Evil: A Challenge to Philosophy and Theology.* London: Bloomsbury Academic.

Ricoeur, P. (2003). *The Rule of Metaphor.* R. Czerney (trans.) London: Routledge.

Ricœur, P. (1998). *Du Texte a L'Action.* Paris: Éditions du Seuil.

Ricœur, P. (1995). *The Rule of Metaphor: The Creation of Meaning in Language.* London: Routledge.

Ricœur, P. (1994). *Oneself as Another.* Chicago, IL: University of Chicago Press.

Ricœur, P. (1986). *The Symbolism of Evil.* Boston, MA: Beacon Press.

Ricœur, P. (1983). *Temps et Recit.* Paris: SEUIL.

Ricœur, P. (1977). *Freud and Philosophy.* D. Savage (trans.) New Haven, CT: Yale University Press.

Ricœur, P. (1970). *Freud and Philosophy.* New Haven, CT: Yale University Press.

Ricœur, P. (1966). *Freedom and Nature.* Evanston, IL: Northwestern University Press.

Ringel, S. & Brandell, J. (2011). *Trauma: Contemporary Direction in Theory, Practice and Research.* London: SAGE.

Roberts, J. (2018). *Trauma and the Ontology of the Modern Subject.* London: Routledge.

Roberts-Cady, S. E. (2009). 'Rethinking Justice with Levinas'. *Essays on Levinas and Law.* D. Manderson (ed.) London: Palgrave Macmillan. https://doi.org/10.1057/9780230234734_14

Robbins, J. A., & Dewar, J. (2011). 'Traditional Indigenous Approaches to Healing and the Modern Welfare of Traditional Knowledge, Spirituality and Lands: A Critical Reflection on Practices and Policies Taken from the Canadian Indigenous Example'. *The International Indigenous Policy Journal,* 2(4), 1–17.

Roseman, S. & Handleman, I. (1993). 'Modeling Resiliency in a Community Devastated by Man-made Catastrophes'. *American Imago.* 49, 185–226.

Rothberg, M. (2009). *Multidirectional Memory: Remembering the Holocaust in the Age of Decolonialization.* Stanford: Stanford University Press.

Rothberg, M. (2008). 'Decolonialising Trauma Studies: A Response'. *Studies in the Novel.* 40, 224–234.

Rothschild, B. (2017). *The Body Remembers. Vol. 2.* NYC: W. W. Norton & Company.

Rothschild, B. & Reid, M. (2006). *Help for the Helper: The Psychophysiology of Compassion Fatigue and Vicarious Trauma.* New York, NY: Norton.

Sadock, B. J., Alcott Sadock, V. & Ruiz, P. (2009). Kaplan and Sadock's Comprehensive Textbook of Psychiatry. Volume 1. London: Lippincott Williams and Wilkins.

Sar, V. (2011). 'Epidemiology of Dissociative Disorders: An Overview'. *Epidemiology Research International,* 1–8. doi: 10.1155/2011/404538

Scheeringa, M. S. & Zeanah, C. H. (2001). 'A Relational Perspective on PTSD in Early Childhood'. *Journal of Traumatic Stress.* 14, 799–815.

Schimmenti, A. (2020). 'The Developmental Roots of Psychopathy: An Attachment Perspective'. *Psychoanalysts, Psychologists and Psychiatrists Discuss Psychopathy and Human Evil.* S. Itzkowitz & E. F. Howell (eds.) London: Routledge, 219–234.

Schonfeld, E. & Ehlers, A. (2017). 'Traumatic Stress Disorder and Autobiographical Memories in Everyday Life'. *Clinical Psychological Science.* 5(2), 325–340. doi: 10.1177/2167702616688878

Schwartz, R. & Sweezy, M. (2020). *Internal Family Systems Therapy. Second Edition.* New York, NY: The Guildford Press.

Scott, C. (2009). 'Trauma's Presentation'. *The Trauma Controversy.* K. Brown Golden & B. Bergo (eds.) Albany, NY: SUNY, 115–126.

Sehwail, M. (2005). 'Responding to Continuing Traumatic Events'. *The International Journal of Narrative Therapy and Community Work.* 3(4), 53–57.

Seiden Henry, M. (2016). 'Speaking of Pain: Yehuda Amichai'. *The Motive for Metaphor.* London: Routledge, 164–168.

Senior, J.. (5 Aug 2020). 'Opinion: It's Not Just You. We've All Got a case of the Covid-19 Blues'. *New York Times.*

Shalev, Y., Peri, T., Gelpin, E., Orr, S. P. & Pitman, R. K. (1997). 'Psychophysiologic Assessment of Mental Imagery of Stressful Events in Israeli Civilian Posttraumatic Stress Disorder Patients'. *Comprehensive Psychiatry.* 38(5), 269–273. https://doi.org/10.1016/S0010-440X(97)90059-6

Sigurdson, O. (2019). 'Only Vulnerable Creatures Suffer'. *Phenomenology of the Broken Body.* E. Dahl, C. Falke & T. E. Eriksen (eds.) New York, NY: Routledge, 87–100.

Sophocles (1994). *Antigone. The Women of Trachis. Philoctetes. Oedipus at Colonus.* H. Lloyd-Jones (trans.) Sophocles Vol II. Loeb Classical Library. Cambridge, MA: Harvard University Press, 21.

Soskin, D. (2013). 'Commentary'. *Academic Medicine.* 88(2), 215. doi: 10.1097/01.ACM.0000426356.35520.8c

Stamatakos, M. & Campo, J.V. (2010). 'Psychopharmacologic Treatment of Traumatised Youth'. *Current Opinions Pediatrics.* 22(5), 599–604. doi: 10.1097/MOP.0b013e32833e26d5

Stanghellini, G., Broome, M., Raballo, A., Fernandez, A. V., Fusar-Poli, P. & Rosfort, R. (2019). *The Oxford Handbook of Phenomenological Psychology.* London: Oxford University Press. doi: 10.1093/oxfordhb/9780198803157.013.106

Stauffer, J. (2015). *Ethical Loneliness: The Injustice of Not Being Heard.* New York, NY: Columbia University Press.

Stearns, P. (2017). 'History of Children's Rights'. *Handbook of Children's Rights.* M. D. Ruck, M. Peterson-Badali & M. Freeman (eds.) London: Routledge, Ch. 1.

Stephens, C. (2005). 'Review: Pathologies of Power: Health, Human Rights and the New War on the Poor. Paul Farmer'. *International Journal of Epidemiology.* 34(3), 718. https://doi.org/10.1093/ije/dyi095

Sveneaus, F. (2018). 'Human Suffering and Psychiatric Diagnosis'. *Bioethica Forum.* 11(1). Available at: www.bioethica-forum.ch/docs/ 18_1/02_Svenaeus_BF11_01_2018.pdf

Sveneaus, F. (2012). 'What is Phenomenology of Medicine? Embodiment, Illness and Being-in-the-World'. *Health, Illness and Disease Philosophical Essays.* London: Acumen, 97–112.

Sveneaus, F. (2011). 'Illness as Unhomelike Being-in-the World: Heidegger and the Phenomenology of Medicine'. *Medicine, Health Care and Philosophy.* 14(3), 333–343.

Sveneaus, F. (2000). *The Hermeneutics of Medicine and the Phenomenology of Health: Steps Towards a Philosophy of Medical Practice.* Dordrecht: Kluwer Academic Publishers.

Sweeney, R. (1996). 'The Body as Expression of Life'. *Life in the Glory of Its Radiating Manifestations. Analecta Husserliana (The Yearbook of Phenomenological Research).* 48. Dordrecht: Springer. https://doi.org/10.1007/978-94-009-1602-9_8

Tahmasebi-Birgani, V. (2014). *Emmanuel Levinas and the Politics of Non-Violence.* University of Toronto Press. Available at: www.jstor.org/stable/10.3138/j.ctt5vkhvz [Accessed on 5 August 2021].

(1984). *The Holy Bible: New International Version.* Grand Rapids, MI: Zondervan Publishing House.

Tedeschi, R. G. & Calhoun, L. G. (1996). 'The Posttraumatic Growth Inventory: Measuring Positive Legacy of Trauma.' *Journal of Traumatic Stress.* 9(3): 455–471.

Tobin, J. (2016). 'Fixed Concepts but Changing Conceptions: Understanding the Relationship Between Children and Parents under the CRC'. *Handbook of Children's Rights.* M. D. Ruck, M. Peterson-Badali & M. Freeman (eds.) New York City: Routledge, 521–546.

Todres, J. (2017). 'Physician Encounters with Human Trafficking: Legal Consequences and Ethical Considerations.' *AMA Journal of Ethics.* 19(1), 16–22. doi: 10.1001/journalofethics.2017.19.01.ecas2-1701.

Umberton, D., Crosnoe, R. & Reczek, C. (2010). 'Social Relationships and Health Behavior Across the Life Course'. *Annual Review of Sociology.* 36, 139–157. Available at: www.jstor.org/stable/25735072 [Accessed on 5 August 2021].

United Nations Human Rights Office of the High Commissioner (2014). *Human Rights and Human Trafficking.* New York, NY: United Nations. www.ohchr.org/Documents/Publications/FS36_en.pdf

Van der Hard, O. & Rydberg, J. A. (2019). 'Vehement Emotions and Trauma-Generated Dissociation: A Janetian Perspective on Integrative Failure'. *European Journal of Trauma & Dissociation.* 3(3), 191–201. https://doi.org/10.1016/j.ejtd.2019.06.003

van der Kolk, B. (2005/2014). *The Body Keeps the Score.* New York City, NY: Penguin.

van der Kolk, B. A. (1984). *Post-Traumatic Stress Disorder: Psychological and Biological Sequelae.* Washington, DC: American Psychiatric Pub Inc.

van der Kolk, B.A. & van der Hart, O. (1989). 'Pierre Janet and the Breakdown of Adaptation in Psychological Trauma'. *The American Journal of Psychiatry*. 146(12), 1530–1540.

van Huijstee, J. & Vermetten, E. (2018). 'The Dissociative Subtype of Post-Traumatic Stress Disorder: Research Update on Clinical and Neurobiological Features'. *Current Topics in Behavioural Neuroscience*. 38, 229–248. doi: 10.1007/7854_2017_33

Visser, I. (2015). 'Decolonising Trauma Theory: Retrospect and Prospects'. *Humanities*. 4(2), 250–265. https://doi.org/10.3390/h4020250

Walsh, R., Danto, D. & Sommerfeld, J. (2020). 'Land-Based Intervention: A Qualitative Study of the Knowledge and Practices Associated with One Approach to Mental Health in a Cree Community'. *International Journal of Mental Health and Addiction*. 18, 207–221.

Walters, K. L., Beltran, R. E., Huh, D. & Evans-Campbell, T. (2011). 'Dis-Placement and Dis-ease: Land, Place and. Health among American Indians and Alaska Natives'. *Communities, Neighbourhood and Health: Expanding the Boundaries of Place*. L. M. Burton, S. P. Kemp, M. C. Leung, S. A. Matthews & D. T. Takeuchi (eds.) Philadelphia, PA: Springer Science, 163–199.

Watkins, H. H. (1993). 'Ego-state Therapy: An Overview'. *American Journal of Clinical Hypnosis*. 35(4), 232–240. doi: 10.1080/00029157.1993.10403014

Weil, S. (1952/2002). *The Need for Roots*. A. Wills (trans.) London: Routledge.

Widiger, T. A. & Samuel, D. B. (2005). 'Diagnostic Categories or Dimensions? A Question for the Diagnostic and Statistical Manual of Mental Disorders – Fifth Edition'. *Journal of Abnormal Psychology*. 114(4), 494–504.

Wildcat, M., McDonald, M., Irlbacher-Fox, S. & Coulthard, G. (2014). 'Learning from the Land: Indigenous Land Based Pedagogy and Decolonization'. *Decolonization: Indigeneity, Education & Society*, 3(3), I–XV.

Wilson, J. P. (2004). 'The Abyss Experience and the Trauma Complex: A Jungian Perspective of Posttraumatic Stress Disorder and Dissociation'. *Journal of Trauma & Dissociation*. 5(3), 43–68. doi: 10.1300/J229v05n03_04

Winblad, N., Changaris, M. & Stein, P. K. (2018). 'Effect of Somatic Experiencing Resiliency-Based Trauma Treatment Training on Quality of Life and Psychological Health as Potential Markers of Resilience in Treating Professionals'. *Frontiers in Neuroscience*. 12(70). doi: 10.3389/fnins.2018.00070

Winnicott, D. W. (1989). *Psycho-Analytic Explorations*. C. Winnicott, R. Shepard & M. Davis (eds.). Boston, MA: Harvard University Press.

Winnicott, D. W. (1971). *Playing and Reality*. London: Tavistock Publications, 1–156.

Winnicott, D. W. (1965). *The Maturational Process and the Facilitating Environment. Studies in the Theory of Emotional Development*. New York, NY: International Universities Press.

Winnicott, D. W. (1949). 'Hate in the Counter-Transference'. *International Journal of Psycho-Analysis*. 30, 69–74.

Wolff, N. & Shi, J. (2012). 'Childhood and Adult Trauma Experiences of Incarcerated Persons and Their Relationship to Adult Behavioral Health Problems and Treatment.' *International Journal of Environmental Research and Public Health*, 9(5), 1908–1926. doi: 10.3390/ijerph9051908

Wolff, N. & Shi, J. (1908–1926). 'Childhood and Adult Trauma Experiences of Incarcerated Persons and Their Relationship to Adult Behavioural Health Problems and Treatment'. *International Journal of Environmental Research on Public Health*. 9(5). doi: 10.3390/ijerph9051908

Woller, W., Leichsenring, F., Leweke, F. & Kruse, J. (2012). 'Psychodynamic Psychotherapy for Postraumatic Stress Disorder Related to Childhood Abuse – Principles for a Treatment Manual'. *Bullettin of Menninger Clinic*. 76, 69–93. doi: 10.1521/bumc.2012.76.1.69

World Health Organisation (2018). *International Classification of Disease.* Geneva: World Health Organisation.
World Health Organisation (1948/2005). 'Constitution of the World Health Organisation'. *World Health Organisation: Basic Documents.* 45th *Edition.* Geneva: World Health Organisation.
Zimmerman, N. (2015). *Facing the Other.* Cambridge: James Clarke & Co.

INDEX

Aboriginal people 155
abuse, intergenerational colonisation 119
Abyss Experience 17
active witnessing 160
addiction, intergenerational colonisation 119
affect, Freud 15
affectivity: Anderson 59; personality 18
Al-Aqsa Intifada 125–6
Alford, C F 44
ambiguity of trauma language 72–5
American Psychological Association (APA) 144–5
Amichai, Yehuda 136
Amira's story 5–7, 26–7, 173
Amrami, Plotkin 125
Andermahr, Sonya 36
Anderson, I 59, 62
anthropocentric view of relationships 170–1
anti-life force 45
Aristotle 122, 174, 175
at-homeness 100–9
attachment figures (AF) 21
attachment theory 20–2
Auerhahn, N C: active witnessing 160; communication 94; consolation 151; forgiveness 158; The Holocaust 140, 159, 175; religious practice 156; transformation of trauma 140–1; trauma and justice 157; trauma representation 38; vulnerability 139
Autonomic Nervous System (ANS) breathing 143
auto-suggestion 13–14, 15

biological model of arousal 32–3
biological reading of experience 56
Boase, E 144
bodied experience, consciousness as 91
body: communication and 95–8; consciousness connection 68; home and 101–5; mind *vs.* 80; phenomenology of 122–3; philosophy of 9, 170; transformation in trauma 103; trauma coding 26; trauma expression 24–5, 102
body-based experiences 22–6
The Body Keeps the Score (van der Kolk) 11–12, 46–7, 143
Bosnian War 29
Bowlby, John 20–2
Brown, Charles 170
Brown Douglas, Kelly 120–1
Brown Golden, Kristen: communication 97; preconscious experience of desire 83–4; speech role 98; trauma narratives 44
Brunner, J: harm definition 131–2; moral injury 160–1; relationship interconnectedness 141
Bryant-Davis, T 144–5
Buzzell, L 167–8

Canadian Legal Human Rights Tribunal 155
Carbone, Mauro 80

Carel, H 87, 155–6
carnal hermeneutics, phenomenology as 124–5
Cartesian dualisation of identity 83
Cassell, Eric 42
Charcot, Jean-Martin 13–14
Charles, Marilyn 45–6, 165
Charon, Rita 70
childhood trauma 21, 38, 117–18
child neglect 84–5
Children's Charter of Human Rights (CHRC) 110; child trafficking 113–14; development of 111–14; implications of 111
child trafficking 113–14
CHRC *see* Children's Charter of Human Rights (CHRC)
Christian scripture 169–70
cogito 106
cognitive function, illness and 82–3
Cohen, Leonard 58
collective trauma 166
colonisation 119–24
communication 83; body and 95–8; justice and 94; limits of 92–3; linguistic communication 64, 93; re-representation of trauma 94–5; transmission of memory 97; trauma healing and 174
community healing 167
concept of flesh 145
conflict experiences 165; mental health 9
connection to nature 168
consciousness: bodied experience as 91; body connection 68; embodied consciousness and language 122–3; material unity 23; passive consciousness 61–2; psychical unity 23; reading of 85–6; suffering 96; understanding of 136–7
consolation 151–2
continuing traumatic disorder (CTD) 165–6
Convention on the Rights of the Child (CRC) 114
corporeality 125
COVID-19 33–4, 36, 151–2
Craps, Stephanie 33
CRC (Convention on the Rights of the Child) 114
Critchley, Simon 52
CTD (continuing traumatic disorder) 165–6
cultural architecture 134–5

Dahl, Espen 170
De Anima (Aristotle) 122
Declaration of the Rights of the Child (Jebb) 113
decolonisation 118–19, 166–7
Decolonising Trauma Studies (Andermahr) 36
definition of traumatic 36–8
definitions of trauma 42, 133
de Marneffe, Daphne 33–4
Descartes 80, 106
description of trauma 11–12
desegregation 86
desire 83
destructive experiences 149–50
diagnosis of trauma 28–30; ambiguity of 30–4; discrepancies in 34–5
Diagnostic and Statistical Manual of Mental Disorders (DSM): intention behind 29–30; post-traumatic stress disorder diagnosis 59
Diagnostic and Statistical Manual of Mental Disorders III (DSM-III), post-traumatic stress disorder diagnosis 161
Diagnostic and Statistical Manual of Mental Disorders IV (DSM-IV), trauma definition 35
Diagnostic and Statistical Manual of Mental Disorders (DSM-V): post-traumatic stress disorder classification 31; trauma classification 34
Diehm, Christian 170
dissociation 14, 18, 85
dissociative states of trauma 144
Dolezal, Luna 120, 121–2
dual understanding of trauma 139
Dutton, Mary Ann 143

ecological relationships, therapeutic benefits 169
ecotherapeutic practice 167
Edwards, E 80–1
ego: development of 85–6; rupture of 93–4; trauma reading 68
ego-perception: construction of 16; Freud 15; suffering and 62
Ego-State Therapy 104
embodied consciousness, language and 122–3
embodied interactions 120
embodied suffering 42
embodied trauma, phenomenology 69–72
embodiment 77–87; *see also* Merleau-Ponty, Maurice
emotional abuse 36

empathy, suffering and 62
enclosure body experience 56
enquiry, objective mode of 80
environment 165
episodic trauma 4
Eros 16, 150
ethical breaches 162
Ethical Loneliness (Stauffer) 54
ethical responsibility 115–16
existential phenomenology 70–1
experiences 103; language and 176–7; prismic qualities of 81, 92; psychological complexes 17; somatic view of 53–4; trauma of 20, 103–4; verbal rearrangements of 97–8
external world 20

Fackenheim, Emil 148–50
faith-base communities 144
Falconer, Robert 104
false comfort 151
Family Systems Therapy 104
Farmer, Paul 111, 117
Feinstein, A 36, 44
figure-oriented open divergence 123–4
First Intifada 5–7
First Nations People (Canada) 121–2, 166, 167
First World War 30
flesh 79
Fleury, Francois: embodied trauma 69, 71; torture 71, 156; trauma narratives 45
forgetting, pardon *vs.* 158
Frechette, C G 144
freedom 56–7
Freud and Philosophy (Ricœur) 68, 70
Freud, Sigmund 15–16; auto-suggestion 15; criticism by Horowitz 23; criticism by Jung 19–21, 153; criticism by Ricœur 65–9; criticism by van der Kolk 23–4; *eros* & *thanatos* 150; false comfort 151; language drawbacks 66–7; psyche of self 42; psychoanalysis 16–17; second innocence 106; trauma and language 135–6; trauma definition 4

generalisation of rights theory 117
Glas, Gerrit 45, 72–3
Graeco-Roman tradition 12
grammar of syntax 66
gross stress response (GSR) 13
growth cessation 158
Gulf War 5–7

Halligan, S 143
Handleman, I 140
harm 131–3
Harris, J. Irene 31–2
healing: adaptive definition 132–3; beyond metaphor 177–8; communication and 174; community healing 167; consolation as 147–52; definition 132; individual healing *see* individual healing; interrelationships 178; interruption & presence 139–41; language and 135; nature and 171; otherness in 124–6; relational healing *see* relational healing; relationships and 153–4
health: cognitive function and 82–3; limits of 134–9; mental health 9; possibility of 134–9; wake of trauma 148
Heaton, John 59, 60
Hebrew scripture 12–13, 169–70
Heidegger, Martin 69
Henry, Seiden 176
Herman, Judith 14–15; justice 155; other and self 159; social relationships 147; trauma diagnosis 32–3
Hind, Joe 168
historical aspects 4
historical trauma 4
The Holocaust 11, 52, 95, 175; healing after 148–9; testimonies of 107–8; writings about 139–40
home 105–8
homelessness 100–9
Horowitz, Gregg M 23–4
Howell, Elizabeth 102
Huber, Machteld 132
Hueneke, Anna 139
humanity 138–9
human rights 111–14; language and 114–15; political theories of 116
human trafficking 84–5, 117–18
hysteria 13–14

ICD-11 *(International Classification of Diseases)* 32, 34
idem, ipse vs. 45
identity 83
IFS Therapy 104, 105
Ignatieff, Michael 111, 116, 117
Iliad 12
individual healing 131–63; harm definition 131–3; healing oneself 134–9
inner event, trauma as 19
Intergenerational Trauma of Residential Schools 155

internal working model (IWM) 21
International Classification of Diseases (ICD-11) 32, 34
interrelationships, healing 178
interruption, healing and 139–41
intersubjectivity of trauma 110–28
ipse, *idem vs.* 45
isolation 164–5
IWM (internal working model) 21

Jabb, Eglantyne 113
Janet, Pierre 14
Jones, Lynne 29
Jung, Carl 17–18, 22; consciousness and 136–7; criticism of 18–19; criticism of Freud 19–21, 153; embodied trauma 71; self and 19
justice 154–6; communication as vessel 94; pardon demands 159; transfiguring trauma 157–60

Kalsched, Donald 18; Jung and 136–7; Jung dissociation theory 24; self-care theory 137–8, 153; trauma as inner event 19
Kardiner, A 135
Kearney, Richard: embodied consciousness and language 122; healing interrelationships 178; phenomenology 124–5; self–other relationship 118–19; suffering 74–5
Kidner, David 167–8
Kilkelly, Ursula 114–15
Klein, Melanie 41
Knotsch, C 167
Kraepelin, Emil 30

Lambek, Michel 32
lament 152–4
Lamouche, J 167
Lang, Berel 94–5
language: embodied consciousness and 122–3; experience and 176–7; healing and 135; human rights 114–15; limitations in Lévinas 92–5; Ricœur 107; trauma and 66, 135–6 *see also* narrative experiences
Laub, D: active witnessing 160; communication 94; consolation 151; forgiveness 158; The Holocaust 140, 159, 175; religious practice 156; transformation of trauma 140–1; trauma and justice 157; trauma representation 38; vulnerability 139
L'automatisme psychologique (Janet) 14
Lear, Jonathan 68
Lévinas, Emmanuel 51–63; anthropocentric view of relationships 170–1; biography 54–5; body vulnerability 105; communication 98; consolation 151; enclosure body experience 56; ethical responsibility 115–16; generalisation of rights theory 117; The Holocaust 149–50; homelessness 100; hospitality 101; language limitations 92–5; limits of being 55–60; loneliness 156; moral injury 160, 161–2; passive responsibility 116; paternalism 115; phenomenology 8–9, 110, 159–60; relational beings 54; self and 58; subjectivity and 55–60, 111, 138–9, 156; suffering 42, 58, 61–3, 96, 148, 150; systematisation critique 58; victim-perpetrator experience 157–8 *see also* phenomenology
Levine, Peter 26; biological reading of experience 56; body-based reading of trauma 24–5; body perception 103; consciousness reading 85–6; COVID-19 36; dissociation 85; living trauma 53; polyvagal theory 8; psyche 12; rupture of trauma 71; somatic psychology theory 135; trauma definition 34–5; trauma transformation 103
Lewis, Sarah 143
liberalism 115
limits of being 55–60
limits of health 134–9
linear interpretation of time 80–1
linguistic communication 64, 93
liquidation 15
lived experience 69–70, 82
living trauma 52–4, 141–7
loneliness 156
Luke, Helen 41

Macbeth (Shakespeare) 92
Macy, Joanna 127
Mageatu, Alexandra 145, 171–2
Mahmoud-Shwana, Shadman: embodied trauma 69, 71; torture 71, 156; trauma narratives 45
martyrs 138
Marx, Karl 106
material freedom 56–7
material unity 23
McDonald, Mary Catherine 77; communication of trauma 83; Merleau-Ponty, experience ideas 86–7; neurological explanations of trauma 84;

prismic experience 92; therapists 152–3; treatment of trauma 133
meaning is meaning 126
meditation 143–4, 146–7
memory: retrieval of 14; transmission of 97; trauma of 67, 97
Menchentiere (human animals) 149
mental health 9
Merleau-Ponty, Maurice 77–57; body in communication 97; body phenomenology 122–3; body vulnerability 105; colonisation 119–24; concept of flesh 145; decolonisation 123; experience, ideas of 86–7; figure-oriented open divergence 123–4; Freud, ideas development 86; healing process 126–7; home and the body 101–2; living trauma 141–2; meaning is meaning 126; narrative experiences 64; phenomenology 51–2, 78–81; phenomenology of existence 171; phenomenology of perception 125; phenomenology of trauma 82–7; philosophy of the body 9; self–other relationship 118; subjectivity and 138–9 *see also* embodiment
metaphorical conception 175
metaphorical transformations 174–7
Michaelsen, Catherine Bjørnholt 43, 93
migrants/migration 45, 108
mind, body *vs.* 80
mind-body practices 145
moral injury 160–2
Morgan, M L 116
multiplicity of being 55
Myers, Neely 143, 146
mythical trauma narratives 38–40, 41, 73–4
mythic time 81

narrative analysis: definition 65–6; lived experience as 69–70
narrative experiences 64–76 *see also* Ricœur, Paul
narrative phenomenology 174–7
narratives of trauma 43–7
nature: connection to 168; healing and 171
negative growth, post-traumatic stress disorder 144
neurological explanations of trauma 84
non-reciprocal responsibility 115

objective mode of enquiry 80
Odyssey 12
O'Neill, B 166
Oneself as Another (Ricœur) 45, 124
ongoing trauma 4
On Psychoanalysis (Ricœur) 42, 65
other, self relationship 96, 159
otherness, healing in 124–6
Otherwise than Being (Lévinas) 101, 102
outcomes of trauma 31–2

Palestine 141
pardon 158, 159
passive consciousness 61–2
passive responsibility 116
paternalism 115
perception, phenomenology 125
personality, affectivity 18
Petherbridge, Danielle 120, 121–2
phenomenology 3, 8–9, 51–63, 120; body of 122–3; carnal hermeneutic as 124–5; definition 80; definition by Merleau-Ponty 78–81; embodied trauma 69–72; existence of 171; experience reading 67; exploration of rupture 68–9; home 106–7; homelessness 107; illness 155–6; Lévinas 159–60; living trauma 52–4; Magearu 171–2; mythic time 81; perception of 125; relation of 110; responsibility and 121; self 158; trauma of 82–7 *see also* Lévinas, Emmanuel
Phenomenology of Perception (Merleau-Ponty) 77, 79, 80–1, 83, 141
Philocretes (Sophocles) 39–40, 41
philosophy of the body 9, 170
physical abuse 36
physiology, trauma definition 34–5
Pilates 145
places 164–5
poena 74
Poetics (Aristotle) 174
political theories of rights 116
political upheaval 165
politics of responsibility 126–7
polyvagal theory 8
Porges, Stephen 8, 25
possibility of health 134–9
post-Freudian theory 17–22
post-traumatic growth 147
post-traumatic stress disorder (PTSD) 7; definition 29; diagnosis 30, 59, 141, 142–3; historical aspects 13; The Holocaust 140; intergenerational colonisation 119; meditation 144; migration 165; negative growth 144;

trauma definition and 35; Vietnam War veterans 29, 31
preconscious experience of desire 83
presence, healing and 139–41
prismic qualities of experience 81, 92
processing of trauma 144–5
Protevi, J 53–4, 166
psyche: historical aspects 12–13; self of 42
psychical reality 22–3
psychical unity 23
psychoanalysis 16–17
psychoanalytic theories of trauma 84
psychological architecture 134–5
psychological complexes 17
psychopathology 37
psycho-physical conditions 96
psycho-physiological conditions 96
PTSD *see* post-traumatic stress disorder (PTSD)

Qigong 145

racism 120–1
Raphaely, Mary 98, 168–9
Raz, Joseph 111, 116–17
reductionism, universalism *vs.* 117
reflective capacity 45–6
relational beings 54
relational embodiment 37
relational healing 164–72; transfigured phenomenology 168–72; trauma and environment 165
relationships 52; anthropocentric view 170–1; breaks 25–6; healing and 153–4; shared world connection 91; trauma effects 42–3
religious practice; post-Second World War 156; processing of trauma *vs.* 144–5
representation of trauma 38
repression of trauma 16
responsibility: ethical responsibility 115–16; non-reciprocal 115; passive responsibility 116; phenomenology and 121; politics of 126–7
Ricœur, Paul 42, 64–76; ambiguity of trauma language 72–5; biography 64–5; decolonisation 123; embodied consciousness and language 122; embodied trauma 69–72; Freudian analysis and 22–3, 65–9; healing process 126–7; humans as thinking things 106; language 107; metaphorical transformations 174–7; mythical trauma narratives 73–4; phenomenology 51; relationships 52; subjective examination 9; subjectivity and 138–9, 156; suffering 108, 148; trauma narratives 45 *see also* narrative experiences
rights of trauma 110–11
rights theory 117
Roberts-Cady, Sarah 157
Roberts, John 41, 134–5
Roseman, S 140
Rothberg, M 36
Rothschild, Babette 103
The Rules of Metaphor (Ricœur) 174, 177
rupture of trauma 68–9, 71

Schimmenti, Adriano 38
Schonfeld, E 150
Schwartz, Richard 104, 105
Scott, Charles 103
secondary trauma stress (STS) 153–4
second innocence 106
Second World War 30
Sehwail, Mahmud 165–6
self: Jung 19; other and 96, 159; protective parts of 105; sense of 44; Staufer 91
self-care theory 137–8, 153
self–other theory, decolonisation 118–19
sensibility 102–3
sexual abuse 36, 84–5
Shakespeare 92
shared world 91
Sigurdson, Ola 137; adaptive healing 132–3; humanity 138–9; lived experience 82; pain 146–7; self-care 137–8
social relationships 147
somatic experience techniques 146
somatic psychology theory 135
somatic theories of trauma 84
somatic view, experience 53–4
Sophocles 39–40, 41
Soskin, David 39–40, 41
South African Truth and Reconciliation Council 107
Spiegel, David 14
Stanghellini, Giovanni 51
Stauffer, Jill 54, 91; communication limits 92–3; language and experience 176–7; trauma exploration 107–8; trauma narratives 142; victim-perpetrator totalities 154–5; vulnerability 139
Stearns, P 113
Stover, Eric 107
stressors 35
STS (secondary trauma stress) 153–4
Studies on Hysteria (Freud and Breuer) 135

subjective examination 9
subjectivity 156, 157
Lévinas 55–60, 111
subjects of trauma 41–3
suffering: ambiguity of 75; consciousness content 96; evil as 73–4, 108; Lévinas 58, 61–3, 150; mediation 152; Schonfeld 150; Stauffer 154; theodicy 148; trauma definition and 42
suicide, veterans 133–4
Sveneaus, F 134
The Symbolism of Evil (Ricœur) 72–3
symptoms, meanings of 134
systematisation critique 59

Tahmasebi-Birgani, V 115
Tai Chi 145
talk therapy 46
terrorism 146
Thanatos 16–17, 150
theodicy 147–52
theology 138, 169–70
theories of self 57, 58
therapists' role 152–4
Tikken Olam 149
time, linear interpretation of 80–1
Toadvine, Ted 170
Tobin, John 112–13, 114
Todres, Jonathan 112–13
torture 71, 156, 168–9
Totality and Infinity (Lévinas) 61, 62, 100, 102–3, 158–9
transfigured phenomenology 168–72
transfiguring trauma 157–60
transformation of trauma 140–1
transmission of memory 97
trauma: ambiguity of language 72–5; childhood trauma 21, 38, 117–18; collective trauma 166; continuing traumatic disorder 165–6; definitions of 42, 133; description of 11–12; diagnosis *see* diagnosis of trauma; dissociative states of 144; dual understanding of 139; embodied trauma 69–72; episodic trauma 4; historical trauma 4; intersubjectivity of 110–28; living trauma 52–4, 141–7; mythical narratives 38–40, 41, 73–4; narratives of 43–7; neurological explanations of 84; ongoing trauma 4; outcomes of 31–2; processing of 144–5; psychoanalytic theories of 84; representation of 38; repression of 16; rights of 110–11; rupture of 68–9, 71; secondary trauma stress 153–4; somatic theories of 84; subjects of 41–3; transfiguring trauma 157–60; transformation of 140–1; treatment of 133; vicarious trauma 153–4
Trauma and the Ontology of the Modern Subject (Roberts) 41
Trauma Complex 17
traumatic ambiguity 28–47
Traumatic Life Events Questionnaire 29
treatment of trauma 133
Trojan War 39–40

unconsciousness, verbalisation of 135
understanding, consciousness 136–7
United Nations Children's Fund (UNICEF) 112
United Nations Declaration of Human Rights (UNDHR) 113
United Nations General Assembly and Human Rights Council 113–14
Universal Declaration of Human Rights 111, 112
universalism, reductionism *vs.* 117
universal rights 114–17
uprootedness 3–4
US Department of Veterans Affairs 161
Useless Suffering (Lévinas) 96

van der Kolk, Bessel 11–12, 26; body perception 103; childhood trauma 118; communication 97; embodied trauma 70; forgiveness 158–9; Freud criticism 23–4; growth stopping 158; language limitations 92, 96–7; living trauma 52; meditation 143; polyvagal theory 8; relationship breaks 25–6; rupture of trauma 71; talk therapy 46; terrorism 146; trauma as relation to place 164; trauma definition 133; trauma narratives 44, 46–7
verbalisation of unconsciousness 135
verbal rearrangements 97–8
veteran suicide 133–4
vicarious trauma (VT) 153–4
victim-perpetrator experience 157–8
victim-perpetrator totalities 154–6
Vietnam War veterans 29, 31
violent pathological force 45
Visser, I 38–9
VT (vicarious trauma) 153–4
vulnerability 139, 148

Weil, Simone 3, 127
Weltanschauung 149
Winblad, N 153–4

Winnicott, D W 22; external world and 20; Freud, criticism of 19–20; trauma situations 20
Wong, E C 144–5
World Health Organization (WHO) 132, 138
woundedness 103
wounded relationships 139

yoga practice 143

Zimmerman, N 55–6